Accessibility and the bus system: from concepts to practice

Accessibility and the bus system: from concepts to practice

Edited by N. Tyler

Accessibility Research Group,
Centre for Transport Studies,
University College London, UK

Thomas Telford

Published by Thomas Telford Publishing, Thomas Telford Ltd, 1 Heron Quay, London E14 4JD
URL: http://www.thomastelford.com

Distributors for Thomas Telford books are
USA: ASCE Press, 1801 Alexander Bell Drive, Reston, VA 20191-4400
Japan: Maruzen Co. Ltd, Book Department, 3–10 Nihonbashi 2-chome, Chuo-ku, Tokyo 103
Australia: DA Books and Journals, 648 Whitehorse Road, Mitcham 3132, Victoria

First published 2002

Also available from Thomas Telford Books

Practical road safety auditing. Steve Proctor, Martin Belcher and Phil Cook. 07277 2938 1
Road lighting for safety. D. A. Schreuder. 07277 2616 1

A catalogue record for this book is available from the British Library

ISBN: 0 7277 2980 2

Typeset by Helius, Brighton and Rochester
Printed and bound in Great Britain by MPG Books, Bodmin, Cornwall

Contents

Contributors

The contents of this book have been drawn from the research being undertaken in the Accessibility Research Group in the Centre for Transport Studies at University College London. Particular inputs from different members of the group are acknowledged in the form of their authorship of each chapter. However, the nature of the work and the way in which we work means that most chapters contain contributions from most people in the group. Apart from the text contributions, members of the group have contributed diagrams and photographs.

Ian Brown was born and educated in England. He graduated in Civil Engineering at Loughborough, followed by postgraduate studies at Imperial College, London. He is an experienced chartered civil engineer who has worked on policy, network management, design, construction and maintenance of highway bridges and other structures, with contractors, consulting engineers, the Department of Transport and the Highways Agency. In 1998 he joined the Accessibility Research Group at University College London. He is currently researching into direct and cross-sector impacts of accessible public transport in rural areas.

Martha Caiafa is a Research Fellow in the Accessibility Research Group in the Centre for Transport Studies at University College London. Martha completed a Master of Science Degree in Transport Science in Brazil, where she worked with computational techniques applied to transport fields, including logistics, public transport and the use of a telematics framework to spread knowledge about transport. Martha joined the Accessibility Research Group in 1998 as the researcher for the EXCALIBUR project, which analysed accessibility for bus systems and the ways in which infrastructure could be designed at bus stops to facilitate accessible bus operation. Martha's current research area is the study of accessible information for public transport, for which she is supported by the ARROW project.

Nick Tyler joined the Transport Studies Group (now the Centre for Transport Studies) at University College London in 1987 to research into the design of high capacity bus systems, for which he gained his doctorate. He is now a Reader in Transport Studies at University College London, where he teaches and researches in the areas of accessibility and public transport. Nick was a member of the Disabled Persons' Transport Advisory Committee (DPTAC) from 1998 to 2001 and continues as a member of DPTAC's 'knowledge pool'. He is a member of the Executive Committee of the Community Transport Association. Nick is also involved with a wide range of research in South America, where he works in conjunction with local academics to promote the incorporation of disability awareness and accessibility.

Two contributors prepared the majority of the artwork:

Chris Cook trained in painting at Camberwell School of Art. He taught on and organised art courses in Adult Education for many years. He has also trained in computer graphics and illustration at the London College of Printing. Since 1998 Chris has worked on publicity, graphics, map design and teaching materials in the Accessibility Research Group at University College London. He has recently completed a project which has worked with children and teachers in a special school to develop ways of helping young people with learning difficulties to travel more independently on public transport and is now working on dissemination methods for the outcomes of this project.

Marcela Wainstein was born in Argentina, where she obtained a degree in Industrial Design at the University of Buenos Aires. She also completed a degree in Social Psychology at 'Pichon Riviere' School of Social Psychology. Marcela worked as a designer of objects for people with special needs and was awarded the MAFRE scholarship to develop research into the area of accessibility in work spaces. She joined the Accessibility Research Group as the researcher for the DIMPLE project, where she is investigating the feasibility of a hand-held mapping device designed for people with learning difficulties.

Three contributors have moved on from the group to take up appointments elsewhere:

Natasha Brown obtained her first degree in aeronautical engineering at Imperial College, London University, followed by an MSc in Transport at the Centre for Transport Studies. She worked at the Centre for Transport

Studies for 18 months in the Accessibility Research Group and then moved to the London Borough of Camden where she has since worked as a transport and traffic planner.

Rodrigo Fernández is a Civil Engineer of the University of Chile (1986), DIC and MSc in Transport (University of London, 1991), and is completing a PhD in Transport Studies at University College London. Since 1992 he has been Assistant Professor at the Transport Division of the Department of Civil Engineering of the University of Chile where he has coordinated the Teaching and Postgraduate programmes. In 2001 he became Head of the Transport Division. Previously, he had held a similar post at the University of Concepción (Chile) from 1986. He teaches the courses on traffic flow theory and traffic engineering to graduate and undergraduate students of the Faculty of Mathematical and Physical Sciences of the University of Chile. In the professional field he is General Secretary of the Chilean Society of Transport Engineering and he has been advisor of many central and local government authorities in Chile. His main research area is traffic engineering and within that area he has been interested in the estimation and mitigation of the urban impacts from traffic and the modelling and design of public transport facilities. As a result, he has been involved in many projects of the Accessibility Research Group since 1994.

Paulo Silva was born in Brazil, where he graduated at the Federal University of Bahia and obtained his MSc at the Federal University of Rio de Janeiro. Before joining the Transport Group at the University of Brasilia, he worked as a traffic engineer for the local governments of Salvador and Rio. He later obtained his PhD at University College London, working with the Accessibility Research Group, with which he remains in close contact seeking the development of joint projects. He is continuing his research into bus systems and traffic management, and teaching transport and traffic engineering at the University of Brasilia.

Preface

The original idea for this book was that it could act as a means of disseminating the outcomes of the research being undertaken in the Centre for Transport Studies at University College London by the Accessibility Research Group. Working in this area means that many of the conventions and mainstream ideas accepted by many people have to be questioned for their validity in a world in which accessibility is a central requirement of society. We wanted to be able to explain how we see accessibility and how we think it fits into the practical world in which it has to be put into place. The book is based on our research and uses examples from our experience to explain and illustrate how our thinking has developed over the past few years and how we have put these concepts into practice. Research is dynamic and never finished: the book is just a snapshot of where we have reached at the time of writing. We have tried to be self-critical and to show where we still have a lot to do.

The Accessibility Research Group has brought together a number of skills from various categories of engineering to design, art and law. This has meant that we have been in a position where each member of the group has contributed to – and questioned – the group's overall view of the topic and the strategy by which we have sought to address it. The essence of our approach is to act as a bridge between the development of theoretical concepts and their implementation in practice. Our research is highly practical – we have constructed bus stops, dealt with the design of vehicles, operated a bus route, carried out public participation processes and seen our designs for user-centred control of local authority transport put into action. The explanations in this book are based not only on theoretical surmises, but also on experience of their implementation in the real world.

Throughout the book we have tried to convey the links between theory and practice. For those who are more interested in the theory, the first three chapters cover: the development of concepts (Chapter 1), the way in which these are currently seen in practice and what we should include in the bus system (Chapter 2), and the ways in which conventional theory with respect to bus network design and operation may need to be recast in the light of the importance of accessibility to the modern world (Chapter 3). Chapter 9 draws these themes together in the light of the practical work described in the intervening chapters.

For people who prefer to work with the implementation of ideas rather than their development, we have used outcomes from our research into bus systems to illustrate the way in which the nodes of the bus system – the bus stops – can provide some insights into the practical aspects of accessibility. We cover the design of bus stops in two parts, in which we show how these all-important (but often disregarded) elements of the bus system can encourage or impede accessibility. Chapter 4 deals with the theoretical approaches to capacity and the way in which bus stops interact with traffic. Chapter 5 introduces the theory behind the design of bus stop infrastructure and illustrates this with examples from on-street implementation. This includes details of the ideals to be sought and covers the implications of not being able to reach them, based on the implementation of the principles in London and Brighton.

We give a brief coverage of accessible information in Chapter 6, in which we seek to open up the questions to be considered. This is an area in which we have a lot of research underway, but much of this is at too early a stage for useful inclusion in this book. We believe strongly in the principles of involving the public and realise the difficulties as well as the opportunities of putting these principles into practice. Chapter 7 describes the processes involved into, and the outcomes of, a number of different approaches to public participation.

One of our research projects incorporates most of the research in the other projects because it set out to put into operation a bus service in a remote rural area and then to study the consequences. This involved consideration of all the above issues and the practicalities of putting them into practice. Chapter 8 describes this implementation, and explains some of the issues raised and what we have learnt from the experience. Chapter 9 brings all the strands together: the importance of developments in conceptual thinking, the improvements in the comprehensiveness of theoretical design and the processes involved in putting it all into practice.

Nick Tyler

Acknowledgements

It is important to realise that one of the key ingredients of the Accessibility Research Group is the way in which all its members interact to provide a full picture of each of the research issues we tackle. The current members of the Accessibility Research Group are: Ian Brown, Martha Caiafa, Chris Cook, Rodrigo Fernández, Patricia Ideawor, Ricardo Marar and Marcela Wainstein. A number of researchers have moved on from the group and these include: Farzaneh Bitarafen, Natasha Brown, Adam Kean, Charles Kunaka, Jenny Lynas and Paulo Silva. My thanks are due to all of these for their contribution to the research and thus the development of this book. I must single out Martha Caiafa, who has provided many of the diagrams in the book, as well as a huge amount of assistance to me during the course of its production. Many others have contributed to this book in various ways. Inevitably, I have had to be selective in putting this book together, and in the end I must take the responsibility for any omissions that lead to confusion or bewilderment on the part of the reader.

The research on which this book is based has been funded by: the Engineering and Physical Sciences Research Council, the Department of Transport, Local Government and the Regions, Bridge House Estates Trust Fund, the Countryside Agency, London Transport and various local authorities.

On a more personal note, I would like to thank my wife, Katrina, who has had to put up with the inevitable absences and other domestic consequences of putting this book together. Without her support, the whole project would have been impossible.

Nick Tyler

Current and Recent Projects Undertaken by the Accessibility Research Group

The list below gives the principal projects which have contributed to the content of this book. For further details about these and other projects and information about publications produced by the Accessibility Research Group, please visit our website at www.ucl.ac.uk/transport-studies/accessib.htm.

A specification for accessible bus stops has been developed, designed, built and tested in the EXCALIBUR project.

ACCEPT discussed a series of possibilities and implications of really accessible public transport systems.

The PATH project worked with Hackney Community Transport to develop and implement an accessible minibus miocronetwork in the London Borough of Hackney.

The concepts and definitions behind the accessibility issue, including the concepts underlying how to evaluate accessibility, have been developed in the APEX project.

APTRA was designed to study the consequences of high frequency public transport services in rural areas.

We worked with Brighton and Hove Council, supplying the council with specifications for accessible bus stops and footways for two bus routes.

A Transport Co-ordination Centre designed by University College London and Hackney Community Transport is now in operation in a London borough to provide the most appropriate least cost transport solution at the time of need for social services users and children with special education needs.

The provision of transport for community healthcare for mentally ill people in rural Kent has been reviewed and an approach to make travelling easier for this group is being developed with the local health trust and local charities.

The detailed study of the interactions within bus stops produced a simulation model (PASSION) useful to improve the design of such facilities, with respect to bus operations and paying particular attention to the ways in which passengers and buses interact at bus stops.

The modelling of interactions between buses and other traffic is the subject of a project that will help the analysis of mixed traffic networks and the design of bus services through the devolopment of a microscopic simulation model (BusSIGSIM).

ELIXIR is the continuation of the APTRA project. We are now examining how the successful accessible bus service can be used to enhance the provision of health and social care in the area.

DIMPLE is developing a mapping device to help people with learning difficulties navigate their way around so that they can begin to use public transport to help them increase their independence and quality of life.

We are working with schools in Southend in a project called TRUMPET which is helping to develop ways of communicating the benefits of our research to children with learning difficulties.

We are working with the Pontificia Universidad Católica del Perú on a project to improve social inclusion, to introduce techniques to enhance accessibility in Peru and to start a programme of disability awareness training in schools.

Together with researchers from the Pontificia Universidad Católica del Perú, we are part of a team which carries out assessments of transport projects in the imperial city of Cusco, Peru.

PUPPIT is introducing a public participation process into the programme of accessible bus stop construction in Brighton and Hove.

TOCCATA is a project in which we are working with the University of Brasilia to introduce disability awareness training to schools in Brazil.

We have been studying the interactions between wheelchairs and historic carpets as part of the National Trust's efforts to open properties to a greater number of disabled people.

Chapter 1

Philosophy and Approach

N. Tyler

Introduction

Our starting point is the general fact that a person who is unable to make use of a system will be unable to obtain any of the benefits it offers to its users. This applies to the bus system just as much as it does to any other system, and we contend that any discussion of bus systems must have at its heart the issue of how the use of buses can be made possible for everyone. In this chapter we consider how society organises itself and the impacts this has on the transport – and notably the bus – system. We explain how we see accessibility as an issue and the way in which this affects our approach to the design and operation of the bus system. We then discuss the reasons for using accessibility and the bus system as the prime example for the rest of the book.

Society

How do People Live in Society?

A society is a social community living in close proximity on the basis that as a group they face a better chance of survival than by acting individually. However, by coming together, people juxtapose their different lifestyles, needs and desires. This can be seen clearly in areas of high population density where many people give up their individual preferences for the sake of living close to their neighbours. However, it is not only a feature of high-density neighbourhoods – people in rural communities also give up individual preferences in order to live in small communities. For many people the anonymity of city centre living is preferable to the common knowledge of one's affairs, which can easily be the experience in village communities in remote rural areas. One of the issues that marks out living in societies is that people, who as individuals choose to take on an activity, often desire – or need – others to participate in order for the activity to be feasible. A football team or an orchestra could not happen without the coming together of a number of like-minded individuals.

There is a functional difference between activities undertaken individually and those which depend on joint or social activity. There is also a difference in terms of where the activity can take place. Individuals could review their stamp collections in isolation at home, but in order for them to trade with like-minded people they must find some place to congregate. Even in these days of electronic trading via the internet there seems to be a need for face-to-face contact between like-minded individuals. Other, more obviously gregarious activities such as football can only be undertaken in places where people can gather.

Some social activities provide pleasure (e.g. sport) and others enable the economy to turn (e.g. employment or trade). Yet others are concerned with the well-being of members of society (e.g. healthcare, social services or education) or of society itself (e.g. the democratic process). These are examples of a notion of 'social activities' and constitute a major part of living in society. If someone is denied access to one of these activities they are being denied full membership of society.

There are many ways in which social activities can be denied to people – either deliberately or unintentionally – because of unsuitable access arrangements, for example:

- locating an activity very far away might make it available only to those with access to a car
- if the only access to an activity is a flight of stairs it prevents a wheelchair user from participating in the activity.

In each case, preventing a person from gaining access means preventing them from participating in the activity. Failure to provide adequate access means that some people will be denied opportunities for leisure, employment, trading, healthcare, education – even for taking part in the electoral process. Accessibility is not just about being 'nice' to people with difficulties, it is about ensuring that the benefits and responsibilities of living in society are truly available to, and are shared between, the vast majority of its members. Understanding this becomes more important if the outcome is likely to result in an unequal distribution of benefits – whether these are of income, accessibility or other societal concerns such as education or health. It is more common to consider distribution of benefits when considering income, so we shall start by considering this and then showing how accessibility is distributed unequally within society.

Trade-offs

Most societies contain rich and poor people. A lot of society's activities are directed towards ensuring that the poorest members of society are not left in a state of unacceptable poverty. The resources used to achieve this are redistributed from people in better economic circumstances, often through taxation. It is not the purpose of this book to discuss the rights and wrongs of taxation or of any particular taxation policy. Nevertheless, there are some issues that arise when thinking about taxation that will help to direct our approach to accessible bus systems.

The first issue is the concept of thresholds defined by society over which it considers that people should not pass. For example, society declares a level of poverty that it considers unacceptable. This can be defined in several ways – one is the level of income below which the State decides to contribute towards household income through some statutory payment (another is the level of income at which income tax becomes payable). However, some people may require more resources than others in order to survive and thus the level of payments needs to be adjusted according to individual circumstances. Another way of describing this process is that some people may be eligible for payments from the State (granted in the name of society) while others may not. Who should be in receipt of such payments or the associated adjustments to their income? The answer to this question is defined by a set of eligibility criteria which are determined by society (by means of intervention by the State or some other body). The general point here is that there is a default level of income which is determined by society (through its willingness to support levels of contribution through taxation) and which can take into account the particular circumstances of different individuals. There may be much debate about what that default level of income actually is, but the principle holds in any case.

Other aspects of communal living are also subject to thresholds. The education system, for example, attempts to ensure that every member of society has some basic skills (e.g. reading, writing and numeracy). We can consider these levels as society's consideration of the basic level of education that its members should have. Society devotes resources towards establishing and maintaining such education standards. The health system is another example where society takes a view about the basic level of health of a member of society and this is set as a default. In the UK this is enshrined in the level and type of healthcare available under the National Health Service. Some treatments are not deemed to be necessary to ensure that every member of society is able to live above a certain threshold, but

3

others are. Some treatments are considered differently in different circumstances. Elective cosmetic surgery might be considered to be beyond the scope of treatment within society's norms in one case, yet if required as the result of injuries sustained in a road accident could be deemed to be within society's scope.

Many approaches to accessibility work on a similar basis: access to a bus may be restricted to wheelchair users who can use a chair up to a certain size. We can debate what is a reasonable maximum size for a wheelchair – and we could change our views about this over time (e.g. as technology changes). However, in the end, society decides on a reasonable size to use when trying to make buses accessible and expresses this decision in the form of legislation that must be followed until a change is deemed to be desirable.

Why are these defaults important? The principles by which decisions are made in the examples just given are examples of society taking a decision about a base acceptable level (e.g. of education or health) and allocating its resources in a way that attempts to establish and maintain the quality of society above that level. Different societies have different views about what should be the default value – the UK is different from the USA, Sweden or France in its choices just as surely as, at a more local level, two counties might make different choices about how society will function in their area. In each of the aspects we have discussed so far (and of course there are many more), we have a concept of unequal distribution. Some people are better off than others – whether we are looking at income, health, education or accessibility – and it is up to society to ensure that nobody falls below its base acceptable level in each case.

We can consider the 'quality' of some aspect of society (e.g. income) in two ways:

- we can measure the default or fundamental level below which it is deemed unacceptable to allow members to fall
- we can count the number of people at various levels above and below the default line (e.g. at different levels of income).

We can consider these as, respectively, the 'level' and the 'distribution' of whatever aspect of society we are considering. In either case, this means establishing some method for measuring the levels attained by members of society. In the case of income this is reasonably easy, and even in the case of health or education this can be done in an understandable way. It is much harder – and no less essential – to measure accessibility in a similar way.

We need to look at both the level and the distribution of 'quality' in order to gain a complete picture of the effects of a given policy and to avoid perverse results. For example, if a policy were based only on income distribution it would take no account of the levels involved and there would be no consideration of what the acceptable threshold would be.

The result of such a policy would be that some people would be in absolute poverty yet still appear to be acceptable to the policy-makers because there is no definition of the 'acceptable level'.

Analysis of only the level means that we would consider only the actual level (e.g. of income). We could choose to examine a high level (e.g. the maximum) or the average or even the lowest level of income. Yet without consideration of the distribution of incomes we would have as false a picture as we had before. The average income could be maintained at an acceptable level, while some people are destitute, simply because there are enough people with enough affluence to offset the effects of the number of people on unacceptably low incomes. Considering only the highest level of income takes no account of how many people are living below the minimum acceptable level.

We therefore need to find a policy appraisal method which takes level as well as distribution into account. John Rawls, a political philosopher, proposed a particularly interesting approach to this problem in his book *A Theory of Justice* (1971). Rawls considered the distribution of economic benefits to groups of members of society. We shall continue to use these as the topic for our discussion, as they are relatively easy to understand. We shall argue that the same principles apply to the consideration of accessibility.

Social Justice and Fairness

Acknowledging the ubiquity and usefulness of utility theory in establishing the distribution of benefits following a given policy decision, Rawls set out to consider how to incorporate the analysis of the level of benefits into policy appraisal. Rawls framed his thoughts in the context of social justice. He felt that the weak consideration of the distribution of benefits usually incorporated in utility-based decision assessments meant that some people could be intolerably worse off as a result of a decision, even though the analysis of benefits showed a net gain to society as a whole. The key word here is 'intolerably': very few policy decisions result in everyone being better off, but Rawls maintained that society, to be just and fair, should ensure that nobody should fall below the minimum acceptable level and that the people who were the worst off before the decision should at least be in no worse a position afterwards. The key issue for Rawls was the difference between the net expectations obtained by the least well-off compared with those obtained by the better-off. Rawls expressed this as:

> ... the higher expectations of those better situated are just if and only if they work as part of a scheme which improves the expectations of the least advantaged members of society. (Rawls, 1971, p. 75)

Rawls called this the *difference principle* and explained it by comparing two groups following a policy decision.

Figure 1.1 shows the contribution to the expectations of the less well-off group (X2) as a result of the increased expectations of the better-off group (X1) following a decision. If X2's expectations increase exactly in line with X1's, both groups benefit in equal measure and the curve would be equidistant from the axes as shown in Figure 1.1 by the line OA.

Rawls considers the situation where the expectations of X2 as an effect of the increased expectations of X1 are represented by the curve OP in Figure 1.2. In this case, the difference principle is perfectly satisfied only where OP is at its maximum (point 'a'). This is where the expectations of benefits from the decision are maximised. Subsequent increases in the expectations of X1 are only achieved as those to X2 are reduced. This suggests that the quality – amount – of justice and fairness in the society thus depicted depends on the state of the least well-off group in that society. This means that a socially just system must search for the solution at which the expectations of the least well-off group are maximised. Seeking to improve the benefits to the other group beyond this point will always be at the expense of the less well-off and thus to the quality of social justice and fairness in society as a whole. Point 'a' in Figure 1.2 represents a compromise. X1 could accrue more benefits

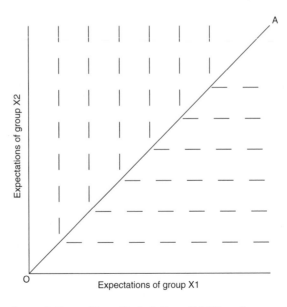

Fig. 1.1   Equal expectations of benefits to better-off (X1) and worse-off (X2) groups following a decision

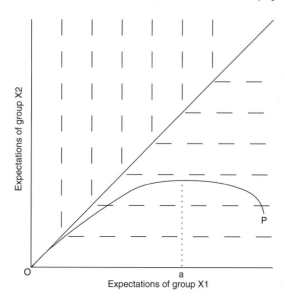

Fig. 1.2   Unequal expectations of benefits to better-off (X1) and worse-off (X2) groups following a decision

(although X2 could not), but would do so only if society were to accept the unfairness of the resulting position for X2. This compromise is not necessarily ideal for any group, but it does seek to ensure that the worst-off in society do not become even more worse off after a given decision has been made.

Rawls was trying to establish how social justice could be brought into the decision process regarding the movement of wealth. There is an equivalent concern in relation to other aspects of society, for example decisions about the provision of healthcare or education. Replacing the idea of poverty with that of healthcare shows how social justice could affect policy decisions about a non-quantitative issue. Consider a decision to locate a certain level of healthcare intervention in a centralised facility. As the concentration of specialisms increases so the benefits to patients must surely increase: patients will be able to reach all the necessary experts in a single place – possibly during the same visit. This presupposes that patients can reach this facility. Those patients with access to their own transport would receive increasing benefits as more treatments become available at the centralised facility and a single journey suffices for a lot of treatments. Those with no such access also receive some benefits if they can reduce the amount of travel by arranging several treatments on the same visit. Even if the journey is longer and more complex than the simple local journeys it replaces, it is still just one journey instead of many.

However, after a certain point patients begin to lose, because the greater concentration means that local facilities, to which they would have access for many treatments, close, thus forcing patients to make the longer and more complex journeys to the larger centralised facility. So concentration of health facilities has a point beyond which it cannot go without causing an overall loss in social justice and fairness. The people who had least access in the first place (because they had no access to their own transport) are even worse off because they are unable to reach any facility at all. We shall discuss below how this approach affects our view of accessibility and the use of the transport system.

Social justice is much more than simply choosing the correct trade-offs. It is about ensuring that everyone has at least some fundamentally acceptable amount of health, wealth, education and so on before determining how the overall benefits should be distributed. Rawls' model shows that simply improving things for one sector of society can only be justified to the point at which another group begins to become worse off. In the end we have to learn to deal with compromises where perhaps nobody feels that they have received as many benefits as they deserve, but where the delivery of social justice is maximised. To make compromises of this sort work in practice we have to be reassured that the improvement in social justice will be delivered, that it is worth having and that the corresponding 'losses' of benefits are justified. One way of providing reassurance that future actions will be delivered is to enter into a contract. In the case considered in this book the contract is between individual members of society and the controllers of its transport system – a sort of 'transport contract'.

A Transport Contract

The first thing to say about our concept of a transport contract is that it is not about the specific duties placed on transport system designers, operators or planners. We are dealing with the wider issues from which such a contract might result: what society needs from its transport system and what the transport system requires from society. In this sense it is similar in concept to the Social Contract of Jean-Jacques Rousseau in which the 'contract' was between a sovereign and their citizens.

So far, we have identified that people living in society undertake a variety of activities, many of which are located some distance from their homes so that at least some people will have to travel to undertake them. We have also established that a failure on the part of society to ensure that such access is possible for everyone results in some people being excluded from some activities, with a consequent reduction in social justice and fairness. The next step is to determine the points at which social justice is maximised – point 'a' in Figure 1.2 – for various aspects of society's needs from the transport system. The Rawls-type approach means that these points are not determined on the basis of a trade-off but are set by the point at which the expectation available to the most disadvantaged groups in society is maximised. To consider this further, we shall consider a simple example concerning access to a health centre.

Suppose that society has determined that an equitable and socially just level of access to a health centre is that everyone should be able to reach it comfortably from their home within 30 minutes. Some people will require more resources than others in order to meet this standard. For example, some people may live within 30 minutes' walk at their comfortable walking speed. Others may need to walk more slowly than this and therefore would require some form of conveyance to the health centre in order to meet the criterion. Their alternative would be to move home, but requiring this would be unlikely to meet social-justice criteria. As a result, a social duty is placed on society to ensure that:

- the provision for walking to the health centre is such that the journey could be completed comfortably, securely and safely
- suitable transport provision is made for those members of society for whom the criterion would otherwise be unachievable.

The requirement for good-quality, safe pedestrian infrastructure is a matter of social responsibility on the part of society. The same also applies to the provision of transport for those who cannot take advantage of that infrastructure. Our transport contract has to define the minimum standards for planning, design, operations and information provision so that socially just access is available to everyone. This could be set out in terms of network design (e.g. a bus stop within 10 minutes' walk from a journey origin), but it should not specify how this would be achieved. These minimum standards are derived from knowledge obtained from people about what they need from the public transport system in order to use it. As we shall see throughout this book, such needs can be expressed – and met – in the form of design criteria for infrastructure, operations, vehicles and the supply of information. As with any contract, evaluation criteria must be set out so that achievements can be checked against the requirements.

So, we can construct a contract between society and its members. On the one side, people can determine what they require from the public transport system; on the other, society can determine what is required of the people. Meeting particular demands might place obligations on the public budgets, thus requiring changes to the amounts, sources and ways in which public money is spent. The concept of a contract has another effect: the statement that there are minimum standards means that the system has to be designed to meet them. Failure to do this means that the contract has been broken. The contract acts as some protection for people who would be disabled by the failure to design a system which provides the ability to reach and use facilities that are available to others. The socially just minimum standards are, by definition, those that can meet the needs of the most disadvantaged groups in society. However, this does not mean that everyone has to have access to a low-price, door-to-door transport service. It acknowledges that some people will require such a service and that this should be provided for them so that the standards can be achieved. There are many reasons why people may need special transport services in order to function more completely in society. These include the presence of some circumstances that make it difficult to use conventional transport services.

Of course, the minimum standards have to be defined. The temptation is to define standards in terms of inputs (e.g. measurements of size or distances). However, these become very inflexible and can become outdated very quickly. Also, it is very easy for a standard which has been set as a minimum to become the norm in practice, thus tending to reduce the possibility for improvements over time. This also tends to reduce the basic standard in the short term to that of the worst acceptable level.

Another way of looking at standards is on the basis of outputs, usually expressed as levels of performance. Performance-based standards determine what should be achievable. For example, rather than define the minimum dimensions for a wheelchair space, a performance-based standard would require that a wheelchair user can reach, enter and leave the wheelchair space comfortably and with dignity in a forward direction. A performance standard needs to be devised with users. It is necessary to find out what users need from the performance, then extract from this the elements that are both repeatable and testable as measures of performance. These might be described in terms of time (e.g. to enter the wheelchair space within one minute of entering the bus, in a forward motion with a minimum of reversing, in a dignified manner and at a safe speed). This would only be to provide guidance to the technicians overseeing the test. It is not a target for 'real' users in a 'real' situation. The test should be designed so that it can be repeated with the same results at different testing stations and when carried out by different people. Performance-based standards are harder for manufacturers than dimension-based criteria, but if determined properly they are much better for users. On the whole, a performance-based criterion means more pre-production practical testing and user involvement, but once a design has been produced that satisfies the performance test its dimensions then become the production design and the manufacturer can construct the product accordingly, safe in the knowledge that the performance test will be satisfied.

Accessibility Issues

Disability

For a long time the concept of disability was dominated by the medical profession. Disability was seen as a problem of a person arising from some form of medical condition or traumatic event that resulted in the loss, or reduction in use, of some physical, sensory or cognitive function. The problem rested with the person concerned and the medical profession attempted to relieve or remove the offending condition. Failure to remove the problem resulted in a person being unable to carry out some function (i.e. they had a disability). The easiest way to treat a person with a disability was to put them in some form of hospital unit at which medical facilities could be provided and, for this reason, many disabled people were kept in institutions, away from any involvement in society.

The medical view of disability ignored many of the social dimensions of the issue, especially where these were not under the direct control of the person concerned. This gave a very narrow view of disability, in which all the problems were seen as 'belonging' to the individual, who therefore had to adapt (or be adapted) to 'fit in' with the rest of society as best they could.

During the latter part of the twentieth century, it became increasingly apparent that the medical model of disability was unable to reflect the needs of disabled people. It was difficult to understand how society could function legitimately while excluding many of its members simply on the basis of a disability. The concept began to emerge that disability was a problem of society rather than the individual. In this view, a person does not have a disability which prevents them from doing something; rather, they might be disabled by society's inability to design a facility in such a way as to permit them to use it. This view has been termed the *social model of disability*.

The consequences of the social model are that much more attention must be paid to the design of all facilities so that people are not excluded from them. People can be excluded from an activity by all sorts of barriers, whether these are physical, sensory, cognitive, social, psychological or economic. The social model places the emphasis on society to resolve the problem: society has the disability which disables the person.

The medical model tends to depersonalise disability in the sense that it views a person simply as a collection of conditions. The social model positions the disability firmly within society, thus removing the problem from the person. This raises the question of how we can ensure that the social justice criteria are being met for everyone. For example, it may prove impossible to provide a bus which everyone can use, and we therefore have to consider how society can meet its social justice obligations in such circumstances. Inevitably, this brings forward the issue of who is excluded from the bus, and this is where the social model is less helpful in suggesting a solution. The broad intention is to provide a bus that is accessible to everyone. The reality is that there will still be some people who will have to use other means of transport to reach their chosen activities because it is currently physically impossible to design a bus to accommodate them. In order to ensure that society can meet their particular needs, their requirements must be taken into the design process. For this we must look at the interfaces between their needs and the facilities that can be designed to cater for them. This would seem to advocate an approach in which we try to ensure that the design process:

- accommodates as many people as possible in a mainstream solution
- determines how to provide the service for those excluded from this mainstream solution
- works continuously to find and incorporate new ideas, materials, technologies and methods into on-going designs so that more people can be included in the mainstream solution in the future.

We agree wholeheartedly with the social model that people are not the problem. We also believe that, far from removing disabled people from the problem, they should be at the very centre of the solution. There is, however, a personal element to the detail of the problem, because barriers have different impacts on different people. This means that designers need to understand individuals' difficulties in depth, with a view to incorporating their needs in the development of a solution. Designers must involve people in the process of establishing their design criteria. This requires people to participate fully in the design process. Everyone must take their share of the responsibility for making society function in accordance with the best principles of social justice and fairness.

Society should seek to include people in all its activities, irrespective of their social status, intellectual capability, economic circumstances, health, age or gender, or their social, psychological, physical, sensory or cognitive abilities. We refer to this as *social inclusion*, and where an activity succeeds in including people in this way, we describe it as *inclusive*.

Accessibility, Movement and Mobility

In order to simplify the discussion in this book, we use particular definitions of the words accessibility, mobility and movement:

- *Mobility* is the ease of movement from place to place, and thus represents the ease with which a person can reach an activity. This consists of two elements: movement and accessibility.

- *Movement* is the act of moving (i.e. the physical displacement required in order to reach the activity). Sometimes the movement required to reach a facility is minimal, but in most cases there is a need to use some form of conveyance (e.g. a vehicle) to enable this displacement to occur. If it is not possible to reach and use this vehicle, the movement is impossible and the activity cannot be reached.
- *Accessibility* is the ability to be approached, reached or entered and in this context represents the ease of reaching and using a bus.

Transport has a leading role in making sure that activities are accessible and available to all. The ability to use a facility is dependent on the ability to reach it (mobility), which is in turn dependent on the ability to reach and use the transport system (accessibility) and the ability of the latter to provide the means of reaching it (movement).

What would be the result if we were to design a transport system on the basis of these terms? For example, a major consideration in the thinking that underlies many transport decisions has been related to facilitating movement between one place and another – seeking time savings, reductions in delay, etc. Making it easier to travel further and faster implies that measures to increase speed would be helpful and the need to locate activities close together could be reduced. Such movement-based objectives could have unfortunate effects – for example, travel time could be decreased by increasing the distance between bus stops and thus increasing the commercial speed of the buses. However, this would make the bus stops less accessible to people experiencing difficulties in walking to the bus stop.

Accessibility to the bus system is the ease with which people can reach and use it. We could, for example, improve accessibility by moving the bus stops closer together, thus reducing the distance it is necessary to walk to the bus stop. However, this would tend to reduce the commercial speed of the buses and thus work against the movement-enhancing objective discussed earlier. In short, an easy way to think of the relationship between these three concepts is in the form of the equation:

mobility = movement + accessibility

which suggests that movement and accessibility are in some way mutually exclusive. If accessibility is increased it is more than likely that movement would have to be reduced, and vice versa.

A failure to meet movement-based objectives will act as a disincentive to travel. However, failure to meet accessibility-enhancing objectives will prevent, rather than reduce, travel and thus would result in the exclusion of some people from society. Indeed, enhancing movement for some may actively reduce accessibility for others.

We can now turn to see how our earlier discussion about Rawls' approach to maximising social justice bears on the provision of accessible transport. We can consider two groups of people: people who expect greater benefits from movement-enhancing objectives (X1) and people who have expectations arising from accessibility-enhancing objectives (X2). We can see from Figure 1.2 that as movement-enhancing objectives are encouraged, people in X1 increase their expectations. Although there is an increase in expectation for people in group X2, this is not at the same rate as for those in group X1. Eventually, the expectations of people in group X2 begin to decline – for example, because movement is being enhanced by increasing the distance between bus stops and this begins to prevent people from reaching the bus system. Increasing the implementation of movement-enhancing objectives beyond this point will result in a reduction in social justice because of the inevitable exclusion from society of those members of group X2 who would, as a result, be prevented from travelling.

The point we are seeking is where the maximum acceptable movement-enhancing objectives coincide with the maximum acceptable accessibility-enhancing ones. As noted above, it has tended to be more common in the past to think in terms of increasing the rate and amount of movement and, as a result, accessibility-enhancing objectives have often lost out. As inaccessibility prevents – rather than discourages – travel, it is better to meet accessibility objectives before tackling movement-enhancing ones. After all, a person cannot benefit from easier movement if they cannot reach the means of transport that provides it. A decision to make society more accessible for everyone means that, even if there are some disadvantages in terms of movement, society will be a more inclusive, more just and fairer place. It would seem that a socially just sense of mobility must place accessibility above movement when prioritising decisions about transport. Design objectives should therefore reflect this order.

The Accessible Journey Chain

Accessibility objectives need to be applied throughout the journey in order to eliminate all barriers. A public transport journey is a set of linked elements, each of which has to be accessible for the whole journey to be achievable. Frye (1996) calls this the 'accessible journey chain'. We can illustrate this concept with the example of a journey involving travel on a bus. This stresses the importance of the accessibility of every link in the transport chain:

- the bus stop will not provide access to the bus if the walk to reach it from the origin is not accessible

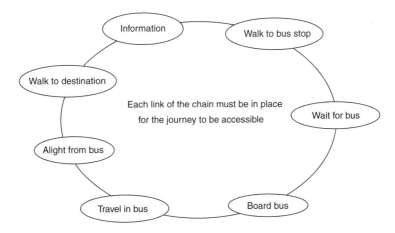

Fig. 1.3   The accessible journey chain

- it will not be possible to enter the bus if either the bus stop or the bus is not designed for accessible boarding
- the bus cannot be used at all if it is not designed to accommodate the needs of users
- the walk to the destination cannot be achieved if it is impossible to alight from the bus because the bus and bus stop are not designed to provide an acceptable interface for alighting passengers
- the destination cannot be reached if the walk from the last bus stop to the destination is impossible
- none of the above will be possible at all if the potential passenger cannot find out that the service exists and how to use it by means of an accessible information system.

The final link is that every element in the chain feeds into the information used when undertaking the next journey, and thus the chain forms a connected whole. Figure 1.3 presents the accessible journey chain and shows that the journey is not possible if any element of the chain is not accessible.

A potential passenger needs to be certain that the entire journey is accessible before they can have any confidence in setting out on the trip. Some people require more certainty than others about more of the journey in order to have this confidence. This is because they are more sensitive to barriers than others and are thus susceptible to very small changes in the details of a journey. Whereas some people could easily adapt to a barrier (e.g. by changing route), others would not be able to do so without a lot of difficulty. In such cases they have to establish that the entire chain is accessible to them, including any possible diversions, before they can contemplate setting out on a journey. This can only be done if the information system is able to provide sufficient information to give this level of confidence. The inability of an information system to provide this exacerbates the difficulties encountered during the actual journey to such an extent that it could prevent journeys from being made even if they were actually quite accessible. Putting accessibility into practice depends on correct and adequate performance in detail of all aspects of the journey chain at all times. It is for this reason that the design details throughout the transport system are so important.

Accessibility gap
What happens if the chain is broken? We mentioned earlier the example of bus stops being set too far apart for some people to reach them. What is the resolution to this problem? To think through the answer to this question, it is helpful to imagine a conventional bus network (large, high-floor buses, infrequent, reasonable route coverage on main routes but poor elsewhere, poor information provision, no special bus stops). For a person who cannot use this bus system – maybe because the bus stops are too far apart – there is no alternative except to rely on a taxi or possibly, in certain circumstances, transport provided on behalf of some statutory authority. For brevity in this discussion, at this point we shall call these *specialised transport services*. There is a difficulty here: a person who is just unable to use the conventional bus system, but who for some reason is not eligible for the specialised transport services, will be unable to make a journey using the transport system. They fall into what we call the 'accessibility gap' which arises between the mainstream public transport services and provision for people for whom these are not sufficient. One reaction to this is for people to use a car for their journeys: another is not to travel at all. Even where specialised transport services are being used, society acknowledges that there will inevitably be people using these where they could use conventional transport if only it were more accessible. The accessibility gap – between the most accessible available conventional bus system and the specialised transport services – is illustrated in Figure 1.4. In this case, the use of the conventional bus services is illustrated by the area to the left of the diagram. Specialised transport services are indicated by the area to the right and the accessibility gap is represented by the area in the middle.

CB	Accessibility gap	Specialised transport

CB, conventional bus

Fig. 1.4   The accessibility gap between conventional bus and specialised transport services

CB, conventional bus
LFB, low floor bus

Fig. 1.5 The accessibility gap between low-floor bus and specialised transport services

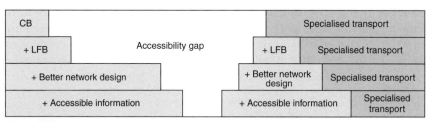

CB, conventional bus
LFB, low floor bus

Fig. 1.6 The accessibility gap between bus (with low-floor buses, accessible network and accessible information) and specialised transport services

If the conventional bus operator were to purchase some low-floor buses, more people would be able to use the new bus system. Some of these 'new' passengers would come from the accessibility gap and some would have been using the specialised services. This is illustrated in Figure 1.5, where the gap as shown in Figure 1.4 has been reduced due to the introduction of the new buses. The reduction in the accessibility gap is shown in two parts: the increase in the area on the left represents the new opportunities for people who are currently in the accessibility gap and cannot travel. The area on the right represents the people who, prior to the change, had to use specialised transport services but who, following the change, can use the improved bus service. Figure 1.6 shows how the gap could be reduced further by improving the design of the network to bring buses closer to the people and by providing accessible information about the services.

Dependence and Independence

For some people, the possibility of using the public transport system means that they can have some control over the choices in life. Most specialised transport services are scarce and must be booked in advance. Therefore a spontaneous journey – whether for pleasure or necessity –

might not be possible if it relies on the availability of a specialised transport service. The opportunity to act spontaneously is a sign of independence and control over one's life, so it is interesting to consider how accessibility and independence interact. To do this, we have divided the concept of independence into five categories, as shown in Table 1.1.

These five categories suggest differences in the need for help, ranging from complete dependence at one extreme to independence at the other. The accessibility gap is one reason why people need assistance to make a journey, and thus reducing the accessibility gap is one way to increase independence. For example, a wheelchair user who is unable to use a conventional bus cannot complete a bus journey. If low-floor buses were introduced (together with the associated infrastructure improvements), they would be able to use the buses (as long as they could reach the bus stop). In this case, they would have increased their independence even though they would remain in the 'technical assistance' category.

Table 1.1   Independence categories

Category	Assistance required to make a journey	Dependence on others
No assistance	People can travel alone without the need for any technical or personal assistance	Independent
Technical assistance	People can travel alone if they have the aid of some form of technical assistance (e.g. hearing aid, assistance or guide dog, wheelchair)	
Personal assistance (localised)	People can travel alone if they have some personal help at specific points in the journey (e.g. to board a train)	
Personal assistance (continual)	People can only travel if they are accompanied by someone throughout the journey	
Full assistance	People can only make a journey if some form of specialised assistance is available throughout the journey	Fully dependent

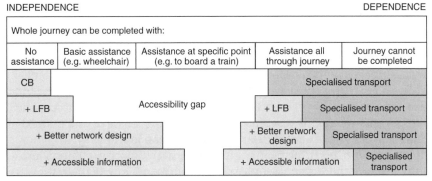

INDEPENDENCE   DEPENDENCE

Whole journey can be completed with:				
No assistance	Basic assistance (e.g. wheelchair)	Assistance at specific point (e.g. to board a train)	Assistance all through journey	Journey cannot be completed
CB			Specialised transport	
+ LFB		Accessibility gap	+ LFB	Specialised transport
+ Better network design			+ Better network design	Specialised transport
+ Accessible information			+ Accessible information	Specialised transport

CB, conventional bus
LFB, low floor bus

Fig. 1.7   Accessibility and independence

Some people could change category as a result of an improvement in public transport. For example, a person might need a wheelchair because the distance to the bus stop is too far for them to walk. An improved network design which brings the bus closer to their house could enable them to make the journey without the assistance of a wheelchair. This would help them change from the 'technical assistance' category to the 'no assistance' category and thus increase their independence. In this way, improved design of the bus system makes a fundamental difference to the choices available and the degree of independence that can be achieved.

Comparing the accessibility gap with the independence categories shows how changes in accessibility can affect independence. The improvements shown in Figures 1.4 to 1.6 reduce the accessibility gap, but it is not removed entirely and it is reduced at each end rather than in the middle. The importance of these reservations, especially the latter, can be seen when we compare the accessibility gap with the independence categories. Figure 1.7 suggests that accessibility is most difficult to deliver to people who require momentary, but vital, assistance. Although people in this category depend on such assistance for only a short time in the journey, the assistance is crucial and its absence will render the journey impossible. It is also extremely difficult to organise such localised assistance so that it can be guaranteed to be present at the right time and in the right place. A traveller cannot start their journey unless they are certain that this assistance will be at the right place at the right time. Unreliability in this respect negates whatever system has been put in place to provide assistance. The same problem arises with the reliability of technical assistance – non-functioning bus ramps have the same effect. This would move the passenger from the 'technical assistance' to the 'personal assistance (localised)' category if they would need someone to help them onto the bus, with the consequent loss of independence. Such failures reduce the extent to which a person can feel able to travel – and make the choice about travelling – independently.

Figure 1.7 also shows that people in other categories can gain independence in the ways described above as a result of improvements in accessibility to the bus system. Accessibility helps to deliver independence, but only if it can be relied on. It is therefore better to design accessibility into a system in such a way that it relies as little as possible on personal or technical assistance at particular points along the journey.

Independence can be challenged unwittingly in some circumstances. For example, consider the case where a person offers their non-car-owning neighbour a lift to the supermarket. Kind and generous though the offer may be, it can put the recipient of the offer in a position where they feel overly dependent. They are unable to refuse because they need to go to the supermarket and have no other way of going, but this reinforces their dependence on the kindness and generosity of their neighbour. The result is a reduction in the amount they travel because the lift-taker tries to reduce inconvenience to the lift-giver (and with it the sense of dependence engendered by the acceptance of the lift). We have found examples of just such a reaction in a number of our research projects. This is not to say that people should not offer others a lift, just that such an act can have unintended consequences.

Transport Provision

The discussion so far has raised some issues about accessibility, independence, the burden of responsibility within society and the concept of social justice and fairness. We now turn to the task of bringing these issues to bear on the process of setting design objectives from which we will be able to consider how best to put the concepts into practice.

Public Transport

A public transport system is one which is available to the general public to use. For our purposes there is no concern about who owns it, operates it or who controls it. The key concern is its availability to the public, and this presents considerable constraints and responsibilities to the designers of a public transport system to ensure that it is accessible. Public transport is the fundamental – default – transport system: the system that should be designed before all others and which everyone should be able to use without the need for private resources such as a car. The prime requirement of public transport design is to ensure that the accessible journey chain is maintained. Capacity (the conventional main objective) only makes sense if passengers can actually reach and use the system, so it must be secondary to accessibility as an objective. Systems must be designed so that they provide accessibility throughout the chain even where different owners and operators are responsible for different parts of the chain. Although the various owners and operators – and their technologies – might be different from each other, this should be transparent to the user, who, after all, is simply trying to make a journey.

One of the difficulties for designers of accessible transport systems is that over the last century or so the main influence on transport design has been the private car. This has spawned design objectives and techniques geared to ease the use of cars and, in addition, has raised expectations of the ease of mobility – or at least movement – for the private individual. As discussed above, accessibility is based on the need for social justice and thus may conflict with design objectives directed towards the enhancement of movement. One of the first impacts of basing transport design on accessibility objectives is that the public transport system would be truly available to everyone in society, whatever their accessibility needs. This does not prevent other people from using their private resources to obtain access to a private car, but it places the requirement on society to design first for the default system, which is available to everyone, and then to design for other forms of movement. If we insist that this default system is accessible to everyone we place constraints not only on its design – of network, infrastructure, vehicles, operating systems and information provision – but also on what we include in this 'public transport system'.

Trains and buses are usually considered to be public transport, but what about taxis, specialised services, ambulances, footways and other pedestrian infrastructure? In the sense of our definition of a transport system that the public can use, each of these examples is public transport. The accessible journey chain includes phases such as the walk to and from the bus stop and the provision of information. As each of these must be accessible in order for the chain to be complete, they must be included in the public transport system. Our search for a just and fair society in which people can reach and use the activities they wish must begin by ensuring that the whole public transport system is fully accessible. Nobody should be excluded from society on the basis of not being able to travel on society's default transport system.

The Bus System

We have chosen in this book to concentrate on the type of public transport offered on roads. Although not every form of road-based public transport might be considered to involve buses, we have used the bus system as the main focus for our research, and therefore this is the main source of examples for our discussion. We chose the bus system as our focus because:

- it incorporates every aspect of the accessible journey chain
- it involves the design of vehicles and infrastructure and the interface between them
- it highlights the conflicts and opportunities between the public and private sectors
- it is far more common than any other public transport mode
- its operational characteristics enable us to think in more practical terms about implementation
- we can test ideas about all of the above more easily (this would be much more difficult if we considered only, for example, a rail-based system).

Even where there is a railway system, it is likely that it will be necessary to use a bus (or some other form of road-based public transport) in order to reach the railway station. Therefore we consider the bus system – in its broadest interpretation – to be the default public transport system: if the bus system is not accessible, the rest of the public transport system is not accessible. We include in the bus system: the network of fixed- and variable-route scheduled bus services; bookable taxi and bus services; on-demand taxi services; specialised transport services provided for reasons of health, social services or education; and, because of its importance in the accessible journey chain, the pedestrian network.

Conclusions

A utopian society, where everybody has instant access to everything, does not exist, but every reduction from this ideal results in someone being excluded from something. So, to increase social inclusion we need to consider how to identify and deal with these exclusions. Some exclusions are the result of a lack of accessibility to the bus system, and these are the subject of this book. Transport is the means by which society coheres, people meet each other and manage to carry out their daily lives. The transport system is the means by which concepts such as freedom of choice and independent living are made real. The provision of more access to all sorts of activities must therefore be available to everyone, and for this reason we must ensure that there is a transport system which really is inclusive. The design of this transport system has to be directed towards eliminating barriers to access (or reducing their impact if they cannot be removed). Not all transport systems can be made completely inclusive: some people will inevitably be excluded from even the most accessible system. However, by including concepts such as justice, fairness, inclusion and accessibility in the creation of the design objectives, we can make decisions about the transport system, where suboptimal choices have to be made on the basis of maximising social justice rather than on achieving some other, less socially coherent, objectives.

The socially just and fair approach to transport policy places public transport at the top of the agenda for transport investment and improvement. This is because it is the practical statement about the level of mobility all members of society require in order to be able to live in a free and independent society. The main aim should be to maximise social justice by taking decisions on the basis of assuring the level of provision for the people experiencing the greatest difficulty in using the public transport system that enables them to be involved in whatever activity they choose.

The design of the public transport system is important because it is the default transport system for everyone in society; the bus system, in its widest sense, is the default public transport system. We aim to encourage design of bus systems that is directed towards the achievement of a fully accessible journey chain for every journey. Where this cannot be achieved in full and suboptimal solutions are required, the key to choosing these solutions rests with maintaining and enhancing social inclusion. The attainment of other transport-related objectives (e.g. time savings) can only be sought after the overall aim for social inclusion has been satisfied.

References

FRYE, A. (1996). 'Bus travel – a vital link in the chain of accessible transport'. *Proceedings of Bus and Coach 96*, Birmingham, UK.

RAWLS, J. (1971). *A Theory of Justice.* Oxford: Oxford University Press.

ROUSSEAU, J.-J. (1762). *The Social Contract* (trans. M. Cranston). London: Penguin, 1975.

Chapter 2

Existing Systems

N. Tyler

Introduction

In this chapter we take the concepts that we discussed in Chapter 1 and view them in terms of the bus system. We start with a brief description of a conventional view of public transport, but then we try to see it from the point of view of users. This involves a simple exercise in examining the types of road-based public transport to see how the multi-barrier nature of the accessibility problem can affect people. We then examine the providers of transport – who they are and what they provide. We discuss how principles can be put into practice and the requirements in terms of policy and legislation for the implementation of accessible transport. We then show how an accessible transport system needs a common mentality between all agents in the system and how this relates to the current legislation in the UK.

Public Transport Systems

The Conventional View

The usual way to view public transport is as a set of modes, gradually increasing in capacity, speed, comfort and cost, from the smallest and slowest component such as a taxi, to the largest, fastest element such as a high-speed train. This concept, illustrated graphically in Figure 2.1, is generally used to determine if a railway, light rail, tram or bus system should be constructed in a particular situation. The aim of most public transport systems is to convey large numbers of people as quickly as possible, usually into or around a city centre. The point past which the largest volume of passengers travels (the *maximum load point*) is the main constraint on the system, as this determines the maximum number of passengers that the system can carry.

The relationship between volume (i.e. passenger capacity) and speed is not simple. This is because the main way to increase passenger capacity is to increase the number of passenger-carrying vehicles able to pass the maximum load point. One way of doing this is to reduce the time that any one vehicle occupies space (i.e. increase its speed). This has implications for the safety of the system: there are limits to how close together vehicles can be, and the safe distance between vehicles changes as speed increases. Lehner (1949, 1950) examined this in relation to railway operation, and discovered that as operating speed increases the capacity at the maximum load point increases at first but subsequently reduces. An example of a *Lehner curve* is shown in Figure 2.2, where the relationship between passenger capacity and operating speed is plotted. Lehner studied the effects of different operating regimes for keeping the trains apart based on the stopping distance required for the following train to stop without colliding with the leading train, but the overall effect was similar in each case. The example illustrated in Figure 2.2 shows the passenger-carrying capacity of a railway line where the operating regime allows the following train to brake at a 'normal' rate while the leading train is decelerating at an 'emergency' rate. Although the actual capacity of the system varies with

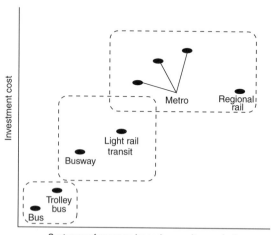

Fig. 2.1 *System performance of different types of public transport (after Vuchic (2000))*

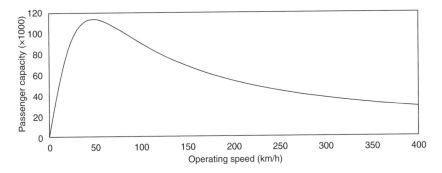

Fig. 2.2   A Lehner curve

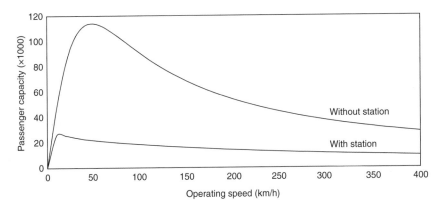

Fig. 2.3   A Lehner curve for a rail system with a station

the carrying capacity of the vehicles, the shape of Lehner's curves remains the same.

An interesting conclusion to be drawn from Lehner's work is that the maximum capacity is obtained at a relatively low speed. However, the separation between moving trains is not the main capacity constraint on a railway system. This is the existence of access points – railway stations – at which the trains must stop to collect and deliver passengers. Lehner estimated the effect of stations on capacity for different operating speeds. The resulting curve is shown in Figure 2.3. This shows the dramatic reduction in capacity that results from adding a station to the railway system. The fewer stations a railway has, the higher will be its operating speed and capacity. As the conventional aim of a public transport system has been to satisfy movement-enhancing objectives, the effect has usually been to ensure that the distance between stations is as large as possible (subject to constraints on reaching the station). Vuchic (1968) pointed out that the distance between stations should increase as a railway line approaches a city centre because the impact of stopping the trains is so great on the passengers – and increases as each train carries more passengers.

Public transport systems have been designed on the basis of bringing people into a city centre since railways started being built in the early part of the nineteenth century. Later, the need was perceived for people to move around the city centre once they had arrived there. This brought the need for thinking about a public transport system that functioned as a network rather than as an end-to-end service. It is very difficult for rail-based systems to operate co-operatively in networks because of the need to deal with the number of junctions and stations, each of which has similar negative effects on both capacity and speed. Mitigation of these effects is extremely costly. Cities which have developed rail-based city centre networks have found them to be expensive to construct and limited in capacity. Examples include London and Paris, with London being particularly prone to the capacity constraints of flat junctions and close spacing between stations.

If network operation is required, it is necessary to have vehicles which can operate independently of each other. Operating on different but complementary routes and being able to overtake other vehicles are prime requirements of a network-based system. It is much easier to design a bus system to operate in this way than to try to force a rail system to work in such a fashion. For example, buses can overtake each other without the need for expensive fixed infrastructure. However, bus systems often have to work at a lower operating speed than is envisaged for a railway system and require more operating staff per passenger (one driver per 100 passengers rather than one per 1000). Bus systems are often thought to be less attractive than a rail-based system, yet the bus system in London carries some 4 million passenger trips per day compared with the 3 million trips on the London Underground system.

London's Underground system has some 270 stations served by 13 lines. The bus system operating in the same overall area operates 700 lines, which call at some 17,000 bus stops. In accessibility terms, the bus system should be far more appropriate than the rail system for moving within and around the city, even if only because the walking distances are likely to be much less to and from bus stops than to and from railway stations. The bus system is often conceived as an end-to-end system (like a railway), yet it functions best as a network: the small vehicles make it unattractive for carrying large numbers of passengers along corridor routes, but make it very easy to reach people in places where railways cannot penetrate. We shall consider bus networks in more detail in Chapter 3. Before doing so, we shall discuss the bus system from a non-operational perspective.

The Users' View

The conventional view of the bus system does not usually place it within a societal context. If we are aiming to produce an inclusive society, we need to ensure that public transport – the default transport system – is truly accessible to everyone. We have pointed out before that we will use the bus system as our example, not least because it is more relevant to the daily needs of more people. As we showed in Chapter 1, we need to aim to satisfy accessibility rather than movement objectives and the bus system is well placed to provide examples of how this can be achieved.

The conventional view tends to concentrate on the operational needs of the bus system to achieve movement-enhancing objectives. If we look at buses from the users' viewpoint, the system looks rather different. We have summarised in Table 2.1 some differences between the perspective of public transport system planners and operators, on the one hand, and users, on the other. Instead of seeing the public transport system as a set of modes, the user sees the means of transport that they can reach and use. In some cases this will be a public bus, but in others it will be some form of 'specialised' transport provided by, for example, a voluntary organisation, a healthcare provider or a social services department. Specialised transport tends to be much less available than public transport, mostly because it is much more expensive to provide and thus the vehicles are more scarce than is commonly the case with a conventional bus fleet. Reliance on specialised transport might provide a greater degree of special care than can be found in a public bus system, but it is likely to mean a loss of independence for the user (see Figure 1.7 in Chapter 1). What specialisation is provided in the specialised service is thus very important to the users – much more so than who is providing the service. To a person who needs to make a journey, the choice is about which of these services they can use, not about whether it is 'public transport' or 'specialised transport'. In this sense, the identity of the provider of any particular service is not of interest – provided that they are competent and that the service is reliable, sufficiently accessible and reasonably priced.

In principle, every member of the public is 'eligible' to use public transport. Specialised transport is just part of the public transport mix for which particular eligibility restrictions are one of the barriers that must be faced. In the UK, some members of the public are also eligible for special transport to a hospital appointment (as a result of provisions in the Chronically Sick and Disabled Persons Act (1970)). However, their eligibility is still based on their being a member of the public and, even though they have to meet certain requirements, they do not have to be a member of a specific club or group in order to qualify (as they would for some forms of transport). Unfortunately, the effect of many eligibility criteria is that they can easily exclude people who should really be able to make use of the system.

Table 2.1   Comparison of different perspectives of the public transport system

	System-centred view	User-centred view
Functionality	Set of different modes Vehicle design Infrastructure design Schedule design	Means of usable transport
Management	Different operating companies	Makes no difference who owns it
	Public versus specialised services	Not interested as long as the services are appropriate and can be used
	Operators and infrastructure providers	If it works, see it as a whole system; if it doesn't, see it as dysfunctional. Many do not see a separation between the operator of the vehicle and the provider of the infrastructure
Control	Eligibility criteria determine who is allowed to use which service	Eligibility criteria determine who cannot use which service
Objectives	Increase capacity Increase movement[*] Decrease costs, increase profit	Increase mobility[*] Increase accessibility[*]

[*]As defined in Chapter 1

From the users' perspective, the transport system is what they can reach and use – whoever provides the service, and for whatever motivation. Our concern is to ensure that these systems are designed and operated to enable people to reach and use the activities they wish to undertake. Services which are the only available means of transport for particular members of the public because of the inaccessibility of the rest of the system are therefore an integral part of what we call 'public transport'. Analysis of public transport that ignores these services is incomplete and inadequate.

Now we can consider how the bus system can be integrated to achieve accessibility rather than movement objectives. For clarity in this chapter, we will separate the bus system into three parts:

- The *mainstream bus service* is the set of services operated using generally large buses and which travel along major roads within and between towns or in rural areas.
- A *micronetwork* is a set of services usually operated with small vehicles and which penetrates smaller areas such as housing estates or remote rural areas. It can act as a feeder service to mainstream buses or other public transport modes.
- *Specialised transport* is seen by the users as either a bus or an alternative to one, and includes three other groups of transport provision:
  - *door-to-door services* are bookable in advance to take a passenger from their origin to their destination, and include pre-booked taxis and services using minibuses such as London's Dial-a-Ride system
  - *special needs transport* includes specialised services which may have escorts, specially equipped vehicles or vehicles that are provided for special purposes (e.g. transport to hospitals or day centres)
  - *taxi services* are non-booked taxis (i.e. those hailed in the street) which can take a passenger from some point in the street to the door of their destination.

We have therefore arrived at a typified set of public transport categories which we will now consider from the users' point of view. The selection we shall consider is listed in Table 2.2 together with a summary of the main characteristics that are important for the discussion in this chapter.

The actions we shall discuss later in this book mean that some people who are currently restricted to using specialised transport will be able to use the mainstream services. However, even if all the suggestions made were followed and the mainstream bus system were very accessible, there will still be some people for whom the only way to travel would be to use one of the specialised services.

The user is not particularly interested in the details of a transport service or who provides it. What is important to them is whether or not they will be able to reach and use it in order to reach and use their chosen activity. If they can use a mainstream bus service, that is all well and good, but if they require more specialised transport they can be at a distinct disadvantage.

Most transport systems confront their potential users with barriers. The barrier could take one (or more) of many forms – for example, financial (too high a fare), physical (too far away), sensory (difficult to see), cognitive (difficult to understand), or psychological (too scary) – and it

Table 2.2 Characteristics of various transport systems

	Characteristics	Comments
Special needs transport	Specialised service: could be a special vehicle, special equipment on the vehicle, or the presence of specialist crew (e.g. escorts)	Operated by local authorities or health authorities or by other organisations on their behalf. Eligibility criteria will apply
Door-to-door (pre-booked)	Car, minibus or pre-booked taxi or minicab service Has to be reserved in advance	Eligibility criteria can apply if this service is being supplied on behalf of statutory bodies Requires the user (or their representative) to make a booking
Taxi (hailable)	Operates randomly along mostly major roads Operates to the door of the destination	Requires knowledge of likely places to find empty taxis Depends on taxi driver stopping to pick up Not everywhere is likely to have taxis readily available (especially in poor areas) Expensive to use: subsidy (via some form of discount scheme) is necessary for people on low incomes to use taxis
Micronetwork	Operates in small areas (e.g. linking housing estates to mainstream bus services and other activities or villages to a local market town) Could be hail and ride Usually fixed route and schedule, but some can divert on request if booked	Operates inside residential areas that are difficult to reach by other services Short routes help reliability If diversions are made, journey times can be unpredictable and pre-booking required

Table 2.2   (Contd)

	Characteristics	Comments
Mainstream bus service	Operates along main and some residential roads Fixed route and schedule (usually)	Can be unreliable if traffic congestion has not been dealt with Vehicles have to comply with Public Service Vehicle Accessibility Regulations 2000

could be the result of a deliberate attempt to exclude some people or just have that effect unwittingly. A key element of the process of designing accessible transport systems is the elimination or reduction of barriers.

The consideration of barriers is a complex business: both the number and variety of barriers are large. The resolutions to some barriers may conflict with others, or even make matters worse in some respects. As an illustrative example of the way in which the barrier concept should be considered, we now describe each category of transport provision in terms of a number of barriers. The selection is not exhaustive, but is sufficient to indicate the implications of this approach – the details of how barriers should be assessed and remedied are discussed later in the book. In order to make the comparison easier to understand, we use different degrees of shading to represent the effect of a barrier: none for the smallest effect, light for a medium effect and dark for the largest effect.

We can see the way this works with a simple example. On the face of it, the preferred transport service for people who experience accessibility difficulties could be to reduce the distance to reach the mode. Thus they might prefer to use transport systems such as door-to-door services or specialised transport. The transport service categories are represented in Figure 2.4, with the shading becoming darker as the distance to reach them increases and becomes more of a barrier to be overcome.

Distance is not the only barrier to the use of a particular type of public transport. What happens when we consider time? The usual way to think about time when considering public transport is in terms of the time taken to reach the bus stop and the time spent inside the bus. However there is another time element that needs to be considered: the time required by a person between deciding to go on a journey and being able to start travelling. We can call this the *reservation time*. Reservation time is imposed on the traveller by the transport system and varies greatly between different types of operating system.

One feature of independence is being able to choose what to do. Another is spontaneity – the ability to choose when to do it. The liberty to choose the departure time for a journey is an important aspect of independence, and public transport systems can limit such freedom. Some types of public transport require pre-booking. In these cases, it is critical to a person's ability to be spontaneous that the reservation time is as short as possible. In some cases – for example, off-peak times for a pre-booked taxi service – the reservation time could be a matter of minutes. However, at other times there can be a considerable delay.

One of the main complaints about door-to-door services around the country is the difficulty of getting through to the control centre to book a journey. Only the most persistent succeed, and most schemes concede that there is some bias in the take-up: a relatively small number of people use the service a lot and a larger number of eligible people use it quite rarely or not at all. Given the persistence that can be required to make a reservation in such circumstances, a large element of the target population is effectively excluded from their chosen activities as a result of being unable to reserve door-to-door transport.

Although some eligible people choose not to use door-to-door services because they already have other arrangements (e.g. private car), there is a general concern that the difficulty of booking a service is acting as a barrier to many potential users. Therefore, one of the issues seen by the users of transport services is the extent to which they can make a trip at short notice. This might not matter too much for a rare journey (for which there might even be a readiness to pay for a taxi service). However, this is a problem for people who cannot reach the conventional bus system but who need to make a journey to carry out simple daily tasks (e.g. the 'normal' shopping journey). We can therefore revisit the spectrum shown in Figure 2.4 to reflect the effect of the reservation time on the availability of the various transport systems. Figure 2.5 shows that the mainstream bus service is easier to use than the specialised transport as far as reservation time is concerned.

A comparison of Figures 2.4 and 2.5 shows that there is a trade-off between time and space. Door-to-door services offer almost zero access

Fig. 2.4   The effect of distance on the accessibility to transport systems

Fig. 2.5   The effect of reservation time on the accessibility of transport systems

| Special needs transport | Door-to-door service | Taxi | Minibus micronetwork | Bus service |

Fig. 2.6   The impact of the functionality of the transport categories on accessibility

distance, but possibly a long time to wait for the vehicle to arrive. A scheduled bus service usually requires a passenger to walk to reach the bus stop, but can offer a much reduced waiting time (even though the departure time is still constrained by knowledge of the timetable). As the frequency of the scheduled service increases, so the comparative attractiveness of the door-to-door service reduces. The key to this is therefore the availability of a sufficient frequency in the scheduled service to maintain some freedom over the choice of departure time.

Accessible bus services can offer more opportunities than the specialised services: they are more available than the other categories and routinely operate longer routes without having to make special administrative arrangements. The micronetwork provides a 'closer-to-user' convenience in that they offer the chance to reach the mainstream bus system from a point nearer to the journey origin (or destination). The success of this depends on a reliable and fully accessible interchange between the micronetwork and the mainstream buses. If these interchanges (and those within the mainstream bus system) are truly accessible, the combination of the two categories provides a powerful and flexible range of opportunities for everyone. Door-to-door and hailable taxi services can also provide a wide range of destinations, but the opportunity to take advantage of this is rarer than for the accessible mainstream buses. This is because providing a special journey for one person is likely to preclude use of that vehicle for anyone else at that time. This effect is observed by many operators of door-to-door services. Hailable taxis can, of course, take a passenger where they can afford to go, but first it is necessary to find the vacant taxi. For this reason they provide fewer opportunities than the more ubiquitous bus system.

However, the range of opportunities offered by the bus system comes at a price. Conventional buses require the user to be able to use them as they are. We can make this easier (e.g. by using low-floor buses, improving the associated infrastructure or making the information accessible) and thus open up the buses and their opportunities to more people. Specialised transport will adapt to meet the explicit needs of individual users, which is one of the reasons it is expensive to operate, scarce and rationed by means of a set of eligibility criteria. We can therefore compare the public transport spectrum obtained when we examine exclusion from the system on the basis of the way it operates (functionality) and of who is allowed to use it (eligibility criteria). Figure 2.6 shows how the functionality of the system affects its accessibility. Specialised transport services adapt to meet the needs of users more than the bus or hailable taxi systems. Figure 2.7 shows the effect of eligibility criteria on the accessibility of the system. Specialised transport is generally subject to eligibility criteria and is thus less accessible than other categories.

It is also worth examining this spectrum from the point of view of cost. The cost of providing a service always passes on to the user in some way or other. Either it is reflected in the fare, the level of subsidy (and therefore in taxes), or in the supply (a service which is expensive to provide will either be highly priced, be scarce, or both). In most cases it is a combination of all three. Door-to-door services that can cost up to £25–30 per passenger trip will necessarily be scarce, whereas a bus service which costs £2 per passenger trip is easier to provide at a high frequency. The cost of providing a given service is therefore a factor that affects its accessibility: as the cost increases, so it is likely that the accessibility in terms of availability will diminish. The spectrum for our services when considering their cost per trip is shown in Figure 2.8, where it can be seen that, in general, the cost falls as we move to the right of the spectrum.

The cost is borne by the provider of the service (or at least the body that purchases the service from a provider on behalf of the users) and they make the decisions about availability as a function of cost. Price, by contrast, is borne by the user. Sometimes the user is charged for transport (e.g. powers exist for local authorities to charge for social services). In these cases, the actual price charged to the user could act as a disincentive. Without a doubt, price is a major element in preventing people from using a transport service, especially where the user groups concerned are predominantly low income. Even where a local authority makes a charge for transport, it is unlikely to be the full cost. Thus the price will be less of a disincentive for transport provided by the local authority than it would be for a public transport service carrying little or no subsidy. Therefore the spectrum should be revisited from the perspective of price to the user. This is reproduced in Figure 2.9.

Reliability is highly important to everyone: unreliability causes stress and could result in all sorts of difficulties for people who need to make

Special needs transport	Door-to-door service	Taxi	Minibus micronetwork	Bus service

Fig. 2.7   The impact of eligibility criteria on accessibility

Special needs transport	Door-to-door service	Taxi	Minibus micronetwork	Bus service

Fig. 2.8   The cost (to the purchaser or provider) of the various transport systems

Special needs transport	Door-to-door service	Taxi	Minibus micronetwork	Bus service

Fig. 2.9   The impact of the price (to the user) of different transport systems

Special needs transport	Door-to-door service	Taxi	Minibus micronetwork	Bus service

Fig. 2.10   The impact of the reliability of various transport services on accessibility

journeys under some form of time constraint. The most difficult service to deal with reliably is a hailable taxi. The time taken for a journey depends on the existence of a taxi in the place where the user is waiting to hail it. This is a matter of knowledge of places where vacant taxis are likely to pass and other issues (e.g. the weather). Users of door-to-door services often complain about unreliability – both in the booking process and in the actual transport. Where minibuses are used to provide several trips in each vehicle, the pick-up time can be changed as a result of new trips being added to the route (or late booking is not permitted, thus reducing spontaneity). This also affects a user's journey time if new trips are added after they have been collected. Mainstream buses are also notoriously unreliable, but at least their stopping points and route are known and thus a reasonable guess based on past experience might help to predict the journey time. If bus priorities are implemented and traffic congestion is under control, reliability of mainstream bus services could be dramatically improved. In one sense, special needs services are more reliable in that they are often provided on a regular basis as part of a scheduled service. Unforeseen delays can be advised to the user as they will be waiting at home (rather than at a bus stop). However, these services are often notoriously unreliable due to managerial and/or operational reasons. The best compromise on reliability comes from the minibus micronetwork: as these are short routes operating on residential streets they are less prone to congestion problems than mainstream bus services. As long as they do not attempt to provide a door-to-door service or permit diversions from the route, journey times will be predictable. The fixed route means that people can understand where the buses will be. The impact of reliability of various transport services on accessibility is summarised in Figure 2.10.

One way to offset the difficulties caused by an unreliable service is to increase the frequency at which it is offered. Frequency has two effects. First, the demand is spread between more vehicles. Assuming that the demand remains constant, a scheduled bus service will have fewer passengers per vehicle at a higher frequency than it would at a lower one, and a door-to-door service will have fewer disruptions to its programmed route if fewer passengers are allocated to it. Secondly, a more frequent service is more attractive than a less frequent one, so demand is likely to increase as frequency increases. The impact of frequency on accessibility is summarised in Figure 2.11.

Generally, apart from the distance criterion, all of the above suggests that working with the bus system as a whole to enhance accessibility and independence is the best way forward. This is likely to cost less and provide more independence for more people than concentrating at the other end of the spectrum. In addition, by making the bus and minibus micronetwork work well for more people, pressure on the more specialised services is reduced. This would enable the providers of specialised services to provide a more accessible service to those people for whom even the most accessible bus system is still out of reach. To resolve the distance problem, the mainstream bus network must be defined in an accessible way, in conjunction with a minibus micronetwork.

It is important to realise that we are dealing with a spectrum, not a competition. All these service types are required in order to make society accessible to everyone. Having an inaccessible bus service merely puts so much pressure on the much more expensive specialised services that they cannot cope and people simply withdraw from society because they cannot go out. Having accessible bus services but no specialised services simply means that all those who cannot reach the bus services are left out of society. The accessibility gap is unforgiving. If a person cannot reach and use the bus system and is either ineligible for the specialised services or no such services are provided, then they are excluded from society.

Similar points could be made in relation to other types of services and their respective characteristics. It is therefore important to be aware of the disadvantages of choosing any particular means of providing transport in terms of the impacts on accessibility and, having made a selection, to deal with the consequent problems for the users. Figure 2.12 shows the users' view of the relative accessibility of each category for each barrier. In practice, this table should be constructed with the active participation of the users defining the barriers and the values. It might be a good idea to construct tables for different groups of users and discuss them as part of a public participation exercise (as described in Chapter 7).

What does all this mean? We have considered in a very simple way a small number of barriers and their potential effects on the users of the five categories of public bus systems shown in Table 2.2. We have presented just a few examples to show how each category can respond to different barriers. Of course, a proper analysis of a transport system would need to include many more barriers than the ones used in our example, but it is possible to have some sort of idea about the way in which a particular barrier (e.g. distance) has a different effect on the ability to make a journey depending on the type of transport service that is being offered.

| Special needs transport | Door-to-door service | Taxi | Minibus micronetwork | Bus service |

Fig. 2.11   The impact of frequency on accessibility

	Special needs transport	Door-to-door service	Taxi	Minibus micronetwork	Bus service
Distance					
Reservation					
Functionality					
Eligibility					
Cost					
Price					
Reliability					
Frequency					
Overall					

Fig. 2.12   Summary of the different transport service types

The effects summarised in Figure 2.12 are intended to reflect the users' perspective. However, the choice of transport to be supplied is usually made by someone else (e.g. a transport planner or a procurer of transport services) and is often made in isolation of the actual users. Their selection of one type of transport service over another can be made on a number of different grounds and the relative importance of these to the chooser will influence which type of transport would be chosen. However, such a choice brings consequences to the user which must not be ignored if the public transport system is to be able to deliver an acceptable set of travel options to everyone.

Having looked at the public transport spectrum in terms of its effects on users it is useful to consider how it appears when compared with the people and organisations who provide the transport.

Transport Providers

Transport providers can be grouped into three sectors (Gillingwater and Tyler, 2001) as shown in Box 2.1. It is important to understand the way in which the spectrum of public transport as shown in Figures 2.4 to 2.12 is supplied in practice. Historically, there has been a split between the services provided by the statutory sector and those provided by the private sector. Until 1986, some local authorities were able to operate their own bus companies, but this was ruled out by the Transport Act 1985. From 1 October 1986 public bus services were provided by the private sector and the statutory sector could only react to gaps between the

Box 2.1   Transport providers by sector

Primary sector   Private sector, motivated by profit. Examples are mainstream bus companies, and taxi and minicab operators (individuals and companies)

Secondary sector   Statutory sector, primarily local authority and healthcare providers who operate transport fleets as a statutory requirement (healthcare or education), or to facilitate the operation of other statutory services (e.g. social services)

Third sector   Voluntary sector, not-for-profit organisations. Examples are community transport operators and some of the larger charities (e.g. Age Concern)

---

services deemed to be 'commercially viable' by the private operators. Statutory services, such as those required under the Chronically Sick and Disabled Persons Act 1970, or education transport services were provided by the relevant health or education authority, and thus provision remained within the statutory sector. Inevitably, gaps in the provision began to appear and, because it was not possible for direct intervention by local authorities, some of the transport provision was taken on by the voluntary sector. Indeed, Sections 19 and 22 of the Transport Act 1985 were designed to facilitate this intervention.

As the statutory sector has been repeatedly pressed for reductions in cost, the level of provision has been reduced and successive managements have examined the law to test the required, as opposed to the desired, level of statutory provision. This often put direct pressure on the voluntary sector: we came across one example during our research where the local health authority removed all transport for hospital outpatient appointments except for those requiring two or more escorts in order to make a journey. Other people were advised to make contact with local voluntary transport organisations (a list was thoughtfully provided). The health authority concerned had made no effort to contact the local voluntary organisations with a view to establishing whether or not they had the requisite organisational or operational capacity. The result of this sort of action was that the voluntary sector tended to become heavily involved in the provision of specialised transport services, including the provision of door-to-door transport. The Community Transport Association has helped to improve the technical and organisational skills of such organisations so that the voluntary sector is now able to provide a professional service to the community. One view of these changes in the supply side is that the voluntary sector has brought its user-focused approach and 'muscled in' on the relationship between the private and statutory sectors. As a result, these sectors have been forced to adopt a more user-centred basis for their provision in order to compete for service contracts.

It could be argued that many of the innovations introduced into road-based public transport in recent years have been inspired, or at least encouraged, by the voluntary sector: door-to-door transport, the use of small vehicles, wheelchair-accessible transport and travel training are just a few examples. Even more recently, some voluntary sector transport organisations have won contracts to operate mainstream bus routes, and have started to develop and operate their own local scheduled services. Later in this book we describe one case where the voluntary sector has taken on the management of a local bus service on behalf of the local community and another where a voluntary sector organisation has taken the role of specifying and organising the supply of specialised transport for a local authority. The voluntary sector is now present throughout the public transport spectrum, sometimes as a provider of transport, sometimes as the procurer of transport and sometimes as the overall manager of the local transport services. The boundary between private and statutory sector activities is becoming very blurred, with purchasing and providing being carried out in the statutory and private sectors, respectively. The voluntary sector is now active in all the activities previously considered to be in the exclusive domain of either private or statutory sectors. This might lead us to think that the voluntary sector is actually subsuming both the statutory and private sectors. For example, the (voluntary sector) Transport Co-ordination Centre in Hackney described in Chapter 7 specifies the service standards to which both the private and statutory sector contractors must adhere in order to provide transport services on its behalf.

The voluntary sector is renowned for its user-based roots and has brought into these areas of operation a sense of user-centred organisation and provision. As a result, with the progressive involvement of the voluntary sector in mainstream activities has come a change in emphasis from provider-based decision-making to user-based decision-making. This change is still at an early stage and some organisations are rather scared of it. Nevertheless, just because an organisation is based in the voluntary sector does not necessarily mean that it is user-focused. It is very easy for organisations to lose their roots as they become more embroiled in the difficulties of providing core services. It is interesting to see how organisations could become remarkably similar in attitude to the private or statutory sector organisations they have replaced. Maintaining the meaningful involvement of the users is a continual task, and user focus needs to be actively pursued at all times.

The issue that bedevils statutory transport provision is the conflict between function and finance. Few people worry about who provides a transport service, as long as it is provided at an acceptable quality and price. However, there is deep concern within many statutory bodies about who pays for and controls the transport service. The local authority department that is funding a transport service believes that it should control the supply and eligibility and, importantly, that it should do so only for its own clients. One department does not want to pay for another's transport unless there is some form of reciprocal arrangement. Sometimes they arrange a set of arcane reasons to explain why a vehicle cannot be used by clients from two different departments at the same time. As this is difficult between two departments of the same organisation, it comes as no surprise to find that it is almost impossible between organisations. The result is that there is a lot of duplication of resources – of the transport as well as administration – and control passes into the wrong hands: we found one local authority where the need for transport meant that the social services being made available to clients were effectively being controlled by the in-house transport management.

There are several ways in which the conflict between function and finance could be resolved. The most obvious is to make the transport department into a cost centre which charges purchasing departments for the transport it provides or arranges. Its objective is to reduce transport costs by obtaining transport at the lowest cost and co-ordinating different requests where possible to make the best use of each vehicle. Devon County Council has been operating a transport co-ordination centre along similar lines for several years.

Another way to tackle cost reduction is to attempt to co-ordinate public transport and statutory provision by means of sensible scheduling of vehicle use. A peak-hour bus could be used in the off-peak period to provide transport for social services, thus sharing the costs of the vehicle and making better use of the operating crews. This can help to secure the public transport service, while allowing social services to take advantage of the existence of the vehicle to provide more and better services to its clients. The Kent Karrier scheme is a version of this mixing of vehicle use.

Another possibility is to place the co-ordination of transport outside the statutory sector. Where the voluntary sector is providing much of the transport in any case this could be seen as formalising the status quo. The voluntary sector, with its user-centred focus is well placed to try to organise the transport to provide the clients with the best service, whoever is paying for the transport. This makes it a lot easier to incorporate the transport needs of different organisations within a single transport entity. By making their vehicles available to such a scheme, the statutory authorities are able to secure the function while resolving the financial aspects through a common charging method. An example of this sort of approach can be found in west Norfolk.

In Chapter 7, we describe another scheme which seeks to make the transport service more user-focused by making the users' needs the first priority, the type of transport to be used the second and the control of the resulting costs the third. In this case, the transport procurement is separated from the purchasing (by the local authority departments) and provision (by various transport operators, including the local authority's in-house operation). The procurement is undertaken by a separate organisation, which is independent of both the purchasers and providers, on the basis of finding the most appropriate transport (for the user) at the lowest cost (for the purchaser). In principle, this arrangement procures transport for any user on behalf of any purchaser from any satisfactory provider, pays the provider and charges the purchaser. In some cases the most appropriate transport could be a mainstream bus service; in others it could be a pre-booked taxi. Sometimes it is an escorted pedestrian journey. The rule is that it should be the most appropriate method available for the user at that time. Thus the transport can function without interdepartmental disputes about whose client is in whose vehicle. Control is exercised through strict service specifications, backed up by strong contractual relationships between the purchasers and the procurer and between the procurer and the providers. The procurement of transport is made outside the statutory sector, with the statutory obligation being met through a procurement contract.

It is becoming clear that the voluntary sector is becoming more involved with mainstream public transport, including both the statutory and public bus services, as well as its traditional 'voluntary' role. Statutory transport providers seem to be retracting – towards organising others to provide transport or, more extremely, to requesting others to organise their transport. The private sector has meanwhile become more involved in statutory provision. The private sector has remained the major provider of mainstream bus services and hailable and bookable taxis. It has not really become involved in more specialised transport services, although there are some examples in London and elsewhere, usually as an offshoot of emergency ambulance services.

The voluntary sector has moved to plug the transport gap arising from the need for the private sector to maintain profits and the desire to reduce costs on the part of the statutory sector. It has increased its involvement from the provision of social car schemes towards the supply of door-to-door services and contract work for the statutory sector. In some cases it has competed successfully against private sector companies to win contracts for the provision of mainstream bus routes and has been involved in the development and operation of minibus micronetwork services (e.g. in Hackney). The voluntary sector is therefore represented throughout the spectrum, with the exception of hailable taxis.

We have discussed the public transport system from the perspectives of users and providers using the concept of a spectrum of transport categories. We can see that in order to provide a reasonable level of independence to users, the full spectrum of public transport has to be available. We have also seen that in order to achieve this providers from all three sectors need to be involved. We have concluded that for users' independence to grow, there is a need for a common mentality amongst and between the transport providers, the users and purchasers. There are a few examples of movement in thinking – for example, a voluntary sector community transport organisation running a mainstream bus service. However, the real sign of progress would be if a primary sector organisation began to function with the community-based objectives which are more common in voluntary sector enterprises. In general, this would need encouragement from outside the transport sector, mostly by means of a 'push' from central government through policy and legislation. We shall now look at recent UK legislation to see if such a push exists and, if so, how it might operate in practice.

Policy Context

Before looking at the legislation, it is helpful to consider the policy context within which the legislation arises. This means understanding how policy works – for example, how society moves from an idea to the set of legislation that enables the associated goals to be reached.

Policy Issues

The provision of accessible bus services is an example of putting a previously stated policy into practice. If the policy is clear, the decision is clear – it is only made difficult when the policy is either unclear or where it involves unforeseen problems at the implementation stage. It is therefore important to make sure that the policy can deliver such clarity.

One of the reasons that a policy fails to provide sufficient basis for a decision is that it has somehow been separated from the guiding principles from which it originally emerged. One can imagine the process. A principle (e.g. universal accessibility) is considered 'good'. A policy is required in order to put the principle into practice because it will usually be necessary to vote public money for such an undertaking. The problem begins here: in order for the policy to be adopted it is often necessary to 'refine' the principle. For example, the principle 'all people are equal' is generally held to be a 'good' principle. In order for such a principle to be enshrined in law it would have to modified – a political party espousing such a principle would, in order to be elected, almost certainly have to concede that some people are 'more equal' than others. In turn, this could become, in practice, the application of tax laws favouring some people

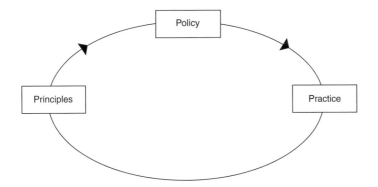

Fig. 2.13   Decisions: principles to policy to practice

over others. It could be argued that politics – the art of the possible – is the process of converting principles into policy.

The practical application of a given policy is usually a question of money – either at the broad macroeconomic level (e.g. spending on health rather than defence) or at the detailed project level (e.g. spending on a project with £X of net benefits rather than another one with net benefits of £Y). It could therefore be argued that the conversion of policy into practice is the matter of economics. This is represented in Figure 2.13, where movement is clockwise: from principles to policy to practice.

Some constitutions exclude certain members of society (e.g. women) from certain activities as a principle. However, very few societies admit to excluding people as a principle on the basis of a perceived disability, yet most – maybe all – societies do disable some people by making it impossible for them to reach and use some activities in practice. The decision process (i.e. the means by which the principle is put into practice) has therefore failed in many cases. A lot of our research has involved developing a principle, finding out how it could be put into practice and then working out the needs for policy and legislation in order for the practice to be more widely adopted. We have therefore had to reverse the conventional route for putting principles into practice as shown in Figure 2.13. Figure 2.14 shows the effect. Moving from principles to practice by means of a series of research studies and practical pilot projects, we can determine the policy needs – not of the principles, but of the practice. In this approach, the policy question is 'What is the policy framework necessary to facilitate this practice?' rather than 'What is the policy representation of this principle?'. Solutions to the new question include setting the policy umbrella under which money is voted for the implementation of some schemes rather than others. The link between policy and principle is then one of checking if the original principle is still being supported.

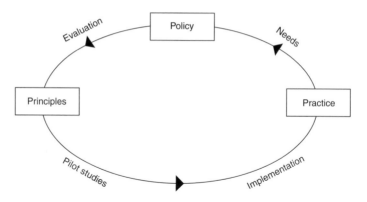

Fig. 2.14   Decisions: principles to practice to policy

We can illustrate the implications of the change in direction by using a recent example. The UK Government's Ten Year Plan (DETR, 2000a) carries many proposals for investment by the public and private sectors amounting to some £180 billion over the period to 2010–2011. Almost 60% of this is directed towards public transport. The plan contains a statement which is very relevant to the subject of this book:

> Building in accessibility for disabled people in all new investment is a condition of public money being spent. (DETR, 2000a, p. 41)

By setting the condition, the government is setting the policy context in which public investment will be made during the next 10 years. The principle of equitable access has therefore become a policy. The problem is to ensure that it will come to fruition in practice. The danger of a policy which is derived from a principle rather than aiming towards one is that it is too easy to satisfy the policy with inappropriate practice (i.e. spending the money without achieving the accessibility). However, in the case of accessible transport, the policy statement has been derived from practice: many of the means of providing equitable accessibility are known and could, with appropriate investment, be put into practice. The difficulty is to ensure that the money will be spent wisely – the test will be that the original principle (equitable access) is satisfied as a result of the investment. For this reason, the approach illustrated in Figure 2.14, with its constant aim of looking towards the original principles, is the better way to put a principle into practice. The evaluation of accessibility is therefore a prime necessity for the successful implementation of the Ten Year Plan – without it, all the money being invested on condition that accessibility is built in will be spent without any way of checking that the principles have indeed been met.

Documents such as the Ten Year Plan are still statements of intent. The reality comes in two ways:

- the policy is adopted voluntarily
- the policy is reinforced by legislation.

In some cases both apply: for example, the accessibility standards for buses incorporated in the Public Service Vehicles Accessibility Regulations 2000 have largely been drawn from recommendations published by the Disabled Persons' Transport Advisory Committee (DPTAC) in 1997.

It is not unreasonable to suppose that when expenditure is required universal implementation of a policy is likely to require legislation. We shall now turn to the main sources of recent legislation concerned with accessibility to bus systems: the Disability Discrimination Act 1995 (DDA), The Public Service Vehicles Accessibility Regulations 2000 (PSVA Regulations) and the Transport Act 2000.

Legislation

The DDA is the primary legislation under which regulations such as the PSVA Regulations have been introduced. As far as bus systems are concerned, the DDA has impacts in two areas. Part III of the DDA refers to access to goods and services and Part V covers accessibility to public service vehicles.

Part III requires access to goods and services to be non-discriminatory. This does not mean that everywhere must be fully accessible: the requirement is that a person cannot be discriminated against in relation to access to, or the standard of, goods and services on the grounds of their disability (Section 19). The DDA requires that alterations shall be made to buildings in which goods and services are available. If this is not possible, a reasonable alternative must be provided. It seems clear that Part III applies to a bus station, but it will remain for case law to establish if it applies to a bus stop or footway.

Part V applies to public transport vehicles (taxis, public service vehicles and rail vehicles). The DDA does not confer a right of access to a vehicle. Section 40 empowers the Secretary of State to make regulations by which the vehicle may, and may not, be accessible. In the case of the bus system, these regulations are the PSVA Regulations. Although the DDA applies to public service vehicles adapted to carry more than eight passengers, the PSVA Regulations currently apply only to vehicles adapted to carry 23 or more passengers. Sections 41 and 42 of the DDA provide that a public service vehicle cannot be used on a road unless it (or a corresponding 'type vehicle') has received an accessibility certificate. The Secretary of State also has the power under Section 43 to issue a special authorisation for vehicles of a specified class or description so that they can receive an accessibility certificate even if they do not comply in some respect.

Until 31 December 2000, accessibility of buses and coaches was dependent on the operator's wish to follow the recommendations of bodies such as the DPTAC. Some local authorities used the opportunity afforded by the tendering process for non-commercial services to stipulate adherence to these or other recommendations. However, there was no general statutory requirement to make a bus accessible to disabled people. Thus, even in an area where accessible vehicles were required as a condition of winning a non-commercial contract, commercial services could still be operated with inaccessible vehicles. The resulting inconsistency of provision made the bus system inaccessible and prevented it from being able to accommodate everyone.

Since the introduction of the PSVA Regulations on 31 December 2000, buses and coaches are required to be designed to afford facilities for disabled people. All new buses and coaches with a capacity of more than 22 seated passengers have to comply with the PSVA Regulations from 1 January 2001, with some limited exceptions. In order to encourage a practicable and consistent improvement in accessibility, the PSVA Regulations include a timetable for implementation depending on the vehicle class and age. In principle, all single-deck buses will have to comply with the regulations from 1 January 2016, all double-deck buses from 1 January 2017 and all coaches from 1 January 2020. These end dates allow for vehicles in use before 31 December 2000 to continue in use until the end of their commercial life. In practice, it is expected that the bus fleet will be compliant long before these dates.

Some vehicles are not covered by the PSVA Regulations (e.g. vehicles operating under permits obtained under Sections 19 or 22 of the Transport Act 1985). Vehicles being used for injured and sick people and heritage vehicles which are only used on a few days a year are exempted from the PSVA Regulations. General compliance with two aspects of the PSVA Regulations will be deferred until 2003. These concern the edges and gradients of boarding lifts and ramps and the illumination for route number and destination displays on the side of a coach.

So, from 1 January 2017, all buses will have to be accessible to the same extent, wherever they are in the country. In practice this will mean many improvements in accessibility inside and some outside the vehicle. Most of these improvements will benefit wheelchair users, for whom access to buses before the PSVA Regulations would often have been impossible. The regulations also contain requirements to improve accessibility for people with other needs. As research and development advances, more enhancements will become available and we can suppose that the regulations will be updated to keep track of such improvements. The PSVA Regulations form an important milestone in the long road to full accessibility. However, there is a long way to go before we can be sure that all aspects of accessibility are able to be enshrined in regulations. For example, a lot more research is still required before a complete information system that is fully accessible to people with learning difficulties could be required on all buses.

The PSVA Regulations therefore constitute a great improvement in terms of the vehicles, but the vehicle is only one element of the accessible journey chain. There is an urgent need to tackle other elements of the chain, notably the interfaces between them (e.g. between the bus and the bus stop, along the footway, or information provision) before we can enable everyone to lead as full and independent a life as they wish.

At the time of writing, we are awaiting outcomes from a trial of audiovisual information in buses and the results of the final consultation exercise of the draft Conduct Regulations which will determine what is required of bus crews and passengers following the introduction of the PSVA Regulations.

Until the enactment of the Transport Act 2000 it was difficult to design and implement a bus network in most of the UK. This was because the Transport Act 1985 placed the burden of network design on bus operators, who were expected to use their commercial expertise and entrepreneurial acumen to design and operate commercially viable services. Local authorities were prevented from entering this market and were relegated to the position of tendering services which they deemed necessary but which were not being provided by the commercial operators. This left local authorities with many problems – for example, the operator's view of the commercial viability of a bus service could change overnight, resulting in a threat to end the service. A local authority in this position is left with a stark choice – either to provide financial support for the service or to lose it. Under the Transport Act 1985, the local authority had 42 days to determine if and how they could respond to the loss of the service. This resulted in unstable provision of bus services in which the prime feature was to lower costs rather than to provide a service. People with mobility problems suffered disproportionately from this as they were less likely than others to have alternative transport. Drivers on low wages with old, ill-equipped and uncomfortable vehicles combined to make bus travel an inconvenient and often unpleasant experience.

The Transport Act 2000 should change this. Section 108 requires local authorities to produce a local transport plan (LTP) and to report annually to central government on progress against targets in the plan. The LTP must include a 'bus strategy' in which the local authority states how it intends to meet the transport requirements of persons within the authority's area, how it will ensure that bus services meet the authority's standards and how it will ensure that necessary facilities and services connected with bus services will be provided (Section 110(1)). Guidance on the preparation of LTPs (DETR, 2000b) indicates that networks should be considered both quantitatively (including network design, frequency requirements and targets) and qualitatively (improving the attractiveness of public transport and reflecting the needs of particular user groups). An important effect of this is to encourage local authorities to think about their transport policies over a longer time horizon than used to be the case.

Sections 114 to 123 of the Transport Act 2000 set out the ways in which 'quality partnerships' between local authorities and bus operators can be constructed. A quality partnership is an agreement between a local authority and an operator in which the operator will provide a given quality of service (e.g. vehicle specification, but not frequency or timing of services) and the authority will provide associated traffic management and/or infrastructure. The idea is developed further into a 'quality contract' (Sections 124 to 134) in which the authority enters into a contract with an operator to provide services within a given area. This is seen as a serious step with which the Secretary of State has to be in agreement. Quality contracts are seen as the option of last resort when it has proved impossible to function properly with a partnership. A quality contract enables the local authority to specify the services that may operate in the area and the operator is allowed to operate in the area without fear of competition from other operators, but will be required to provide the services as specified by the local authority. Quality partnerships and contracts provide a mechanism by which a local authority can plan to provide enhancements to bus systems in their area, including bus priorities and improvements to bus stops. Unfortunately, there is no requirement to include users as partners in any such scheme. Although a local authority must be satisfied that such an improvement will bring benefits to 'persons using [the bus] services' (Section 114(3)), it is significant that it is the local authority – and not the users – who have to be satisfied that this is the case. There is therefore a risk that such enhancements might benefit bus operators or local authorities without providing the improvements wanted by bus users.

Information provision has historically been poor for bus services, with timetables – if they exist at all – often illegible, out of date and unintelligible. The importance of good-quality information in an accessible format is recognised in the Transport Act 2000. Section 139 places a duty on local authorities to review the provision of information about bus services as provided by operators, in terms of the information provided and the way in which it is made available. This review is required to include consultation with users' groups. If the local authority finds that the appropriate information is not being made available or is not being provided in the appropriate way, it is required to make arrangements 'under which those operators agree to make the information available (or to make it available in that way)'. The required information relates to routes and timetabling, fares and other facilities for disabled persons, travel concessions, connections with other public transport services or 'other matters of value to the public'. If the authority is unable to make satisfactory arrangements, Section 140 requires them to provide the information in the appropriate way and gives them powers to recover the costs of so doing from the operators concerned. These actions must be carried out with a view to the 'best value' criteria of economy, efficiency and effectiveness.

Sections 139 and 140 are very powerful because they place a duty on the local authority to find and judge what is meant by 'appropriate'. We would argue that the 'appropriate way' in which information should be made available is that it should be accessible to, and understandable by, everyone – including people with learning difficulties and people with sensory impairments. 'Appropriate information' is all the information necessary to make an entire journey. The power to recover costs from defaulting operators means that there is no reason why the appropriate information should not be provided in the appropriate way. Together, these sections constitute an excellent opportunity for the disabled community to express their needs and to have them met in practice – if they have an active participation in the process. We shall discuss each of these issues later in the book.

Section 145 of the Transport Act 2000 provides another major change for elderly and disabled people. A national concessionary fare scheme for bus services seeks to ensure that, at the very least, elderly people and eligible disabled people will be able to have a half-fare concession on bus services. The scheme will not necessarily replace existing schemes that provide greater discounts, but will ensure that a minimum scheme is available to anyone using buses anywhere in the UK. Section 146 sets out the basis for eligibility for the concession. These include elderly people of pensionable age and various categories of disabled people. This is a second fundamental change for disabled people because there is a national standard for eligibility to the scheme. This removes local arbitrariness in terms of who is entitled to local concessions in different local authority areas. The inclusion of people with learning difficulties marks a notable change from previous eligibility under which they were often ignored. This reflects an increasing awareness of problems caused by transport systems for people with learning difficulties (previously highlighted by the King's Fund (1996, 1998). Section 151 ensures that the same descriptions are used in Greater London.

The combination of the DDA, its associated Regulations and the Transport Act 2000 should result in a noticeable change to the accessibility of conventional bus services in the UK.

The PSVA Regulations apply only to buses and coaches with more than 22 seats. The forthcoming European Union Bus & Coach Directive will, however, apply to vehicles with nine or more passenger seats. At the time of writing this directive is still in its progress through the European

Parliamentary process, and could therefore change in detail before implementation. In principle, the draft EU directive is similar to the UK PSVA Regulations, although some details are currently different. As the draft directive has not been finally approved there is little value in discussing it here; the main point is that the directive will apply to smaller vehicles (including minibuses), which will be required in the not too distant future to comply with a set of regulations with respect to their accessibility. DPTAC has produced a set of recommendations (DPTAC, 2001) for minibuses, which seek to encourage minibus manufacturers, purchasers and users to start thinking in terms of improving the accessibility of smaller passenger-carrying vehicles. This follows the method successfully adopted for larger public service vehicles (see above).

Conclusions

The bus system is made up of a range of different categories of transport which are available to the public and these must work together to deliver a fully accessible system. The relationship between the purchasers of transport, the providers of transport and the procurers of transport is being made clearer as statutory purchasers are shedding in-house provision in favour of contracted provision and transport providers are learning how to fill the various gaps in provision. The procurer of transport has the key role of ensuring that the user has a transport service that is the most appropriate possible and at the lowest cost. The voluntary sector is essential in the mix of transport providers: it provides a user-centred focus to the provision of transport and it has shown that it is capable of filling gaps between the provision offered by others.

It is unlikely that any transport system to be used by the public would ever be complete without contributions at all levels by the public, private and voluntary sectors. The boundaries that have divided these sectors are becoming increasingly blurred, with private companies taking over elements of public provision and the voluntary sector bringing its culture to the realms of commercial operation. All sectors can learn from each other to help work together towards a complete and fully accessible transport system.

In policy terms, accessibility is in the strongest position that it has ever been. There is a strong condition on the expenditure of public money on transport investment that accessibility for disabled people must be included. The importance is therefore to ensure that the practice meets the policy and the original principles by ensuring that good-quality, accessibility-enhancing projects are implemented. This requires user involvement at every stage of the process. It also requires a serious rethink at an even more fundamental level: What are the best methodologies to use when trying to put principles into practice, and how do we ensure that policy serves to assist this process and not to impede it?

The legislative position is that there are powers and duties to ensure that at least the local authorities and operators work together to improve the bus systems and to involve users in some aspects of this. However, the legislative context, while necessary, is not sufficient. The local authorities and bus operators must join with two other parties – the local community (including users) and the contractors involved in the supply and construction of materials and infrastructure – to obtain a successful implementation of an accessible bus system. In order for the interactions between the four groups to be plausible each party needs to be able to understand the perspectives of the others. This will require a culture change, in which people begin to look beyond their own direct experience towards the needs of others – an area where the voluntary sector has a lot to contribute. In particular, those in authority should become more open to help develop ideas and objectives coming from people who will have to use and live with the resulting systems. It is important to realise that accessibility for one section of society might mean reducing current freedoms for another (e.g. clearing parking in order to guarantee access to a bus). All decisions involve compromises. In order to achieve a fair result, people need to understand the reasons for the compromises and their impacts on all members of society.

In the next chapter we consider three aspects of putting these principles into practice: accessible networks, accessible infrastructure and the relations between the bus system and the public.

References

DETR (2000a). *Transport 2010 – The Ten Year Plan*. London: Department of the Environment, Transport and the Regions.

DETR (2000b). *Guidance on the Preparation of Full Local Transport Plans*. London: Department of the Environment, Transport and the Regions.

DPTAC (1997). *Recommended Specification for Low-floor Buses*. London: Disabled Persons Transport Advisory Committee.

GILLINGWATER, D. and TYLER, N. A. (2001). Specialized transport. In: *A Handbook of Transport Systems and Traffic Control* (eds K. Button and D. Hensher). Oxford: Pergamon Press.

KINGS FUND (1996). *Changing Days* (ed. A. Wertheimer). London: King's Fund.

KINGS FUND (1998). *Days of Change* (eds B. McIntosh and A Whittaker). London: King's Fund.

LEHNER, F. (1949). 'Menge, Arbeit, Leistung und Wirkungsgrad im Verkehr'. *Verkehr und Technik*, Nos 8, 11 and 12. Bielefeld: Erich Schmidt Verlag.

LEHNER, F. (1950). 'Menge, Arbeit, Leistung und Wirkungsgrad im Verkehr'. *Verkehr und Technik*, Nos 1 and 20. Bielefeld: Erich Schmidt Verlag.

VUCHIC, V. (1968). 'Rapid transit interstation spacings for maximum number of passengers'. *Transportation Science*, Vol. 3, No. 3, pp. 214–232.

VUCHIC, V. (2000). *Transportation for Livable Cities*. New Brunswick: Center for Urban Policy Research, Rutgers University.

Chapter 3

Accessibility and Networks

N. Tyler

Introduction

The concepts discussed in Chapter 1 are implemented in the form of the public transport network. As pointed out in Chapter 1, bus services deliver the fundamental element of that network. This chapter considers how we approach the implementation of a bus network.

For anyone who wants to know about public transport operations, Vuchic's *Urban Public Transportation* (1981) is a good option. Vuchic's book has all the details of how to analyse public transport operations from first principles. However, it does not consider the issue of making the bus system accessible in the way proposed in Chapter 1 and for which the legislation discussed in Chapter 2 is encouraging us to work.

Approaching bus system design from the point of view of accessibility means thinking first about what both existing and potential passengers need in order to use buses. This raises implications for the needs of buses and their drivers, in order to ensure that the buses are able to deliver their part of the accessible interface. We also need to ensure that we consider the relationship between the bus system, including its passengers, and the rest of society who choose not to use this particular form of transport.

We can look at the bus system from four perspectives in relation to its bus stops: global, macroscopic, local and microscopic. The global view corresponds to the users' needs in order to reach the bus stop, and the requirements of buses with respect to the number and location of bus stops. The macroscopic view of a bus stop corresponds to the extent to which the bus stop operates within the system as a whole, and is concerned with the ability to deliver sufficient capacity. It thus relates to the specification of the bus stops in terms of the number of berths for buses and the available space for passengers. The local view corresponds to the way in which a bus stop interacts with other activities nearby, such as pedestrian or vehicular traffic. Finally, the microscopic perspective concerns detailed design of various elements of a bus stop, such as the vertical and horizontal gaps between buses and the platform, the position of a shelter, information or seating. One can think of these perspectives in other ways as well.

As mentioned in Chapter 1, at a global level, society determines what people should be able to do and the way in which they can make use of the bus system as passengers. The detailed nature of their needs determines what the bus system must deliver. In turn, the bus system has requirements of the macroscopic environment in order to deliver these needs. This has impacts on the local traffic management systems, and the way in which these are allowed to affect and react to these demands is an indicator of the way in which society really operates at a global level. The message is therefore that we need to consider all these levels in order to determine how to deliver a bus system that can begin to meet the demands of the civilised and inclusive society as required following our discussion in Chapter 1.

We deal with these perspectives over the next four chapters. This chapter considers access to the bus system and the implications for buses of imposing passengers' access needs on the design of the network. Chapter 4 is concerned with the macroscopic view and considers the way in which bus stops should be specified so that they can provide an accessible interface for passengers while ensuring that any disturbance to the bus and traffic system is kept under control. Chapter 5 shows how the infrastructure should be designed in order to provide a good interface between the pedestrian footway and the vehicles. Chapter 6 discusses how the accessibility of the bus system needs to be reflected in an accessible information system and considers how this might be approached.

Users' Perspectives

Although, as mentioned in Chapter 1, the bus stop is the gateway to the bus, it is not much use if an intending passenger cannot reach it. Therefore a key element to be designed into the bus network is the distance that a passenger has to walk in order to reach a bus stop. In this section we will look at some basic principles of bus stop location: how far apart they should be and the implications of this for accessibility.

Accessible Networks for Users

Normally, bus stop location is thought about after a bus route has been determined. However, the location of bus stops within the street network

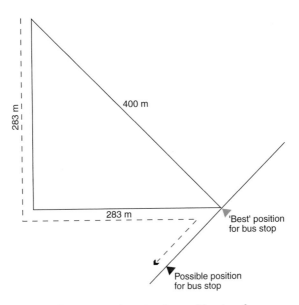

Fig. 3.1   The walking distance to a bus stop in a grid network

defines how far we expect people to have to walk in order to reach the bus system. This is one of the first issues to address when designing an accessible bus system. Most conventional approaches to the location of bus stops at this scale consider only the distance between bus stops along a route. We need to explore the relationship between this distance and the distance required of a passenger to reach a bus stop (the *access distance*). First, we need to explore how people and their activities are distributed around an area and the ways in which people travel to reach the bus. We need to find an answer to the question: How can we define a bus network so that accessibility to the bus system might be set as part of a policy?

First, to make the analysis of network density easier, we could assume that the road and footway network is a grid pattern. In the worst case, the straight-line distance between two points is the hypotenuse of a right-angled triangle. The other two sides of the triangle are then the representation of the actual route to be followed along the footways between the two points. Transport for London (TfL) uses a norm of 400 m for the straight-line distance from a journey origin to a bus route. When considered in this way, a 400 m straight-line distance means a walking distance of up to 566 m to reach a given point. The best that can be achieved under these conditions would be to locate the bus stop at the point where the access route meets the bus route, in which case the walking distance would be 566 m. It may not be possible to put a bus stop at this point, in which case the walking distance would be even greater (Figure 3.1).

If the straight-line access distance to the bus stop is 400 m, the worst situation for the inter-stop spacing would be 566 m, as shown in Figure 3.2. This would provide rather less than 2 stops/km. If the shortest distance to the bus route is 400 m, the resulting distance between the bus stops could be as much as 800 m, as shown in Figure 3.3.

We tested these walking distances in Bloomsbury in London (Tadesse and Islam, 1996), which has a street network that is as near to a grid pattern as any in London. We examined a number of bus stops and identified a selection of random locations at a straight-line distance of 400 m from these bus stops. Although the TfL norm refers to reaching a bus route, we used a bus stop as the defining point for two reasons. First, there is little point in reaching the route if you cannot board the bus at that point and, secondly, the bus stop provides an easily defined 'target' for the analysis. We then measured the shortest distance along the footway network from each selected location to the associated bus stop and calculated

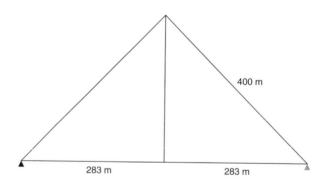

Fig. 3.2   Inter-stop distance in a grid network based on a 400 m straight-line distance to a bus stop

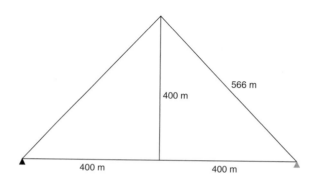

Fig. 3.3   Inter-stop distance in a grid network with straight-line distance to a bus route of 400 m

Table 3.1   Percentage of people with a mobility impairment able, with assistance, to move at least the stated distance without a rest[*]

Group	Distance (m)				
	18	68	137	180	360
Wheelchair users	100%	95%	95%	40%	15%
Visually impaired	100%	100%	95%	50%	25%
Stick users	90%	75%	60%	20%	5%
Ambulatory, no walking aid	95%	85%	75%	30%	20%

[*]Source: Barham et al. (1994)

the overall mean access distance to reach a bus stop where the straight-line distance was 400 m. We found that the mean access distance was 528 m. This was more or less expected – the higher figure mentioned earlier would be the worst case (i.e. when the right-angled triangle was isosceles).

We then repeated the exercise assuming that there was an additional constraint: the access route used in the exercise had to be accessible to a person in a wheelchair. This constraint had a dramatic effect: the mean travelling distance between the selected points and the associated bus stops rose from 528 to 930 m. Similar effects can be found if other accessibility constraints are applied. For example, a blind person may need to adapt their walking route in order to cross roads in locations where they can hear traffic more easily or can take advantage of accessible pedestrian crossings. Similarly, a deaf person may need to find crossings where they can see traffic more easily, or a person worried about their personal security might wish to alter a route to avoid a threatening street environment.

However, is the 400 m norm adopted by TfL appropriate? In these circumstances, we should consider how far people can actually travel before the distance becomes a problem which is sufficient to cause them to abandon or avoid the journey altogether. Research carried out at Leeds University showed that these distances are actually quite short. Table 3.1 shows a summary of the distances achieved by people walking along a measured path and observed during that walk (Barham *et al.*, 1994). It can be seen from the table that only 15% of wheelchair users and only 5% of people with a walking aid could manage a distance of 360 m without stopping for a rest. The distances mentioned above therefore exclude many people from using the bus system, simply because of the distance required in order to reach it.

The effects on people of the location of points of access to the bus system can be examined by bringing together the two notions of bus stop distance and the distances people are able to walk. This involves comparing two views of the same object: what is a bus stop to a bus driver is an access point to the passenger. Assuming the grid network as before, we can see that if we were to adopt a maximum walking distance of 360 m, the straight-line distance to an access point would be 254 m and the distance between the bus stops would be 360 m (about 3 stops/km). Table 3.1 shows that this would still exclude some 95% of people using sticks as a mobility aid from using the bus system. We could make the bus system accessible to another 15% of elderly people with a walking aid by reducing the walking distance to the access points from 360 m to 180 m. This would give a straight-line distance of 127 m and a distance between the bus stops of 254 m, yielding about 4 stops/km, but even so we would still be excluding some 80% of elderly people with a walking aid from the bus system. This problem can be ameliorated to some extent by providing comfortable, secure and protected seating along the access routes so that people can rest if they need. However, the corresponding effects on the time taken to reach the access point should be taken into account when considering the costs and benefits of a particular bus stop location policy. We shall return to this issue below.

The theoretical examples above based on a simple grid network are much simpler than would be the case for most real networks. Kunaka (1996) examined the nature of the footway network bringing people to a bus stop and how this related to the 'main route' where the bus stop was located. In the environment considered by Kunaka, the passengers selected the access points and the vehicles stopped where the passengers had accumulated. This was therefore a case where the convenience of passengers' access determined the location of the bus stops. One of the results of Kunaka's work is that, under these circumstances, the design of the access network has a strong impact on the location of a bus stop. A minor change in bus stop location could have a profound effect on the walking distance in one case, yet a much larger change elsewhere could make hardly any difference because the access network provided a different level of access to the main route served by the buses. Knowledge of the access network must include a detailed knowledge of how people use it and the impacts of different barriers. It is therefore necessary to examine the access network to establish actual access routes in some detail before deciding on bus stop locations.

It is unlikely that the required level of knowledge about the access network will be obtainable from maps. Our study in Bloomsbury showed that the access route differs for people who are disabled by different barriers. We need to evaluate all these access routes for people who are affected by different barriers when determining the accessibility of a pedestrian network. These assessments need to be undertaken on site – they can rarely be made from maps because of the nature of the detail concerned (e.g. available footway width, sightlines, echo effects from buildings or bridges).

The bus stop is an important element of the accessible journey chain, but it is worth considering the locations of the actual origin and eventual destination of a journey. Many of these will be buildings which, if new or recently constructed, should be accessible according to the Building Regulations Part M or will be covered by Part III of the Disability Discrimination Act 1995. The ability to reach these buildings is not covered in the same level of detail and not always considered in the design. Yet a failure to ensure that the access routes to the building are accessible will result in the exclusion of people from the possibility of using it. Is a building accessible if you cannot reach it?

We should bear in mind that the whole point of accessible public transport is to make places and activities accessible to people. It is worth spending a lot of effort to consider how accessibility will be dealt with when planning the location of places and activities. Poor consideration of accessibility at this stage may render a new development inaccessible to people who rely on public transport. The accessibility of the pedestrian access network is therefore the starting point for planning and developing bus stops, bus services and bus routes and should be worked out before considering other issues such as operating costs, traffic impacts or environmental effects.

The London Borough of Hammersmith and Fulham has developed an interesting measure which takes into account the distance from public transport access points to a given location. This is combined with the service frequency to provide an estimate of the *public transport accessibility level* (PTAL). The model only includes quantifiable measures, such as time and distance, and does not incorporate issues such as perception and degrees of mobility impairment. As PTALs only consider walking distances and public transport service frequencies, they do not take any other form of barrier into account. As a result, they do not measure 'accessibility' in the sense that it is used in this book – or, for that matter by the government (e.g. DETR, 2000). It might, therefore, be better to consider the PTAL approach as a means of including the 'availability' of public transport rather than its 'accessibility', given the current use of the latter term.

PTALs are calculated on the basis of the measured walking distance from a proposed development to the various public transport access points within a maximum distance (15 minutes for rail and 10 minutes for bus (London Borough of Hammersmith and Fulham, 1994, p. 187). There has been a move to represent this in terms of distance (960 m for rail and 640 m for bus). If a straight-line distance is used, a factor is applied to account for the difference between the straight-line and the actual walking distance. The factor normally used provides an estimate of walking distance that is broadly in line with the results from our Bloomsbury work noted above. Walking speed is assumed to be 4.8 km/h. Access time is then calculated by adding the walking time from the 'doorstep' of the location of interest to the boarding points and the scheduled waiting time (adjusted by an assumed reliability factor). The *equivalent doorstep frequency* (EDF) for each boarding point is taken as the reciprocal of the access time. The EDFs are then summed over all boarding points, with the smallest access times multiplied by 30 and the others by 15, to give an *accessibility index* (AI). Ranges of AIs are then used to divide the borough into zones, currently ranging from 1 with the lowest accessibility level (AI between 0 and 5) to 6 for the highest level (AI greater than 25). The zone value is then used to determine aspects of a development (e.g. the amount of office space to be permitted).

PTAL analysis is an attempt to ensure that public transport availability is included in planning decisions which might otherwise only consider access by private car. However, there are difficulties with PTALs. For example, no account is taken of differences in accessibility obtained by people with different walking speeds. A speed of 4.8 km/h may be an average value, but it is quite a high average – reasonable estimates for walking speed (e.g. TRB, 2000) tend to suggest a rather lower speed (4.3 km/h). However, even these estimates do not take into account the slower walking speeds obtained in practice by elderly and disabled people (we have measured examples as low as 0.25 m/s (0.9 km/h)). Akcelik & Associates (2001), in a study of crossing speeds at mid-block pedestrian crossings, showed that the 15th percentile for walking speeds by people with a walking difficulty in this environment was 1.0 m/s (3.6 km/h). However, this is an environment where people feel under pressure to walk faster and the distance is relatively short. In addition, 'people with walking difficulty' was taken to include people pushing baby buggies, who one might expect to have very different walking speeds in comparison to elderly people with walking aids.

Rest periods to allow for the need of many people to rest at intervals while walking (as discussed above) are not included in PTAL calculations. Another gap is that there is no allowance made for people to choose routes other than the shortest in terms of physical distance because they are more accessible. PTALs are used when making decisions about planning consents. As PTALs do not explicitly include such routes in the analysis, disabled and elderly people will be effectively excluded from consideration in some planning decisions unless there is a conscious effort to ensure that they are included. Failure in this respect could, for example, exclude disabled people from working in a new office development even though the development itself complies with current accessibility regulations and is fully accessible. This could also apply to new facilities such as healthcare or day centres which, although accessible in themselves, may only be reachable in practice by specialised transport or private car because suitably accessible access routes from local public transport are not assured. This is not only an issue for urban areas. The nature of the bus network and the location of bus stops is also a key issue for rural areas. Indeed, in some cases the problem is much worse in rural areas. The sparse road network and lack of roadside footways mean that people are often required to walk along the road in order to reach a formal bus stop. This is neither attractive nor safe.

There is a relationship between the access network and the bus network: the two networks are superimposed onto the same geographical area but they only connect at the access points. The upper limit of possible walking distances is, as discussed above, a hard constraint on the design of the access network. Therefore, the location of bus stops with respect to the access network is a critical factor in determining the accessibility of the bus system. Every time the required access distance is increased more people will be excluded from using the bus system. This means that both the bus network and the access network need to be adapted in order to accommodate the accessibility needs of the population. The result of this approach is that it is necessary to fix the bus stop locations before worrying about the design of the bus routes that will join them together.

Accessibility Standards Throughout a Network

A number of issues should be considered with respect to the bus network in both urban and rural areas:

- Formal bus stops are needed so that they can:
    - provide an accessible place to board and alight from the buses
    - provide appropriate waiting facilities and shelter
    - act as a source of information about the bus service
    - act as a source of information about the local area.
- Bus stops must be located so that access distances are appropriate. This may mean ensuring that buses go into villages or local residential areas rather than pass them by on the main road.
- Bus services must serve the local community, making it easier for people to move around, shop and work within their local area, as well as making it easier to travel further afield.
- There must be accessible interchanges between the local services and longer distance services (bus and rail) to provide access to activities that are not available locally.
- The level of demand, which is determined to a great extent by the density of local residential or other activities, dictates the amount of transport required. This could affect frequency, the size of the vehicles and the density of the route network. It is important to

recognise that in order to achieve the civilising objectives raised in Chapter 1, there is a minimum level of accessibility that society must provide, and this could indicate requirements in terms of the demand to be met which are quite different from those obtained from the conventional calculations.

We can define a set of issues that need to be considered in terms of the needs of bus users – including potential users – to be included when considering the design of an accessible bus network. The first step towards an inclusive bus system is to set out the accessibility requirements for reaching and using the bus stops. Without this, all the other measures will be wasted. This involves ensuring that the pedestrian network is accessible, and that the bus network ensures that access distances are appropriate and the time taken to reach a bus stop is reasonable. Then it is necessary to determine the maximum waiting time. This indicates the service frequency, which determines the number of buses needed to operate the service and thus the number of buses that each bus stop has to accommodate. The overall passenger demand then determines the required capacity of the bus stop for passengers (and, therefore, the associated facilities) and the size of the buses. Once all these factors have been finalised, it is necessary to work out the provision of the accessible information that will guide people to and from the bus system. Once this has been completed, the whole system can be put in place. In summary, the essential ingredients of an accessible bus system include:

- Provision of an accessible pedestrian network, including:
  - the removal of sensory, cognitive and physical barriers, or the reduction to an acceptable level of their impact on users
  - the provision of sufficient accessibility enhancements (e.g. dropped kerbs, increased footway widths, seating, information and signage (Institute of Highways and Transportation (1991)).
- The definition of appropriate access times and distances between journey origins/destinations and bus stops, and thus the location of bus stops
- The definition of accessible service schedules, including consideration of the effects on accessibility of frequency, route and interchange (e.g. waiting times and journey times).
- The definition of appropriate capacities, such as bus stop capacity (for passengers and buses) and bus size.
- The provision of appropriate passenger facilities at bus stops, such as seating and shelter.
- The provision of adequate accessibility features on and in vehicles and training for staff in their use.
- The provision of updated training in disability awareness for all staff associated with the bus service.

- The provision of accessible information throughout both the access network and the bus network, including access to information at journey origins.
- The implementation of the accessible bus system.

Spatial accessibility

Some accessibility issues are defined in terms of space: we have already mentioned some aspects of distance. The principles underlying the notion of this 'spatial accessibility' to the bus system have been raised above, namely the distance between a bus stop and a journey origin or destination. Analytical models currently used to analyse the distance between bus stops take passenger access times into consideration, but they all accept the premise that all passengers have the same value of time, concept of walking and waiting times and ability to walk at a given speed. We believe that it is not reasonable to hold such a view. We will now discuss the effects of considering the possibility that different pedestrians might have different needs with respect to the distance between their journey origins/destinations and the bus stops. Basically, this means considering how to ensure that people are not excluded from the bus system because their journey origin or destination lies too far away from the bus network.

Exclusion penalty

Every bus stop is unreachable for someone. Therefore, no matter how accessible the system, it still will be inaccessible to some people and this should be reflected in any analysis of a bus stop. Bus stops have to be located around the network in such a way as to provide reasonable access to the bus system. Although in many cases bus networks are thought of primarily as sets of bus routes, it might be better to think in terms of a network of access points, i.e. bus stops. The measurement of the adequacy of a physical bus network is the extent to which people are able to reach its bus stops. If the access distance to a bus stop becomes too large, some people will be unable to reach it and will be excluded from the activities they would otherwise be able to reach by using the bus system.

We can therefore divide the area surrounding the bus network in terms of parts where a bus stop is reachable and other parts where it is not. The two types of zone based on each bus stop in the network are an *inclusion zone* where the journey to the bus stop is accessible and an *exclusion zone* where it is not (Figure 3.4).

Kunaka's approach suggests that the access distance is not so much a function of the distance between the bus stops along the bus route, as it is of the actual network leading from the journey origins to the bus stop. This is essentially a spatial issue depending on the particular access network, the geography and the accessibility features associated with

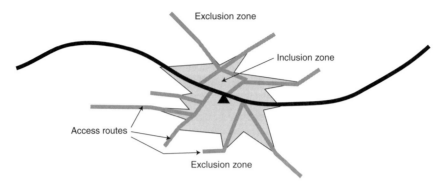

Fig. 3.4   Inclusion and exclusion zones around a bus stop

each bus stop location. If we determine the location of bus stops – and therefore the distance between them – on the basis of the access network, we are cutting across the conventional models for bus stop location, which are based on the distance between the stops. We can expect the bus network to look quite different as a result, and it means that we can include a major component of the accessibility problem in the analysis of bus stop location.

The example of Bloomsbury, quoted above, revealed that wheelchair users, blind people and deaf people chose different routes to reach a bus stop from the same journey origin on the basis of their needs (e.g. when crossing a road). An inclusion zone with a 10 minute maximum access time could be associated with different distances by elderly people and young people, by visually impaired people and by people in wheelchairs. The differences arise partly as a result of different walking speeds, differing needs for rests along the journey or because different people have to choose different routes to reach the stop. This is pertinent because it is important to know who is being excluded from the bus stop so that steps can be taken to remedy the situation. Broad policy statements about access (e.g. the 400 m norm used in many cities) miss the essential point about accessibility, namely the individuality of the access problem. We need to address the ability of people to reach the bus system and not just to satisfy a broad compromise between a so-called access distance and inter-stop distance. This means being explicit about who is being excluded from a bus stop and for what reason. Then we can devise an ameliorative approach, such as redesign of the network, provision of a specialised service or enhancements to the access network. Unlike the PTAL example discussed above, this approach emphasises the need to understand the requirements defined by a person's needs and places these as constraints on the design of the access infrastructure between the public transport system and the journey origin/destination. Our approach directs these requirements towards the integration of these needs with the public transport system.

Conventional economic analysis of bus stop location considers the time taken by people to reach the stop, usually in terms of the distance parallel to the bus route. A factor of 2 is normally used to reflect the widely perceived dislike of walking and waiting for public transport compared with the same amount of time being spent in the vehicle. However, this ignores people who cannot reach the bus stop as well as those who can reach it albeit with some unacceptably high degree of difficulty. These two groups of people combine to form the population that is excluded from the bus stop – and thus excluded from the bus system as a result of inadequate provision of bus stops.

It is important to include in the analysis of bus stop location those people who are excluded from the system, because they impose two costs:

- a direct financial cost of the provision of an alternative means of reaching the activity they wish to pursue
- the disbenefits imposed on society as a result of the fact that the bus stop is inaccessible.

These combine to form an *exclusion penalty* which is imposed by the system on society because the bus stop is inaccessible. We can use studies such as the one by Barham *et al.* (1994) and official population statistics to estimate the number of people affected and then apply the exclusion penalty on behalf of these people. The work undertaken by Barham *et al.* involved what was considered to be a barrier-free route. It is important to remember this when considering using their outcomes, as a real access route may be obstructed in some way for some people. We shall see below how the exclusion penalty affects the analysis of bus stop location.

What is this exclusion penalty? One element of it is essentially qualitative – for example, the lack of independence and the resulting loss of quality of life. Other elements are more quantitative – for example, the cost of a specialised transport service (such as a non-emergency ambulance), which is required because people cannot reach the mainstream bus system for a journey to hospital. Another example is to think of the cases in the USA where the Americans with Disabilities Act (ADA, 1990) requires that a company can only operate a bus service in an area if they operate a parallel paratransit service for people who cannot reach the mainstream buses. In the former case, the cost of non-emergency ambulances is so high that they are heavily rationed; in the latter case the overall costs can be so high that neither the paratransit service nor the mainstream buses can be operated. The exclusion penalty can therefore be extremely expensive as well as socially divisive. We should attempt to locate bus stops to make the exclusion penalty as low as possible. This requires detailed thinking about the way in which the access network feeds into the bus network.

So far, we have thought of exclusion in terms of distance, but the 'distances' used to define it are usually described in terms of time. This is because a person's access speed is an indication of how difficult it is for them to walk a given distance. It therefore seems more sensitive to describe access to the bus system in terms of time rather than distance. We could stipulate a maximum access time of, say, 10 minutes and then determine how far people can travel in that time. The inclusion zone would become smaller (and the exclusion zone larger) as the access speed decreases. A single stop could have several inclusion zones to allow for people with different maximum access distances as a result of their different access speeds. The advantage of this is that it is possible to have a consistent policy ('Everyone should be within 10 minutes of a bus stop'), yet allow it to be interpreted flexibly to take account of the needs of different people and the different environments they encounter on the way to the bus stop. This also encourages the identification of access problems so that remedial measures can be identified and implemented. Access time includes waiting time, so the expected waiting time should also be taken into account (how this can be estimated is discussed below). The further away a journey origin is from a bus stop, the more likely it is that some form of personal or technical assistance might be necessary in order for a journey-maker to be included within the inclusion zone. The more accessible the access network, the more inclusive the bus system will be. We noted in Chapter 1 how important independence is to the development of a high-quality society and the crucial role played by accessible public transport – especially bus systems – in the encouragement of independence. The design of an inclusive access network is central to the development of an inclusive bus system and thus to the encouragement of this independence.

Access distances are determined along the pedestrian routes leading to the bus stop and include consideration of the physical environment (e.g. crossings, availability of dropped kerbs, obstacles in the footway, or gradients) which could affect the access speed. Access distances, to be acceptable in an analysis, must be accessible. An accessible access distance is defined precisely for a person under the particular circumstances that arise for them in the location of interest. This is the actual access distance which they can achieve comfortably within the access time considered to be inclusive. The access distance can therefore be radically changed by the addition (or removal) of infrastructure (e.g. a footbridge or accessible crossing). The use of geographical information systems (GIS) for this purpose could help to show the effects on access distance as a result of the introduction or removal of such infrastructure or the removal of certain barriers. We can then define who is being excluded from the

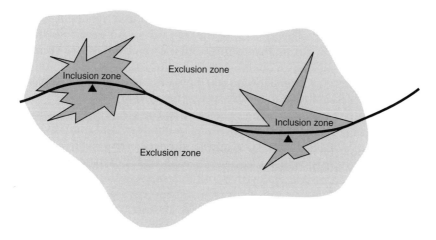

Fig. 3.5 Inclusion and exclusion zones for two bus stops

bus system by the combination of bus stop locations and the access network.

People who are unable to reach a bus stop for any reason are located in its exclusion zone. This can be remedied in principle by the addition of another bus stop, not necessarily on the same road or bus route as the (exclusive) original stop. Plotting these access points on a map will yield a mass of dots and inclusion zones spread over the area. Figure 3.5 shows how two bus stops each have an inclusion zone (as in Figure 3.4), but that the area as a whole still has a large exclusion zone. The process of network design is then one of defining the access points (bus stops) needed in order to make as much of the overall area as possible lie within inclusion zones. The next step is to design the ways in which these points could be joined together to form a set of services.

There are many ways in which a set of points can be joined to form a bus route. In the simplest case, it is a question of joining them together and then working out how feasible the resulting service would be. The set of bus stops selected in order to maximise the amount of an area that can be considered to be within inclusion zones can then be compared with the operating cost of a bus service which is required to call at the stops under the desired operating regime (e.g. whether buses can overtake each other or not).

The consideration of inclusion zones for bus stops as described above and shown in Figures 3.4 and 3.5 means that we are defining areas around a bus stop which exclude certain people from using the bus. This is set against the operational idea of a bus route which has constraints on the number of times it is sensible to stop a bus on its journey. One solution to such exclusion is to have more bus routes spread around the area and thus to have more opportunities to have bus stops without imposing too many stops on each route. This increases the amount of an area which falls within the inclusion zones. Bus routes combine to form networks and it is these networks which can help to reduce the exclusion from the bus system. We therefore need to look at networks in order to establish a reasonable accessibility to the public transport system.

A bus network needs to be designed so that the bus service is inclusive (i.e. the number of people in exclusion zones is minimised) and comprehensive (i.e. a full range of destinations is available, either directly or with accessible interchange). In this inclusive approach we design a network to provide adequate and accessible pedestrian and bus services to the set of access points. The actual bus routes resulting from this approach are then determined on the basis of operational and financial constraints.

Defining a network on the basis of bus stops and thinking in terms of access distance means bringing buses nearer to journey origins and destinations. This is not good for longer routes as the increased number of bus stops would increase the journey time and thus the number of vehicles required to operate the route. One way of solving this problem is to have a network that works on the basis of feeder routes and main routes. This sort of network has main routes which provide the high capacity point-to-point bus services and smaller routes which feed into the main routes from outlying areas. The concept is quite common, but it is important to think about it in more depth. A network designed on the basis of feeder services will have a number of small services serving a main interchange point. Usually the feeder services will start some distance away from the interchange, call at a few intermediate points and end at the interchange. This is analogous to the sort of arrangement envisaged for an integrated inter-modal system where the main mode is a railway. In this case it is an 'intra-modal' integration between different types of bus service.

Feeder services: micronetworks

Whatever the design of a feeder service, its viability is important. These services bring people from parts of the network that are more difficult to reach by conventional bus services (maybe because of distance, road type or traffic restrictions) to meet the main services at a convenient point. If there is a reasonable demand for the main service, the feeders may well bring additional passengers who simply cannot reach the main service at its current location. The design of a bus network which is integrated in this way allows the main services to follow more direct routes, thus reducing their journey time. However, it is important to realise that the level of demand for a service is not the only reason for having it: providing access to the local high street or other public transport services may outweigh the simple profit and loss analysis of any route.

It is a mistake to view feeder services merely as tributaries to the main network: we must also think of the way in which the transport system interacts with the area in which it is situated. A well-designed feeder service also provides a service in its own right which enables people to travel out of one area into another, whether or not this is for the purpose of changing bus. It is important to realise that in providing transport to ease travel from one area to another, this is also removing someone from the first area and taking them to the second. If this person is making the journey to purchase something which might have been bought in the first area, there is a loss to the local economy of the first area and a gain to that of the second. This could be a problem if the first area contains a local shopping centre, such as a small high street, where there are small shops that cannot easily compete with the larger supermarkets of the second area.

The small high street may only be surviving by serving those people who have no access to transport to take them to the larger supermarket in the second area. Small shops often also find it very difficult to offer the same breadth of goods at the same quality and price as their larger supermarket counterparts which are reachable by private car. People without access to transport – including those on restricted incomes – are therefore often condemned to buying more expensive, poorer quality goods with less choice than their better-off neighbours. The provision of accessible intra-community bus services is, therefore, one way of enhancing choice and inclusion. It should also encourage the local community to be cohesive, paying attention to how people in the community interact with each other in both social and economic terms. The provision of a transport system can threaten this cohesion as well as facilitate it, and it is important to design the service to ensure that the encouragement of social cohesion outweighs any potential economic disadvantage that might be perceived. As we shall see, a well-designed bus service can encourage people to shop locally: access to a car is much more of a threat to the local community than access to a bus service.

We could devise a bus service that encourages people to come to the local high street rather than go to the more distant supermarket. This suggests a network design that consists of joining the access points in such a way that buses are led towards the local shopping streets. Making it easier to shop at the local high street helps to sustain the local economy and provides opportunities for local social cohesion. This is not to say that it should be impossible to reach the supermarket. The supermarket could be reached via an accessible, well-designed interchange, i.e. it is still possible, but slightly less convenient than going to the local shops.

One way of approaching this would be to locate the interchange between the feeder services and the main services in the local high street. Bus services (possibly using small accessible buses) could provide a frequent service from the hinterland towards the local high street, where they provide an interchange that enables people to transfer easily to another service which will take them to other parts of the hinterland or further afield. However, a local area exists as a community in which activities happen. A bus system is the default means of transport which society should design in order to ensure that all these activities are accessible to everyone. A bus network which is conceived just as a main service and its feeder services is in danger of ignoring this issue. Simply designing a bus network to provide access to itself is a waste, especially if this means that it is easy to leave a local area to carry out activities elsewhere. We should think about the way in which the bus network could help the local economy to survive a little better.

A bus service aimed to help a local high street would need to provide a service from neighbouring areas (whether these are local villages in a rural area or residential areas in a town) to the high street and back again. Inevitably, the high street will attract a number of bus services, thus affording the possibility of interchange between them. Some of these bus services may connect with other communities, thus providing the possibility of travelling further afield in order to visit amenities that are not available in the immediate locality. The high street would become the focus of these services. This suggests that a small interchange facility, designed to ensure accessible transfer between vehicles, should be included. This need not be a major structure – in most cases it would be a set of well-designed accessible bus stops. However, remembering that the aim is to support the high street, the concept of interchange alters a little. Instead of trying to accommodate the interchange between two services as quickly as possible, we could try to insert enough time to allow some activity to take place in the high street during the interchange period. Thus a passenger could arrive on one service and make some purchases, visit the post office, or whatever, before boarding the second service that will take them onwards. The concept is not novel – airports thrive on forcing passengers to loiter in the proximity of retail and catering facilities while waiting for transport services. The difference is that 'bus stations' are not normally the sort of place one would expect to do this – they are often located too far away from the high street, or are too complicated with too many badly integrated services to make such a scenario attractive. They are also often designed to accommodate the bus operations rather than the passengers – and they rarely attempt to integrate with the local community in this way.

We see a bus network as a set of micronetworks, in which accessible bus services operate at reasonable frequencies, work together to form an overall network for the area, make it easy to make journeys between local centres and connect with longer distance services. The micronetworks are each defined on the basis of access points as described above. Each micronetwork provides transport for the inclusion zones – in combination they should be able to reduce the number of excluded people so that they can be accommodated by other means. The micronetwork then acts as a feeder service to longer distance services, providing access to other areas by means of a simple and accessible interchange.

Why have we come to this view about the bus system? In this book we will discuss two projects which involve micronetworks: the Hackney and the Cumbria Plusbuses. Although we will leave the detailed description of these projects until later, there are some features of these projects that help to explain the progression of our thinking.

When setting up the Hackney Plusbus, we wanted to incorporate the views of potential users in the route design. Working with Hackney Community Transport, we tried to find out where people wanted to go, but instead we found that they were unable to tell us. This was because their transport had been so inadequate for so long that they had simply closed down their world to the activities that they could reach on foot or via a specialised transport service organised by someone else. To establish the Plusbus route required by the local community in Hackney, we had to plot the access points as best as we could and then join them together, taking into account operational requirements and other factors such as traffic management (Lynas, 1998). As we shall see in Chapter 7, we then put this route into operation and revisited the users a few months later. The Plusbus had awakened their interest in activities outside their hitherto normal regime and thus other destinations had become desirable. We then adjusted the route to include as many of these as we could.

The Cumbria case was a little different. Before the start of the Cumbria Plusbus operation, journeys were undertaken by car or not at all (with the occasional exception of journeys made on foot or bicycle, some over quite long distances). For a non-car-owner or driver in Cumbria, the need to travel meant an infrequent trip to one of the larger towns (about 30–35 miles away), made with the help of a car-owning neighbour or family member. Before they could make such a journey they had to ask for a lift: independent travel was not possible. We discuss in Chapter 8 some of the implications of the need to accept a lift.

In establishing the Plusbus route in Cumbria, we set out criteria that we believe should apply to any new service in a rural area. These are summarised in Box 3.1 for easy reference. Although these are specific to the case in question, it is not too difficult to see how they would apply in other cases. Additional criteria for purposes of the research are given in Chapter 8.

In both the Hackney and Cumbria cases, the demand for transport within the local area was not apparent due to the ways in which the residents dealt with the lack of accessible transport. Once the Plusbus services were introduced, the attractions of local activities were made available to people. Independent travel became a possibility and quite suddenly – and seemingly on a reasonably long-term basis – people opted

Box 3.1   Criteria governing the selection of the Cumbria Plusbus study area

---

Geographical and social characteristics

- *The area should contain at least one potential attraction for passengers* (e.g. a market town with substantial activities compared with the outlying villages) – there had to be some reason for people to use the bus service.

- *The market town should not be too large compared with the size of the outlying communities.* The intention was that the service would support both town and village activities and businesses. However, the provision of an accessible public transport service could make it easier for people to travel to a market town rather than to use the village shop. This would be less likely to happen if the villages were not too small compared with the size of the market town.

Operational factors

- *There should be no or very few complementary bus routes already operating within the area.* The new service was aimed at providing accessible public transport where none currently existed.

- *The possibility should exist for connections between the new service and existing train and bus routes.* We wished to investigate the extent to which passengers would use the opportunity to interchange with existing services. In practice this meant that a connecting service along the boundary of the area would be an advantage.

- *The area should not be too large.* The length of the route was constrained by the need to operate a service with one vehicle. We also needed to conduct surveys and obtain feedback with relatively small resources.

- *The area should not be too small.* The area needed to be large enough to contain several settlements and to provide an adequate route length.

- *The bus service should be in an area that can be supported by the bus operator, either from an outstation or from a main depot.* The prospective bus operator had to be content that it could operate and manage the service from its existing network of depots and outstations.

---

to use the new bus to reach local activities independently rather than to visit places further away as part of a pre-arranged trip.

Why is this? A number of issues seem to be important in answering this question:

- People could make their own decisions about when and where they went out.
- The difficulty of travelling was eased so that people could choose how to undertake an activity (e.g. to shop locally rather than far away).

- Some trips (e.g. to a hospital out-patient appointment) could be undertaken without the need to wait around for the 'official' vehicle, even though this would have provided a door-to-door service.
- Apart from the occasional trip on the bus 'just to get out of the house', journeys generally have a non-transport purpose. However, what makes people choose a service that is not door-to-door, is scheduled and is restrictive in terms of destination and departure time, rather than the apparently more comfortable and convenient alternatives? It seems it is the freedom to make that choice and the social interactions that arise. In both Hackney and Cumbria people of all ages make trips for social reasons: shopping or even visits to a health centre become a social event in addition to their prime purpose. In some cases the availability of company on the bus acts as a means to reduce isolation. Transport can therefore be seen as playing an active role in the local economy and social life of a community, rather than as simply being a bus service. We conclude from this that one of the effects of a community-centred micronetwork is to facilitate social cohesion – helping people to function within their community rather than merely helping them to travel to the locations further afield.
- The Hackney Plusbus has opened up opportunities outside the local area: it has provided interchange with accessible mainstream buses which enable users to reach the centre of London (some 10 km away), a journey which might have been unachievable on an independent basis for many years. The Cumbria Plusbus has enabled people to travel between villages in the area, thus making visits to friends and family – and even some work trips – easier.

The difference between the Hackney and Cumbria cases is that in Hackney the journeys were either not made at all or were made on specialised transport before the arrival of the Plusbus, whereas in Cumbria journeys were generally being made to distant locations by car. In Hackney, the specialised transport journeys transferred to the Plusbus but the destinations did not really change. There were also many new trips to the local facilities. In Cumbria, the longer car journeys were exchanged for shorter bus journeys to the local market town. Often several short bus journeys each week replaced one car trip to a distant town for ostensibly the same purpose (Brown and Tyler, 2001). In both cases, the new transport service has provided some independence, resulting from the ability to choose, which is so important in the quality of life of the community.

Time and frequency
We discussed above the issues surrounding the access to a bus stop and how that affected our thinking about network and bus stop density. Now

we need to think about the way in which the service density is affected by accessibility. This has an impact in two ways: the effect on departure time choice and the impact of service frequency on waiting time. We shall consider waiting time first.

We found a fairly common consensus that a 10-minute wait was about the maximum that was tolerable for many people – for some this would be an absolute maximum as a result of pain resulting from standing or sitting. There is, therefore, a need to ensure that this limit is not exceeded. This can be achieved by having a high frequency service or by having a service that is so reliable that it is unnecessary to wait for longer than 10 minutes. Shorter routes, being easier to operate reliably, are therefore useful in this respect. This is another reason for using a micronetwork to provide access to local services (including other bus services). The ability to operate reliably is also an important way in which to reduce the need to run a high frequency service.

The theoretical mean waiting time for high frequency services (usually considered to be six or more services per hour) is half the headway. This is true if the service runs perfectly reliably. If not, the waiting time increases. This effect has been modelled by Holroyd and Scraggs (1963):

$$T_w = \frac{h(1+V^2)}{2} \tag{3.1}$$

where T_w is the average waiting time, h is the mean headway and V is the coefficient of variation of the headway.

The coefficient of variation acts as a descriptor of unreliability because it compares the variance of the distribution of headways with the mean. As the variation of headways increases, the waiting time increases with the square of the coefficient of variation. In effect, even a high frequency service could be so unreliable that it would provide waiting times which are so long on average that they exceed the maximum acceptable length of 10 minutes. However, reducing unreliability is very difficult, especially in mixed traffic conditions. The average waiting time provides a description of the service. However, without an associated indicator of the service reliability (e.g. a comparison between actual and scheduled waiting times) the average waiting time is fairly meaningless. In accessibility terms, the important issue is the maximum rather than the average waiting time. We need to base the service frequency on the longest time that people can wait and to ensure that this is not exceeded.

An important element of thinking about accessible bus systems is the need to think of frequency as a part of the service rather than as a means to provide capacity. The conventional view about service design is to think in terms of calculating how many buses of a given size are required to provide sufficient capacity for the number of passengers to be carried past the maximum load point. For accessibility purposes, we need to shift the perception towards that of the user rather than the operator or planner. The key issues are then based on how a user could use the bus service:

- how long a user must wait for a bus
- how long before it is possible for the user to make a return journey
- the freedom of choice of departure time.

Although a maximum waiting time of 10 minutes implies a maximum headway of 10 minutes, this is not necessarily required. Where a service is relatively low frequency, an acceptable maximum waiting time can be arranged if the service is able to deliver a reasonable level of reliability. Thus the Hackney Plusbus operates at 30-minute intervals, but waiting time is rarely as much as 10 minutes because of the reliability of the service and thus the predictability of its arrival time at a stop. The same applies to the Cumbria Plusbus, which operates with a 3-hour headway.

Making a return journey is important for most trips. The ease of arranging this depends on the frequency of the service in the same way as the freedom to choose the departure time. However, there is a difference between the outward and return journey in terms of being able to know about the available services before departure. Some rural services may not even provide a return service, and in almost every case it would be necessary to know the times of the last available connections of the day.

Bus Needs

In Chapter 1 we argued that bus stops are the principal points of access to the transport system, so it is important to understand how they might affect accessibility. Some aspects of this are of course concerned with the actual design, construction and operation of the bus stops, and these issues will be discussed in Chapters 4 and 5. We discussed above the effects of bus stop location for passengers. That discussion did not take into account the needs of buses in relation to the location of stopping points. It is also important to determine how the accessibility effects of the relationship between the location of bus stops and the access network will affect the bus operation. We need to know what costs and difficulties the design of an accessible access network imposes on the bus system before we can work out how to ensure that such a system cold be implemented and made viable.

Most models used to optimise distances between bus stops are derived from the approach used for railway stations, where the issue is to find the distance at which operating costs and overall access costs are equal. In these models, no account is taken of the distance of a journey origin or destination away from the route: the access path is only considered in terms of travel parallel to the route. Inter-stop distances have traditionally been treated in terms of economics, but this approach barely touches on the accessibility issue. We are going to look at the bus stop network and we will use some simple models to indicate the effects of different locations of bus stops. We are not suggesting that these models, or any others based on similar principles, are the best means for locating bus stops: we are just using them to illustrate the effects of different bus stop densities on bus operations, passenger access and so on. In reality, bus stops are located according to the practicality of placing them near to suitable origin and destination points (network effects of bus routes are discussed below). Simple economic models are not useful in determining where a bus stop should be located, but they can help to show how operations might appear if different policies about location were to be adopted.

The density of bus stops is the number of bus stops per unit area. As far as a single bus route is concerned, this is derived from the number of bus stops in a given route distance, and this is where we start our discussion. To consider this in more detail we need to look at some simple models of bus operations. Before doing so, we need to clarify the difference between what we shall call 'stops' and 'stoppings'. We use the word *stop* to refer to a formal or permanently generally recognised official place where buses stop. A *stopping* is the act of the bus coming to a halt. This may be due to congestion, or it could be in order to pick up passengers at a formal or informal stop. A bus may or may not stop at a bus stop or, in some cases, it could stop more than once at a bus stop, and thus the number of stoppings along a route could be different from the number of stops.

Speed

We will be considering some aspects of speed and, to avoid confusion, we need to describe briefly what we mean by speed:

- *Design speed* is the speed for which the infrastructure is designed.
- *Maximum speed* is the highest permitted speed.
- *Operating speed* is the speed at which the vehicles are able to travel.
- *Running speed* is the highest cruise speed obtained under the relevant infrastructure and traffic conditions.
- *Average speed* is the mean speed over a distance while the bus is in motion (e.g. between two bus stops) and includes consideration of acceleration and deceleration.
- *Commercial speed* is derived from the time for which the bus is in business, namely the average speed calculated from the time of departure from the first stop on its route to the time of arrival at the last stop. It includes consideration of delay resulting from bus stops and general congestion.

Comparing these speeds can give a very rough impression of where an operational problem might lie:

- The difference between design speed and maximum speed indicates the extent to which it is believed that the design is safe. A large difference here would indicate that, for some reason or other, the design is not perceived to be as safe in practice as it was designed to be.
- The difference between maximum speed and operating speed indicates the extent to which the vehicles are capable of achieving the maximum speed (or of over-achieving it).
- Comparing the running speed with the operating speed shows the extent to which the infrastructure or traffic conditions reduces the cruise speed for the vehicles of interest. This might indicate that it is necessary to look at traffic management, bus priorities and other such measures.
- The difference between running speed and average speed gives an indication of the loss in performance resulting from aspects of the bus operation, such as its ability to accelerate and the distance between stoppings. The more stoppings there are, the more it will reduce the average speed compared with the running speed.
- The difference between average speed and commercial speed indicates the effects of bus stops (congestion will have been included in the consideration of both running speed and average speed). This shows the effects of the delay at bus stops caused both by passengers boarding and alighting and by congestion between buses within the bus stop area.

Table 3.2 summarises the different speed types and indicates a possible place to start analysing the system, given large differences between these speeds.

The relationships between the maximum, running, average and commercial speed for a hypothetical road with a length of 5 km as a function of the stop density are shown in Figure 3.6. For this graph, the maximum permitted speed (V_{run}) is 40 km/h, the running speed (V_{max}) is 18 km/h, and the average (V_{av}) and commercial (V_c) speeds are calculated using equations (3.3) and (3.2), respectively (see below). The graph indicates the effect of stopping a bus and thus shows at what point attention should be paid to the quantity of bus stoppings. This illustrates why we distinguish between stops and stoppings – the accessibility of a bus system is, as we have discussed above, heavily concerned with the distance it is necessary to walk to reach a bus. This is inevitably connected to the number of bus stops along the bus route. At first sight, an improvement in accessibility would therefore seem to provide a devastating effect on the commercial speed of the bus service. The resulting journey times would not be attractive to other passengers. To understand why this appears to be so, and how this problem can be resolved, we must examine the issue of commercial speed in more depth.

The time taken to travel between two points on a public transport route is a function of the number of stoppings, the running speed of the vehicle and its rates of acceleration and braking. Three equations are useful for this. The first is a general empirical equation (Gibson *et al.*, 1989) which shows the way in which the commercial speed changes with respect to the stopping frequency (stoppings per kilometre):

$$V_c = V_0(e^{-Bf_p}) \tag{3.2}$$

where V_c is the commercial speed (km/h), V_0 is the speed in uninterrupted conditions (km/h), B is a parameter and f_p is the stop frequency (stoppings per kilometre).

Table 3.2   Different ways of looking at speed and what this can indicate

	Description	A large difference between the speed defined in this and that in the previous row indicates:	Look at first:
Design	Speed for which infrastructure was designed		
Maximum	Highest permitted speed	(a) Inadequacy of design (b) Cautious speed limits	(a) Design of infrastructure (b) Speed limits
Operating	What the vehicles can achieve	Extent to which vehicles can achieve maximum speed	Adequacy of vehicles for this operation
Running	Normal cruise speed attained	Extent to which vehicles are affected by congestion	Congestion measures and bus priorities
Average	Mean speed while in motion	Extent to which vehicles are affected by the number of stoppings	(a) Route and service design (b) Power/weight ratio of vehicles
Commercial	Mean speed including stopped time	Extent to which vehicles are affected by the duration of stoppings	(a) Number of bus stops (b) Bus stop design

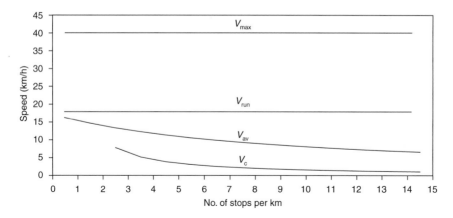

Fig. 3.6   *Comparison of the maximum, running, average and commercial speeds*

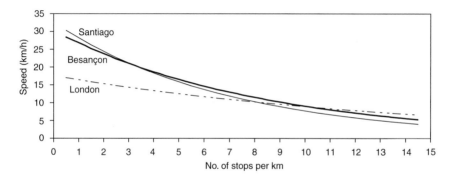

Fig. 3.7   *Commercial speeds calculated from equation (3.4)*

As the stopping frequency increases, the vehicle can no longer achieve as high a running speed, thus there is less time spent on acceleration and deceleration. The parameter B is a measure of the effect on the commercial speed of the act of stopping. It is also indicative of the behaviour of drivers in the city of interest: a higher value of B suggests more aggressive driving (higher acceleration and braking rates), increasing the effect of each stopping. Figure 3.7 shows curves obtained from equation (3.2) for data with respect to Santiago (Chile), Besançon (France) and London. The more aggressive driving in Santiago is reflected in the higher initial running speed and the stronger impacts resulting from the stoppings compared with the Besançon example.

Cohen (1984) points out that the problem in Besançon was mainly concerned with congestion at intersections, which accounted for 20% of bus journey time. The bus priority system introduced there set out to reduce these delays and after implementation intersection delay accounted for less than 9%. This contrasts with the situation which arises where bus stops and their associated operations are less fixed. In the case of Santiago, Gibson *et al.* (1989) give an example where the stop frequency is 10.4 stops/km, of which only 4 stops/km are attributable to picking up or setting down of passengers and a further 4.7 stops/km are due to buses being caught up in delays caused by other buses within the bus stops. The result is a commercial speed of less than 8 km/h. London is characterised by a low running speed but less impact from the stoppings compared with the other cities. More formalised bus stops, with less informal bus operation leading to bus stop congestion results in rather better performance in London than in Santiago at higher stop densities.

The inference is that, depending on the nature of the problem in a given street, attention should be spent on either the reduction of traffic impacts on bus operation or on the effects of poorly designed bus stops. This is an example of why it is helpful to analyse the different types of speed, as described at the beginning of this section. It is therefore useful when collecting speed data to include an assessment of the reasons for the stoppings, as this will help to direct attention to the cause of the problem of bus delay in each situation.

The second equation, derived from Vuchic (1981) shows how the average speed changes with respect to the distance between the stops on a particular route:

$$V_{av} = \frac{D}{D/V_{run} + V_{run}/2(1/a+1/b)} \tag{3.3}$$

where V_{av} is the average velocity, D is the distance between stops, V_{run} is the running speed, a is the acceleration rate (average) and b is the braking rate (average). This equation requires an estimation of average acceleration and braking rates. It reflects the degree of congestion by using running speed rather than maximum speed.

Finally, the third equation shows how the commercial speed may be calculated from knowledge of the distance between bus stops. This takes into account the time spent stationary at stops, although for practical reasons this does not include estimates of the amount of time spent stationary due to congestion effects, except through the use of running rather than maximum speed.

$$V_c = \frac{L}{\sum_{i=1}^{N-1} \{[V_{run}/2(1/a+1/b)] + D_{ij}/V_{run}\} + (N-2)T_s} \tag{3.4}$$

where L is the total distance between first and last stops on the route, N is the number of stops on the route, T_s is the stationary time at each stop and D_{ij} is the distance between stops i and j.

If the distance between the stops is constant, equation (3.4) can be changed to simplify the summation into a multiplication:

$$V_c = \frac{L}{\{[V_{run}/2(1/a+1/b)]+D/V_{run}](N-1)\}+(N-2)T_s} \qquad (3.5)$$

The curves shown in Figure 3.6 were derived using equations (3.2) and (3.3). The commercial speed curves shown in Figures 3.6 and 3.7 assume that the stationary time at each stop is the same, irrespective of the distance between the stops. In reality, as the stop density increases, we would expect the number of passengers at each stop to decrease. The empirically based model expressed by equation (3.2) is the result of a study of real practice, where buses compensate for such differences. The theoretical model expressed by equation (3.4) is derived from models used in railway systems, where a station acts as a single attractor for many people. Bus stops are more widely distributed and thus the demand is spread between them. The comparison of the theoretical and empirical models suggests that bus operations differ from railway systems in the way in which they interact with the pedestrian access network.

The commercial speed given by the model proposed by Gibson *et al.* (1989) as defined for the London example above would be of the order of 14 km/h if the distance between bus stops were 250 m. With a stop distance of 500 m, the commercial speed would be higher (a little under 16 km/h). A 10-km journey would take (under the same congestion conditions) 43 minutes and 38 minutes, respectively. As we shall see below, the reduced inter-stop distance will have an important impact on the cost of operation (one extra bus and crew to keep a 10-minute headway). The impact on bus operations of making the network accessible is, therefore, potentially considerable. We need to ensure that increased costs that arise from a more accessible service are compensated through better operational conditions and reduced impacts of bus stops.

Access Costs and Accessibility

We have just seen one view of the impacts of the number of stoppings on a bus operation, taking into consideration the impacts on accessibility arising from changing the distance between bus stops. We should note that the models just discussed do not include passengers except in the most simplistic way as an element of the dwell time of the buses at the bus stops. We can now discuss what happens if we include passengers in the consideration of the optimum distance between bus stops by examining some bus stop location models.

Most bus stop location models are derived in some way from railway station location models. This is quite understandable: inter-station distances are important on railway systems, given the capital cost involved and the impacts on operations. It seems only natural to consider buses as small trains and to use the same model. After all, they are both based on fixed routes and schedules. However, these models only consider vehicle operations – there is no direct reference to passengers, except in the simplistic treatment of dwell time. We can start to introduce passengers to the bus stop density models by including a simple valuation of time associated with arriving at a bus stop located at a given distance from its neighbours.

Taking the simple case first, the conventional wisdom examines the 'cost' of access and the cost of stopping the bus at the stops. In order not to give precedence to either group of people (those trying to reach the bus stop and those already on the bus), we want to find an optimal distance where these costs are equal.

The costs associated with access are the time costs associated with getting to and from the bus stop (assume walking for now) and the number of passengers doing this. A simple model for this, based on the distance between bus stops, is given by:

$$C_a = \frac{dP_a WC_t}{4V_p}$$ (3.6)

where C_a is the nominal access cost, d is the distance between two adjacent bus stops, P_a is the passenger density associated with the bus stop (passengers per hour per kilometre), W is a weighting factor to represent dislike of time spent on access compared with in-vehicle time, C_t is the value of time and V_p is the access speed.

The costs associated with stopping are the time costs imposed by decelerating, accelerating and standing at the stop while the access passengers get on and off. These costs will be felt by the bus (in the sense of operating costs) and by the passengers inside. We only need to consider the time between the departure of the bus from the first stop to the time it arrives at the second. In-vehicle costs C_v are given by:

$$C_v = \frac{T_1(C_t P_v + C_o)}{d}F$$ (3.7)

where T_1 is the lost time, P_v is the number of passengers in the vehicle arriving at the (second) station and C_o is the operating cost per vehicle.

When C_a (as calculated using equation (3.6)) and C_v are set to be equal, and the equation solved for the distance, an optimum value for d can be obtained:

$$d = \sqrt{\frac{4V_p T_1[C_o + (P_v C_t)]F}{WC_t P_a}}$$ (3.8)

This function provides the optimum distance between a pair of bus stops on the basis of the ratio of vehicle flow to passenger density (e.g. 20 buses/h

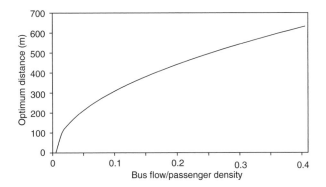

Fig. 3.8   The optimum distance between bus stops, assuming no overtaking

and 100 passengers/h/km gives a value of 0.05), with no recognition of differences in access difficulty and assuming that everyone can reach the bus stops (whatever the distance between them).

Figure 3.8 shows the curve that results from using equation (3.8). This is representative of the normal result of inter-stop distance analysis: the optimum distance increases at a decreasing rate as the vehicle flow increases relative to the passenger density. This is because the model assumes that when one vehicle stops all the others will have to stop behind it. Thus, as the frequency increases, the effect on the overall delay to the bus system increases. This delay should be caused as infrequently as possible, and therefore the distance between bus stoppings should be increased.

We have discussed above the need to consider an exclusion penalty in the consideration of bus stop location. The exclusion penalty should apply to everyone who:

- is within the inclusion zone, but whose access speed is different from the average
- is outside the inclusion zone.

The Rawlsian approach suggested in Chapter 1 would say that nobody should be in an exclusion zone, so we should not begin to calculate distances between bus stops until we have satisfied this condition. Nevertheless, it is interesting to see what would happen to the optimum stop distance if excluded people were taken into account. First, we have to consider all the people within the inclusion zone who cannot reach the bus stop and those who can reach the bus stop albeit at a slower walking speed than the average assumed in equation (3.6). Then we need to count all the people outside the inclusion zone who might have been associated with this bus stop. If we assume that the exclusion penalty is simply the local taxi fare for a short distance, say £2, then we can begin to see the effects.

When the outcomes of this approach are plotted alongside those for equation (3.6) as a function of inter-stop distance, it is possible to see what

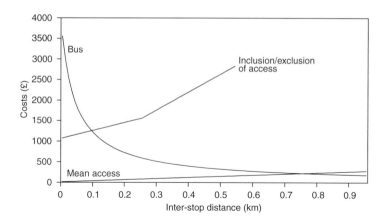

Fig. 3.9   Access costs, differentiating between inclusion and exclusion, compared with the costs of stopping buses as a function of inter-stop distances

would happen to the optimum inter-stop distance. Figure 3.9 shows that this gives a surprisingly short inter-stop distance compared with the one that would be calculated with the same parameter values using equations (3.6) and (3.7). This suggests a rethink about how bus networks are designed and evaluated.

What Figure 3.9 shows is that when we include the effects of exclusion the access costs are so high that they completely dominate the consideration of inter-stop distances. In fact, the situation is much worse than this: the real 'cost' to people who are excluded from the system because they cannot manage the access distance from their home to the bus stop is that they cannot go out at all. As we discussed in Chapter 1, we do not accept that a society should be designed in such a way that some people are excluded. Also, as we have noted in Chapter 2, such exclusion imposes costs on society in the performance of its other duties (e.g. the provision of healthcare, social care or education).

We therefore need to resolve the issue of how we enable buses to operate feasibly within a system conceived to be accessible to the people who need to use it. For this reason we ought to consider again how the bus system operates, but from the point of view of some other characteristics. For example, in principle, and unlike trains, buses can overtake anywhere. This is not considered in any of these models. Buses work in networks, and this is not considered anywhere either.

Bus Operations

It is easier to understand the effects of overtaking if we consider the comparison between bus operating costs and mean access costs without complicating the issue by incorporating the exclusion issue. If we allow overtaking at bus stops, we can observe three effects:

- a bus is not delayed by another bus stopped in front of it because it can leave when ready and overtake the stopped bus
- a bus does not have to stop at every stop
- as there is a reduced impact from the bus stop, stops can be placed closer together.

The first two of these can be incorporated quite simply as a probability of stopping, which is effectively related to the passenger density and the flow of buses, so that only buses that collect or deliver passengers at the stop are considered. This gives a probability K:

$$K = \frac{P_s}{1 + P_s} \tag{3.9}$$

where P_s is the number of boarding and alighting passengers per bus.

The third point can be incorporated by assuming that the optimum distance between two stops is actually made up of two elements:

- the optimum distance that would arise if overtaking were not possible
- a distance by which this is reduced as a result of the relationship between the number of buses and the passenger density.

The second of these elements can be imagined by thinking of the reduction caused by the bus not being constrained to stop at a formal bus stop in order to collect its passengers. As this is given by the relationship between the bus flow and the passenger density, it turns out to be:

$$R = \frac{1}{P_g} \tag{3.10}$$

where P_g is the number of access passengers per bus per unit distance. As a result, the equation for the optimum distance between two bus stops where overtaking is permitted is:

$$d = \sqrt{\frac{4V_p T_1 [C_o + (P_v C_t)] FK}{WC_t P_a}} - R \tag{3.11}$$

As can be seen in Figure 3.10, the resulting curve looks rather different from the one for the non-overtaking situation shown in Figure 3.8. Figure 3.10 shows the curve from Figure 3.8 for reference. The first difference is that the optimum distances are much lower when overtaking is allowed. Secondly, there is a maximum optimum distance after which, as the ratio of buses to passengers increases, the optimum distance reduces. This is because when there are lots of buses and relatively few passengers, few

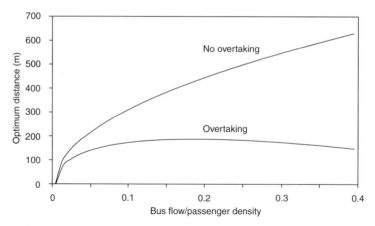

Fig. 3.10   The optimum distance between bus stops, allowing for overtaking

buses actually stop for the passengers and the others can pass by without stopping. The the overall cost of stopping the buses is thus reduced.

The effect of overtaking at bus stops is important for our consideration of accessibility because it shows that there is a way of reducing the impact of bus stops. This permits us to reduce the distance between bus stops without necessarily increasing the impacts on the bus operation. Thus we should be able to increase accessibility to passengers without always increasing the costs of bus operation. Overtaking at bus stops is therefore a key part of the development of an accessible bus system.

Another issue to consider is whether bus stops are necessary. In Figures 3.8 and 3.10 the *x* axis is the ratio of buses to passengers per kilometre. The left-hand side of the graph represents the situation where there are (relatively) lots of passengers and few buses. The right-hand side of the graph illustrates the effect on inter-stop distance of a large number of buses relative to the number of passengers per kilometre. The left-hand side could therefore represent a situation where there is one bus and 100 passengers/h/km (or 10 buses/h and 1000 passengers/h/km – each would yield a value for F/P_a of 0.01). The right-hand extreme could represent 400 buses/h and 1000 passengers/h/km ($F/P_a = 0.4$).

Under these assumptions, it is possible to establish a principle for the optimum distance between bus stops. Figure 3.10 suggests that if you can design the stop to allow overtaking, bus stops should be about 200 m apart if your bus service provides, for example, 2 buses/h and you have a passenger density of 20 boarding and alighting passengers per kilometre. With a stop spacing of 200 m this passenger density gives 0.01 passengers/m, and thus a figure of two boarding and alighting passengers per hour, or one passenger per bus.

As a bus service reaches areas with small numbers of passengers per bus, it may be better to operate a hail-and-ride service so that passengers are not forced to walk to formal bus stops in order to reach the bus. This would reduce the access distance for those people living along the route and for some people living away from the route (the exact benefits depend on the detail of the access network). Under hail-and-ride conditions it would be necessary to ensure that overtaking is possible wherever the bus can stop to collect passengers. Otherwise, the additional stops would be imposed on all other buses in the system and the benefits reduced as a result. It is important that overtaking is possible if the overall service frequency is such that more than one bus might appear at the same time. The overtaking facility means that only the buses actually collecting or delivering passengers at the stop will be delayed, as the others will pass the stopped buses. However, as discussed in Chapters 5 and 6, formal bus stops are also points of information and provide accessible access to the bus system and cannot be abandoned on capacity grounds without imposing additional barriers on people who have difficulty in reaching the bus system. Formal accessible bus stops should, therefore, be included at appropriate locations relative to the access network even where hail-and-ride systems are in operation. Our experience of operating a service in this way shows that, on the whole, people board buses at formal bus stops (or, in the case of the Hackney Plusbus, consistent access points), but tend to alight at points which are more convenient for their destination. This applies in both urban and rural areas.

The model as described in equation (3.11) was derived from an empirical analysis of an express bus corridor in São Paulo, Brazil, in which the bus stops were constructed 600 m apart. The analysis indicated that the bus stops could have been about 280 m apart under the same operating conditions. Using this as a design approach, the bus system could therefore become more accessible by reducing the distance it is necessary to walk to reach a bus stop.

This approach also shows that thought should be given to the number of boarding and alighting passengers to accommodate at a bus stop. This is related to two elements of the bus system: the service frequency and the distance between bus stops.

As the service frequency increases, the number of boarding and alighting passengers per bus decreases (assuming demand is constant). At this point it is useful to note that using this factor as a design constraint places the emphasis on the need to deal with the bus stop as the main constraint of the bus system. The more common consideration is that the main constraint is the provision of adequate capacity at the maximum load point (the point along a route where the largest number of passengers is carried). This ignores the difficulties faced by buses at bus stops, where they are subject to the most severe effects of congestion and thus to much of the overall delay encountered by bus services. Bus stops have to be designed to accommodate the flow of buses that need to use them, so that bus stops do not impose unnecessary delays on the bus system. As we shall see in Chapter 4, this can be achieved if the bus stop capacity is sufficient for the services and passengers using the stop.

As the distance between bus stops decreases, the number of passengers using each stop decreases because they are spread between more stops. As a result, the number of stoppings at each stop would decrease. The number of stoppings per bus would remain about the same (i.e. the buses stop and collect about as many passengers as in the non-overtaking case), but each stopping imposes less delay because the stops are less congested.

Thus, the order of constraints to deal with for bus operation design is:

(1) Locate bus stops appropriately for the access network and conditions.
(2) Determine an initial operational service to join these stops together.
(3) Find the passenger density for each section of the bus route.

There is then an iterative process to establish both the service frequency and the bus stop locations:

(4) Identify the bus stop where one could expect the longest dwell times (the critical bus stop).
(5) Estimate the optimum bus stop spacing given the overtaking conditions.
(6) Estimate the service frequency necessary to bring the number of passengers per bus at the critical stop to a manageable level.
(7) Confirm the operational feasibility of the bus service under these conditions. If it is not appropriate, go back to step (2) and try again.

Then:

(8) Determine the size of the buses necessary to deal with the maximum load point at this frequency.
(9) Design bus stops to accommodate the required number of vehicles (including overtaking if necessary). If it is impossible to accommodate the desired services, go back to step (2) and try again.

A network designed on the basis of the non-overtaking model is likely to result in a much less accessible system than a network designed to take overtaking into account.

Flexible transport services – such as extensive use of taxis, door-to-door services or similar non- or semi-scheduled systems – are attractive but expensive, and their use needs to be thought about in terms of the best use of resources. This is not to say that they should not be used, but the high cost of providing an adequate service means that it will inevitably be scarce and therefore should be made available primarily to those people who have no alternative. We have also found that the need to telephone the control centre in advance in order to book a vehicle works against those people who find such a process intimidating or difficult and can therefore become exclusive. Looking at the user profiles for such systems often reveals a relatively small number of regular users and little evidence of use by the wider, more socially excluded, community. In Hackney, experience suggests that some 50% of door-to-door service users would be better served by some form of well-designed group-based transport, about 30–40% could (and would, when given the option) use a minicab or taxi service, leaving 10–20% of existing users for whom the pre-booked door-to-door service using specialised vehicles is really the only option available. These estimates do not include those that have already transferred to the Hackney Plusbus for the journeys in question. The overall effect in that case is that a more targeted approach to the service yields considerable cost savings to the majority of users and better service to those who have to use the door-to-door service.

Scheduled services also have their difficulties. We must include the design of bus stops, as discussed in Chapter 4, in the consideration of network density because the way in which they are designed may influence the extent to which they make interchange easier or more difficult as well as the delays they may impose on the buses. Before considering bus stop design, however, we need to consider the impacts of decisions about network and stop density on the cost of providing a given level of service.

First, we have to establish how the operating costs of a bus service are determined. The cost of the crew can be 70–80% of the operating costs of a service, so it is useful to consider how these are generated. As crew costs are related to the number of vehicles in operation, we must decide how many vehicles will be needed to provide the service. The cost of providing a bus service depends largely on the number of crews required to operate the service. This depends on the number of vehicles required to operate the service at the required frequency.

The first principle to consider when deciding how many vehicles it is necessary to use to provide a scheduled service is that it is impossible for a vehicle to be used on a second service until it has completed the first one. This means that a bus travelling from A to B will not be available to work from A to B for a second time until it has returned from B to A after the first trip. In addition, it is almost certain that some layover time will be required at each end (i.e. at B and A) for the driver. Therefore, the time after which a vehicle is available for a second service is the travel time from A to B plus the travel time from B to A plus two layover periods. This is known as the *cycle time*.

The cycle time is critical in establishing the fleet size required for a level of service:

$$F = \frac{T_c}{Ah} \tag{3.12}$$

where F is the fleet size (vehicles), T_c is the cycle time (minutes), h is the service headway (minutes) and A is the availability of vehicles. The outcome for *F* has to be rounded up to the next whole number (it is hard to make use of half a bus!). If the route length were 10 km, the commercial speed 15 km/h and the layover time 15 minutes, the cycle time would be 110 minutes. With a 10-minute headway and 90% availability of the buses, the fleet required for this service is 13 vehicles.

The key to cycle time is the length of time it takes to travel along a route taking into account all the time spent at bus stops and dealing with traffic congestion. It is therefore the time taken to travel along the route at the commercial speed. The cycle time is important in establishing how many vehicles and drivers will be needed in order to provide a given frequency and capacity. As noted above, however, the commercial speed is strongly affected by the stop density and congestion.

Each vehicle requires a driver, and so the number of vehicles determines the number of drivers (crew) required to operate the service. However, more than one driver can drive the same vehicle at different times of day. Drivers' constraints are mainly concerned with working hours and other regulations. For simplicity, consider the case where drivers are based near the start of a route and are not subject to drivers' hours regulations. In this case, the important issue is the length of the service day (i.e. the number of hours in a day during which the bus service is in operation). The first thing to consider is the number of drivers required to operate one vehicle during the service day. This is calculated by dividing the number of hours in the service day by the number of driving hours per working shift that can be used in the actual operation of the service. For this calculation, the time spent by a driver in travelling between the depot and a bus service should be deducted from the working shift, as these hours would not contribute to the service delivery. Thus an operator would like to have services that are routed as near to their depot as possible. We can express this as:

$$S = \frac{H_w}{H_s - H_h} \tag{3.13}$$

where *S* is the number of drivers per bus per service day, H_w is the length of the working day (h), H_s is the length of a driver's shift (h) and H_h is the 'housekeeping' activities in a shift (i.e. the time during which a driver is working but is not driving a vehicle in service) (h).

Take, for example, a service day of 18 h and a bus service where the drivers can take over the service at the depot without affecting their shift patterns. If the number of in-service driving hours in a shift is 6, then three drivers will be required to keep one vehicle on the road during the whole day. Now suppose that the drivers require 1½ h to travel from the depot to pick up the bus at the beginning of their driving shift and 1½ h to return at the end. This would result in three in-service driving hours, thus requiring six drivers per day to keep one vehicle in operation for 18 h.

Now, consider the number of buses to be used for the service. As shown in equation (3.12), this depends on the service headway h and is given by the fleet size F. Multiply this by the number of drivers per vehicle and you obtain the number of drivers it is necessary to have to maintain the service level for the given period. Then, add one spare driver per shift (more if driver unreliability is high) and you have the crew requirement for the service.

In our 'near-to-depot' example, 13 vehicles each have to be driven by three drivers over the service day. This gives a total of 39 drivers. There are three shifts during the day, so adding the one spare driver per shift gives a total requirement of 42 drivers. The 'far-from-depot' example would need 78 drivers plus three spares (although it might be necessary to have more spare drivers per shift with such a high number of drivers being required to operate the service). This all assumes that the service operates at the same frequency all day. If not, the peak vehicle requirement should be calculated for the peak periods, and the off-peak needs worked out separately. Then it is a matter of sorting out the drivers' shifts to give the best use of their permitted driving hours.

The issue of how many spare drivers to carry illustrates an important point about crew costs. As you increase the crew requirement for a service, the probability of absence also increases. Thus requiring 78 drivers to be at work carries with it a greater possibility of absence than would arise if only 39 drivers were needed. The same thinking applies if the crew were increased to two (e.g. if a driver and conductor were required in order to run the bus). One of the main problems of operating such a service is that it requires both members of the crew to be at work before the bus can go into service. The increased risk of absence means that an increased number of spares would be required. The cost of two-person crew operation is therefore very high, and the benefits provided by such a service need to be considered very carefully to be sure that they are worth the additional expense.

Multiplying the number of drivers (crew) by the full employment cost gives you an estimate of wage costs: the fleet size figure enables you to estimate the vehicle costs. Thus the operating cost of the service can be estimated quite simply. Of course, in these simple examples, problems such as maximum driving hours have not been included (these are a major constraint for bus operators). Also, an allowance for the fixed costs and management overheads will need to be included when estimating the full cost of a particular service. Nevertheless, this sort of calculation is quite useful for estimating the impacts of changing the service level, altering the commercial speed, extending/contracting the operating hours, etc.

A cost which is often underestimated is the cost of controlling the operation of the service. This can, of course, be spread over several services and thus its impact on any one service can be reduced if more services are operated. The basic cost depends on how decisions about remedial action can be taken in the circumstances. At one extreme, decisions could be left to drivers to work out on their own: at the other, drivers could be left with no independent discretion and rely totally on instructions from a service controller. The reality lies somewhere between these extremes and depends in part on the level of service (it is much easier to control a small number of vehicles/drivers) and in part on the type of service problems (operation is more difficult to control in highly congested traffic conditions than in a quiet free-flowing traffic stream). An operator needs to take a decision about the level of on-street control that is necessary and the extent to which centralised control can be helpful.

As the calculation of fleet size depends on the cycle time, which in turn depends on the commercial speed, which in turn depends on the stop density, which in turn depends on the desired accessibility level, accessibility can have a dramatic effect on the cost of providing a bus service. How do we compensate for this? To achieve satisfactory accessibility standards, we need to think about what a bus does when it calls at a bus stop and ensure that each of these activities causes the minimum disruption to the smooth operation of the bus stop. This is the subject of the next chapter.

Conclusions

Earlier in this chapter we asked the question 'How can we define a bus network so that accessibility to the bus system might be set as part of a policy?'. We have considered a number of issues that go towards answering that question, looking at various aspects of network design, users' perspectives and operators' problems. To conclude the chapter we shall try to draw the various threads together to provide some sort of answer to the question.

First, bus systems – as with any public transport system – involve the superimposition of two networks: the access network used by people to reach the system and the bus network provided by bus operators as a response to their perception of users' needs. The connecting points between these two networks are formed by bus stops, and these are seen differently by passengers and operators. Passengers see them as access points to the bus system and thus as the gateway to activities they wish to pursue elsewhere in the network. Operators see them as points at which buses must stop to collect and deliver passengers, thus incurring delay to the operation of the bus. The location of these access points is therefore a key issue to both parties and needs to be resolved to their mutual satisfaction.

Normally, a policy concerning the distance between bus stops is described by stating maximum straight-line distances from journey origins to bus routes or by explicitly stating a normal inter-stop distance. Various models have been produced to show the optimum distance between bus stops on the basis of economic considerations of access and in-vehicle costs. These ignore the passengers' needs, which are characterised by being highly individual. We therefore suggest taking as a starting point the definition by local people of the access points they need. Inclusion zones (where people are able to reach a bus stop) and exclusion zones (where they cannot) can then be defined for each bus stop. Different inclusion zones should be defined for people with different access needs so that it becomes clear who is being excluded and for what reason. Once a full and inclusive set of access points has been defined, these should be joined together in the most helpful (for passengers) and convenient (for operators) way, to form a bus network.

A policy about a bus network should be set on the basis of access time (e.g. 'Everyone should be able to reach a bus stop within 10 minutes'), with this being converted to distance according to a relevant set of access speeds. Based on the actual access network, an inclusion zone could then be defined which would fulfil the policy. Study of the resulting exclusion zones should then open up possibilities for redesign of the network and the development of new services or other provision so that the overall objective of enabling everyone to be able to reach their chosen activities can be met.

Even though hail-and-ride services can provide good accessibility along the route, it is necessary to have formal bus stops at accessible intervals so that people who need accessible infrastructure to enable them to board and alight buses can still reach the system. These bus stops should also provide accessible information about the bus services and the local area, forming part of a local information network: a place where people know they can find information.

Bus services must work within the community, taking into account the opportunities they can provide for economic development. They should be designed so that they bring people towards local resources rather than take them away. Careful design of interconnecting micronetworks using small, accessible vehicles can help to provide a useful support to social cohesion in local areas and thus act as a positive element of the local community. It is important to remember, for example, that although journeys are generally made for some reason other than the trip itself, social interactions are often part of the benefit of making the journey. People make journeys because they might meet someone at the shops or on the bus, even though the ostensible purpose of their journey is to go shopping.

We have shown that, with good design, bus networks can be made accessible and the costs of so doing can be analysed and determined. The main difficulty is to ensure that all the elements are in place. This is especially difficult where different entities own and operate each element.

The deregulated environment outside London certainly makes it a lot more difficult to keep these matters under control, but it is not impossible: for example, the Cumbria Plusbus operates in the deregulated environment. Whether or not a regulated situation is helpful depends entirely on the objectives of the regulation. If the objective is to foster better accessibility, then we can expect the design and development of an accessible bus network to be easier. If, however, the objective is to reduce cost, increase passenger mileage or reduce journey times, this will tend to push network design towards corridor-based routes. These can easily fail to serve the less dense residential areas and the needs of sections of the community who need the transport system to come nearer to them before they would be able to use it. The more regulated situation in London does not necessarily make it any easier. It is not immediately clear that this is necessarily any more responsive to the needs of local people – especially people with particular needs of the transport system – than the more commercially oriented systems outside the capital.

References

ADA (1990). Americans with Disabilities Act. Washington, DC.

AKCELIK & ASSOCIATES (2001). *An Investigation of Pedestrian Movement Characteristics at Midblock Signalised Crossings*. Technical report. Melbourne: Akcelik & Associates.

BARHAM, P., OXLEY, P. and SHAW, A. (1994). *Accessible Public Transport Infrastructure*. London: Department of Transport.

BROWN, I. E. W. and TYLER, N. A. (2001). 'Users' responses to the implementation of an innovative accessible bus service in a remote rural area'. *9th International Conference on Mobility and Transport for Elderly and Disabled People*, Warsaw.

COHEN, S. (1984). 'Indicateurs d'allure et de consommation d'un autobus en exploitation'. *Recherche, Transport, Sécurité*, Vol. 1, pp. 16–22.

DETR (2000). *Transport 2010 – The Ten Year Plan*. London: Department of Transport, Environment and the Regions.

GIBSON, J., BAEZA, I. and WILLUMSEN, L. G. (1989). 'Bus stops, congestion and congested bus stops'. *Traffic Engineering and Control*, Vol. 30, No. 6, pp. 291–302.

HOLROYD, E. M. and SCRAGGS, D. A. (1963). 'Waiting times for buses in Central London'. *Traffic Engineering and Control*, Vol. 8, No. 3, pp. 158–160.

INSTITUTE OF HIGHWAYS AND TRANSPORTATION (1991). *Revised Guidelines for Reducing Mobility Handicaps: Towards a Barrier-free Environment*. London: IHT.

KUNAKA, C. (1996). Modelling paratransit services: a microscopic simulation approach. PhD Thesis, University of London.

LONDON BOROUGH OF HAMMERSMITH AND FULHAM (1994). *Unitary Development Plan*.

LYNAS, J. R. (1998). *The Hackney Plusbus Scheme: Initial Monitoring and Review*. Working paper. London: University College London, Centre for Transport Studies.

TADESSE, D. and ISLAM, M. (1996). *Accessibility to Public Transport in Bloomsbury*. Project report. London: Department of Civil and Environmental Engineering, UCL.

TRB (2000). *Highway Capacity Manual*. Washington, DC: Transportation Research Board.

VUCHIC, V. (1981). *Urban Public Transportation*. Englewood Cliffs, NJ: Prentice Hall.

Chapter 4

Operational Impacts of Bus Stops

N. Tyler, P. Silva, N. Brown and R. Fernández

Introduction

The models described in the previous chapter, like all other stop-spacing models, assume that the access network is a grid pattern and that passengers can only choose between one stop and another along the same street. The distance away from this street is therefore not considered. The reality is that most people live their lives in an area and not along a bus route. Therefore we have to consider how the bus services can be designed to serve an area rather than a route, and thus the way in which the network is considered. We have already discussed some aspects of this when considering inclusion and exclusion zones and access distances for passengers.

Figure 3.9 in Chapter 3 shows the effect of comparing access costs with bus operating costs for different inter-stop distances, taking into account people who are excluded by the design of the system. The curves of optimum distance shown in Figure 3.10 merely indicate that bus stops can be closer together when designed to permit overtaking than when overtaking is impossible, suggesting that we can design a bus system with a more accessible view of the spacing between bus stops. These considerations bring together the access needs of passengers and the operational impacts of these on the buses. We noted the importance of overtaking in reducing the distance between bus stops and thus how bus stops could be made more reachable for passengers.

We now begin to consider what the bus stops should look like. In this chapter we look at the operational design of the bus stops: how many buses they need to accommodate, the impacts of the design on bus operation (especially in relation to the effects on queuing and other delays imposed on buses) and the effects of the bus operations on the design. Except in a few cases, buses operate in the general traffic system. Sometimes they have the benefits of bus lanes and other priorities to offset the effects of traffic congestion, but unless they are completely segregated from general traffic they are subject to the vagaries of congestion, whatever its cause. Bus stops constitute one potential interruption to smooth traffic flow. As this could easily affect buses, we need to see how we should examine bus stops for their impacts on traffic. This chapter examines these issues in principle. Chapter 5 considers how the outcomes from such analyses can be incorporated with the needs of passengers into the design of accessible bus stop infrastructure.

Buses and Bus Stops

What do buses need from the bus stops in order to make them accessible? We shall see some detailed answers to this question in Chapter 5, but for the moment we can consider some simple concepts. Basically, buses need to be able to reach the kerb and to be able to enter and leave the bus stop without interruption from traffic, parked vehicles or other buses. This presents a fairly standard queuing problem, in which the bus stop provides a service to the buses, taking a certain amount of time for this. As the number of buses attempting to use the stop within a given time period increases, a queue will form. We therefore have the concept of bus stop capacity, i.e. the number of buses able to enter the bus stop area in a given time period. This, as with most queuing problems, depends on the number of buses attempting to do this, and thus on the service frequency. Unlike many queuing problems, the service time at the bus stop is also a function of the frequency, because this will affect the amount of time spent by a bus at a bus stop. All the models discussed in Chapter 3 either ignore this issue or assume a simple constant value.

The main part of the stopped time at a bus stop is spent setting down or picking up passengers. This is known as the *passenger service time*. However, this can be managed, at least to a certain extent, by the use of frequency. As the frequency increases, the number of passengers being processed by each bus reduces. Therefore, if the demand were to remain constant the passenger service time would reduce. There is some evidence to suggest that frequency has a positive elasticity, so one might expect the reduction to be less as more passengers are attracted to the more frequent service. However, in principle, the number of passengers per bus should reduce even if the overall number of passengers increases.

The difficulty is that as the service frequency and thus the bus flow increases, the number of buses attempting to enter the bus stop increases. This gives rise to congestion between the buses and a queue of buses forms

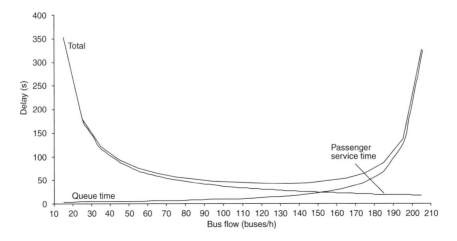

Fig. 4.1   Delays at bus stops as a function of frequency

before the stop. The amount of time spent by a bus in this queue (*queuing time*) increases dramatically as the bus flow approaches and then exceeds the capacity of the bus stop. Although there are other factors which have effects on the overall time spent by the bus at the bus stop, we shall consider just these two at present (the whole bus stop capacity issue is covered in more detail below).

Just taking the passenger service time and the queuing time into account, the overall delay to a bus at a bus stop is the sum of these two times. Each is affected by frequency but in different ways. Figure 4.1 shows a simple example of the nature of the effects that arise. As the bus frequency increases, the amount of time spent serving passengers falls because each bus serves fewer passengers. As the congestion increases the amount of time each bus spends in the queue before the stop increases. The total time has a minimum between the lowest and the highest frequencies. If the frequency of a service is low, the best way to improve passenger service time would be to deal with the boarding process (including the ticketing system, use of doors and design of the entry area of the bus and bus stop). Where frequency is high, a better course of action would be to resolve the capacity problem at the bus stop so that it could cope with the large number of buses trying to use it.

Bus Stop Capacity Issues

As we shall discuss in Chapter 5, a principal requirement for an accessible bus stop is that the horizontal and vertical gaps between the platform and the bus are small. This requires the bus to be able to approach and stop at the bus stop close to the kerb. In most cities in the world this is very difficult to achieve because of the obstacles presented to the bus driver by vehicles parked near to the stop and the need to accommodate too many buses at the bus stop, thus causing inter-bus congestion. The congestion between buses is a function of the bus stop capacity and, just as with any other system bottleneck, the capacity has to be sufficient for the system to operate properly. Capacity at bus stops is rarely considered in the UK because the view is that buses are relatively few in number (compared with, for example, the traffic approaching a junction) and that a bus stop is merely a point in space that identifies the place where a bus might stop. In each case, the view is too simplistic to reflect reality. As we shall see in Chapter 5, we can design a bus stop to achieve sufficiently small vertical and horizontal gaps, but this can only be successful in practice if the bus stop has sufficient capacity to cope with the required numbers of buses and passengers.

To study the capacity of any service, we have to analyse the performance under saturated conditions. The best opportunity to do this lies where the operation is very intensive. In the case of bus systems, the majority of bus stop capacity work has been undertaken in Latin America (mostly in Chile) where bus flows of several hundred buses per hour are the norm. The capacity issue is profound where such flows occur, and these cases provide a rich source of data for analysis of the capacity limits of bus stops with different characteristics. Although it would be unusual to have such flows in the UK, the situation here is more complex because the arrival patterns of both buses and passengers are less predictable.

Even though bus flows are low in the UK relative to cities in Latin America, we still see the effects of congestion at bus stops. The reason for this is that the bus flows, although low, are not regular and thus are characterised by very high flow rates over short periods of time. The high arrival rate causes a queuing effect which outlasts the original problematic event. The most visible effect of this is a queue of buses and this, together with the resulting confusion for passengers and drivers, characterises many bus stops today. One effect of this congestion is that buses stop away from the bus stop. In doing this, they require passengers to walk towards them, sometimes along the footway, but often into the roadway and into what can be a difficult and confusing traffic system around the bus stop. As we stress throughout this book, passengers need buses to come close to the platform so that they can board easily and safely. Therefore the infrastructure needs to be in place to ensure that buses can reach the bus stop in order to connect with the accessible infrastructure. Buses can only achieve this if the bus stop has sufficient capacity to accommodate them.

The easiest way to consider a bus stop when thinking about capacity is as a one-armed signal-controlled junction. In these circumstances, we imagine a bus stop to contain a fixed location with one berth in which a bus can stop. If a bus is occupying the berth, no other bus can enter. Capacity is determined by the length of time a bus spends occupying the berth and the number of buses that could pass through the berth within a defined time period. The capacity of a bus stop is expressed in terms of the number of buses that can enter the stop area within a specified time period (usually an hour). As with any capacity problem, we compare the flow of buses actually using the bus stop with its capacity to obtain the degree of saturation.

To introduce the principle, we will discuss the issue of capacity at a bus stop with just one berth. Figure 4.2 illustrates eight stages of bus stop operation. In this case, the empty berth (a) awaits the arrival of a bus (b), which decelerates from its running speed to enter (c) and come to a stop in the berth (d). The bus then opens its doors to allow passengers to board and alight according to the design of the bus and the operating rules of the system. Sometimes another bus arrives and has to queue behind the stopped bus (e). When all the passengers able to board and alight the bus have done so, the bus closes its doors and leaves (f), first checking that its exit path is clear and for an available gap in the traffic stream. The bus accelerates away from the berth, permitting the subsequent bus to enter the berth (g). The second bus then stops in the berth (h) in the same way as the first bus (d).

Time Periods

We can define six time periods which we can use to analyse how the capacity might be affected by changes to bus stops:

(1) *Queuing time*, the time spent in the queue prior to entering the stop.
(2) *Clearance time*, the minimum time between the departure of one bus and the arrival of a subsequent bus in the berth.
(3) *Dead time*, the time to open and close doors, lower the bus, extend ramps and operate any other equipment necessary to permit boarding or alighting to occur.
(4) *Passenger service time*, the time for passengers to board and alight.
(5) *Internal delay*, the time waiting to leave the stop (when the bus is ready to leave but is obstructed by other buses in the stop area).
(6) *External delay*, the time waiting to leave the stop (when the bus is ready to leave but is obstructed by other traffic outside the stop area).

The total time spent by a bus at a bus stop is called the *dwell time* and is the sum of the time periods (3) to (6). The clearance time (2) has to be added to this to take into account the time taken to enter and leave the

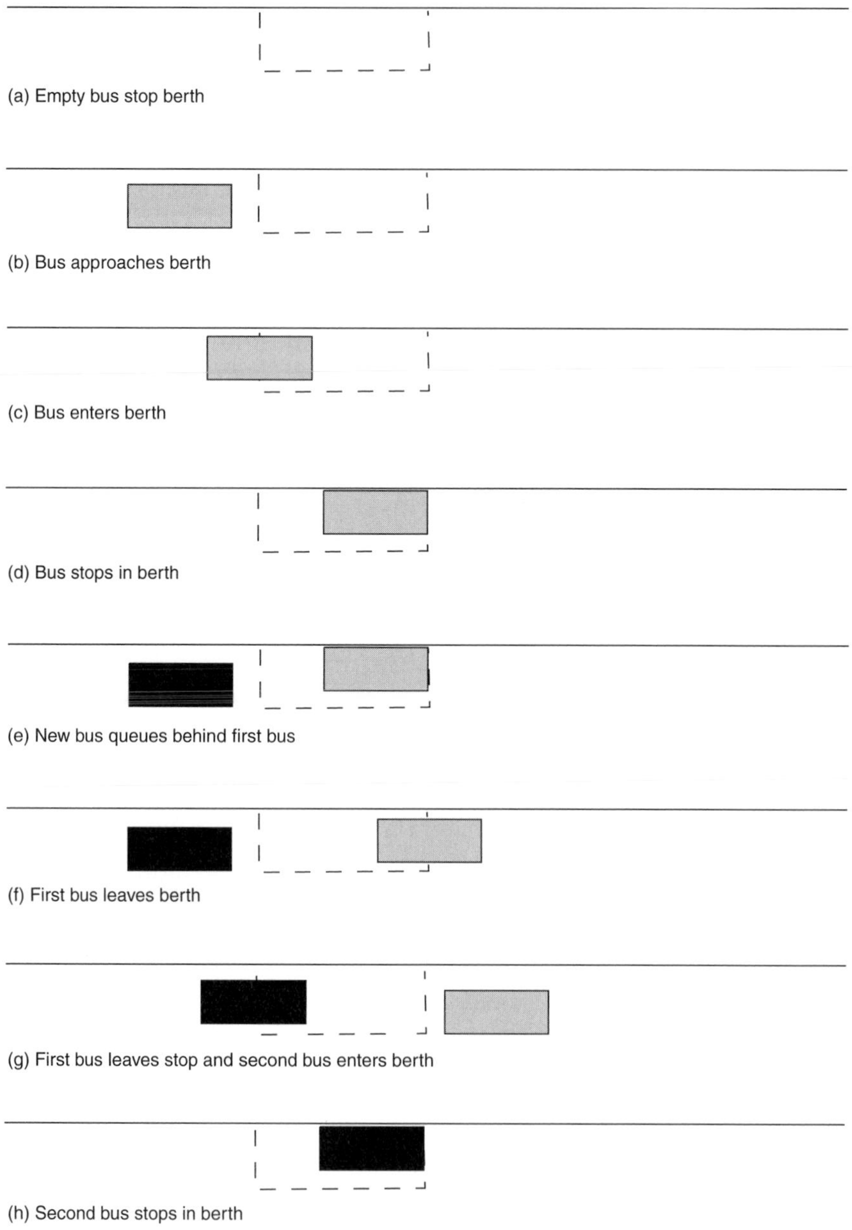

(a) Empty bus stop berth

(b) Bus approaches berth

(c) Bus enters berth

(d) Bus stops in berth

(e) New bus queues behind first bus

(f) First bus leaves berth

(g) First bus leaves stop and second bus enters berth

(h) Second bus stops in berth

Fig. 4.2   The eight stages of bus stop operation

berth. In some cases, (5) and (6) are concurrent, in which case the greater of the two is used in the estimation of the dwell time and capacity. The queuing time (1) is a useful indicator of the adequacy of the bus stop capacity. The time taken to decelerate for, and accelerate from, the stop (*lost time*) applies to all bus stops and thus would not be affected by the bus stop design. Apart from the direct effects on bus stop capacity, the sum of all these time periods shows the delay imposed on the bus by the bus stop. This in turn affects the commercial speed of the bus service because it adds to the time taken to operate from the start to the end of a bus route.

The capacity problem is how to design a facility so that it can accommodate the demand for its service. We need to design a bus stop so that it can accommodate the number of buses wishing to use it in such a way that they can all perform properly (i.e. stop close and parallel to the platform). In this case, the service being provided by the bus stop is time. One of the first difficulties is that the time being supplied and consumed at a bus stop is actually made up of different groups of time periods:

- time that is available for a bus to serve its passengers (passenger service time)
- time to arrive and depart (queuing time, internal delay, external delay, clearance time)
- time to carry out other functions (e.g. open and close doors, or extend ramps (dead time)).

The time is allocated to space in the sense that these operations need to take place in space and thus the time is allocated to the utilisation of a defined amount of space. In most urban areas, such space is a scarce resource. Therefore we need to know how much space we need in order to obtain an accessible bus stop under local operating conditions such as bus flow and passenger demand. Only once this has been achieved can we consider the detailed position of the bus stop and its accessibility. This is because a bus stop with insufficient capacity will be incapable of delivering buses close enough to the kerb to provide acceptable accessibility for the passengers.

Some of the time periods described above can be considered to be constants – for example, clearance time and dead time. There is a strong case for allowing dead time to vary depending on the need to operate ancillary boarding equipment. However, other periods depend strongly on the actual arrival times of the individual buses and the numbers of passengers boarding and alighting as a consequence. For example, a bus arriving after an interval of several minutes following the departure of the previous bus can expect to pick up more passengers than one that arrived after only a few seconds. The latter example would suggest a very short passenger service time, but possibly an increased internal delay as the previous bus could obstruct its departure. Instances of such time-dependent obstructions can only be analysed through the use of microscopic simulation models, and this is one of the reasons why such models have been developed.

Passenger Service Time

The passenger service time is perhaps the most obvious time period to consider first. A passenger takes a certain amount of time to board and alight. This can be averaged to give a marginal boarding time per passenger, although it should be recognised that this will give misleading results if we wish to consider people who might have difficulties in boarding or alighting, such as frail elderly people, people with children or shopping, or people in wheelchairs. The ticketing system has an enormous effect on the marginal boarding time: if a passenger has to pay a driver and collect change as they enter the bus, this will inevitably tend to increase the marginal boarding time. However, this has other effects. First, if all passengers must pass the driver in order to show a pass or pay a fare, this places a constraint on how many doors could be available for boarding and increases the passenger service time. Secondly, passengers have to pass the driver in more or less single file, whether they have to display a pass or pay a fare. This reduces the rate at which people can enter the vehicle and thus increases the marginal boarding time.

Passenger service time must include times for boarding and alighting passengers and must consider all the doorways on the bus. We can generalise the problem into two conditions: those where passengers must wait to board while passengers alight (serial) and those where passengers may board and alight at the same time (parallel). The situation where only boarding or alighting occurs is merely a case where the number of passengers carrying out the 'other' activity is zero. Passenger service time can therefore be represented by two models, depending on whether the conditions are serial or parallel.

Serial conditions:

$$T_{pst} = \max_{i=1}(P_a T_a + P_b T_b)_i \qquad (4.1)$$

Parallel conditions:

$$T_{pst} = \max_{i=1}[\max_i (P_a T_a, P_b T_b)_i]_i \qquad (4.2)$$

where T_{pst} is the passenger service time, P_a is the number of alighting passengers per bus, T_a is the marginal alighting time per passenger, P_b is the number of boarding passengers per bus, T_b is the marginal boarding time per passenger and i is the index for each door on the bus.

Queuing Time

Queuing time is another important way in which the design of a bus stop can affect the way in which a bus service operates. It is also an outcome of a bus stop with insufficient capacity for the number of buses wishing to use it. If a bus cannot enter the stop area it must wait in a queue before the stop until a berth is available. This causes delays to passengers in the vehicle and creates problems for passengers wishing to board the bus when it eventually comes to a stop in the bus stop. The length of this queue and the time a bus has to spend in it indicate the extent to which the bus stop is lacking in capacity.

One way of increasing the capacity of a bus stop would be to increase the number of berths, as this would allow more buses to call at the stop at the same time. We will consider first the case where the new berth is immediately adjacent to the current one. In this case, the berths are not independent: a bus in the rear berth would not be able to leave if there were a bus occupying the front berth. Under these conditions, the additional berth does not double the capacity of the stop. Even with a very high flow of buses, there will be periods when only one bus can be accommodated at the stop (e.g. when the front berth is unoccupied and a bus is stopped in the rear berth). The addition of a second berth would increase the capacity by about 50%. Similarly, a third berth would add a further 30%, a fourth 20%, and so on. Even these increases only apply when drivers stop as a matter of course in the berth that they can occupy nearest to the exit – poor performance in this respect will reduce the capacity of the stop.

Internal Delay

If the number of berths is increased, this brings another aspect of bus performance into play, namely the effects of internal delay. This arises when one bus is obstructed by another after it is ready to depart. The obstruction could be caused because the offending bus is still serving passengers, or because another bus has stopped in such a way as to prevent exit from the stop. Internal delay increases as the number of adjacent berths increases because the probability of such obstructions increases with the increased number of berths.

External Delay

External delay applies when buses are obstructed from leaving the stop by the flow of traffic in the adjacent lane.

It is useful to consider how the various time periods affect the performance of the bus stop. For example, Figure 4.1 shows how queuing time and passenger service time are affected by changes in the number of buses using the stop (for clarity, internal and external delay were ignored in this example). The interesting outcome of this is that the total time involved here has a minimum, although it is insensitive to the actual flow of buses for much of the range.

The dwell time can therefore be calculated as the sum of the time periods:

$$T_{dwell} = T_{dead} + T_{pst} + T_{int} + T_{ext} \tag{4.3}$$

where T_{dead} is the dead time, T_{int} is the internal delay and T_{ext} is the external delay. Each of these processes depends on the exact time at which different buses arrive at the bus stop. As we have noted, they also have a direct effect on the ability of the bus stop to accommodate the desired number of buses and passengers. A useful measure of performance of a bus stop is the degree of saturation. This is calculated by dividing the hourly bus flow through the stop by the theoretical capacity. Returning to Figure 4.1, we can see two bus flows at which the total time increases markedly: in this example, these points are found at bus flows of about 60–70 buses/h and about 170 buses/h. These figures correspond to different degrees of saturation at the bus stop: about 40% for the lower flow and about 80% at the higher flow. This effect is quite common and gives rise to the suggestion that a reasonable design flow for a bus stop is approximately 60% of its theoretical capacity.

We need to find a way of estimating the bus stop capacity to ensure that we can design the bus stop to accommodate the required number of buses and passengers. If we wish to design bus stops with appropriate capacity, we need to understand these arrival-dependent processes in considerable detail. Calculations based on average arrival rates and process times are not sufficient for the analysis of arrival-dependent processes and so we have to turn to microscopic simulation to study operations at bus stops.

Bus Stop Analysis

Arrival Patterns and Number of Berths

There are two microscopic simulation models for bus stop capacity. One, IRENE (Baeza, 1989; Gibson *et al.*, 1989), examines a set of adjacent berths (up to six) at a bus stop under conditions where buses arrive at either constant intervals or randomly (i.e. selected randomly from a probability distribution). IRENE allows different operating practices at the stops to be considered (e.g. controls over the number of times a bus stops at the stop, where the driver should stop in the stop, ability to leave the stop using the adjacent lane, overtaking). This is very useful in estimating the theoretical capacity of a bus stop in terms of the number of buses that can enter the stop area, and indicates the likely queuing patterns if the degree of saturation is too high.

IRENE was developed for the situation in Chile, where bus flows are extremely high and where a passenger can select a bus from almost any that arrive at the bus stop. In Europe, however, the bus flow is typically much lower than in Chile, but the need for passengers to select a particular bus line is greater. Also, the different bus lines operate independently of each other, may have different operating problems and are often arriving at a stop from different routes with different traffic patterns. This provides a different set of problems when dealing with bus stops in the European, rather than the Chilean, context.

Although the European case provides much lower bus flows than those found in Chile, the bus flows can be very high over short periods. One result of these differences is that it is necessary to be able to model bus arrivals exactly as they occur. Models such as IRENE consider all buses to be available to all passengers and assume that the distributions of both bus and passenger arrivals is aleatoric. This makes the modelling convenient, as probability distributions can be used to represent the distributions of bus and passenger arrivals, and techniques such as Monte Carlo simulation can be used to select the exact arrival time of each bus and passenger in the simulation. In the European case, although the bus system might appear to be similar in these respects, it is often a mistake to make these assumptions because:

- passenger arrivals are often influenced by circumstances outside the bus system (e.g. arrivals of metro trains at a nearby station)
- the problem for passengers of waiting for a particular bus line is important
- bus arrivals, although they might appear random, are actually highly dependent on the earlier performance of the buses within the particular traffic stream and passenger boardings encountered in the course of each route.

For these reasons, it is important to be able to represent each bus and passenger explicitly in the simulation. To illustrate this discussion, we use a microscopic simulation model which was developed as part of our research (Fernández, 2001) and which allows us to see what would happen at a single-berth bus stop under a variety of operating conditions. The complexity of the problem is such that the development of the model required a parallel computer to represent all the various concurrent processes. Once we could understand what was going on at the bus stop, it was possible to represent the problem in a serial computer and accordingly a PC-based simulation model (PASSION) was written. A full comparison of the resulting differences in outcomes using IRENE and PASSION is made in Fernández (2001).

For example, take a bus service of 72 buses/h arriving at a bus stop (i.e. one arrival exactly every 50 s). Table 4.1 shows the outcome of a simulation run for such a service. In this case, one passenger arrives every 10 s so five passengers board each bus. The passenger service time is 11.1 s in each case and the clearance time is 10 s. A bus is effectively occupying the bus stop for 21.1 s, giving a berth capacity of 170.62 buses/h. The degree of saturation is 42%, suggesting that there is no particular capacity problem under these conditions. Table 4.1 also shows other data which will be useful for comparison later on and will be explained at that stage.

It is extremely unlikely that the buses would arrive neatly every 50 s. For example, imagine that the service of 72 buses/h which call at the stop is actually composed of three different bus lines, each providing 24 buses/h. It is quite likely that the buses of each line could arrive in pairs, with each pair arriving at intervals of twice the scheduled headway. In this case, the arrival pattern for each line would be two buses about 4 s apart and then an interval of 5 minutes before another pair. This would lead to a period of 20 s in which six buses arrive, followed by a gap of 280 s before the next arrival. In effect, the arrival bus flow in this case is of the order of one bus every 4 s, which gives an hourly rate of 900 buses/h. Table 4.2 shows the

Table 4.1   Simulation outcome for a regular bus service

Routes using stop	1
Simulation period (min)	60
Average bus flow (buses/h)	72
Entry bus flow (buses/h)	72
Boarding demand (passengers/h)	360
Mean passenger waiting time (s)	28.8
Maximum passenger waiting time (s)	49.2
Mean passengers on platform	5
Maximum passengers on platform	5
Mean bus delay for passengers (s/bus)	11.1
Maximum bus delay for passengers (s/bus)	11.1
Mean bus delay in queue (s/bus)	0
Maximum bus delay in queue (s/bus)	0
Mean bus total delay (s/bus)	21.1
Maximum bus total delay (s/bus)	21.1
Berth capacity (buses/h)	170.62
Saturation	0.42
Effective saturation	0.42
Mean bus queue length (buses)	0
Maximum bus queue length (buses)	0
Exit time deviation (s)	2.5

Table 4.2   Simulation outcome for an irregular bus service

Routes using stop	3
Simulation period (min)	60
Average bus flow (buses/h)	72
Entry bus flow (buses/h)	74.82
Boarding demand (passengers/h)	360
Mean passenger waiting time (s)	59.8
Maximum passenger waiting time (s)	279.0
Mean passengers on platform	14.33
Maximum passengers on platform	28
Mean bus delay for passengers (s/bus)	11.1
Maximum bus delay for passengers (s/bus)	21.1
Mean bus delay in queue (s/bus)	47.75
Maximum bus delay in queue (s/bus)	95.5
Mean bus total delay (s/bus)	68.85
Maximum bus total delay (s/bus)	106.6
Berth capacity (buses/h)	170.62
Saturation	0.42
Effective saturation	0.44
Mean bus queue length (buses)	3.44
Maximum bus queue length (buses)	5.00
Exit time deviation (s)	74.47

equivalent outputs to those in Table 4.1, but in this case the operation being modelled is as just described.

The arrival rate of 900 buses/h alluded to above is of course the rate at which the buses appear before the stop. Once the first bus of a batch has stopped, the others must wait in a queue. The rate at which the buses enter the bus stop is therefore much lower and is determined by the dwell time of the bus currently stopped and its clearance time. As a result the entry flow is much lower than the arrival rate, the difference being absorbed by the queue. It is this entry rate that must be used in the design of the bus stop and not the average flow (72 buses/h in this case). Table 4.2 shows that in this case the entry flow is slightly higher than the actual flow (74.82 buses/h). Given the resulting berth capacity, the effective saturation is a little higher than in the regular case (0.44) but is still low and appears to be quite satisfactory. So what is the problem?

Some evidence of the problem can be seen in the data in Table 4.2, which shows the details of the delays. The first warning sign is that the passenger waiting time is much higher (although still quite short) but with a much greater variation (the maximum waiting time is 4.65 minutes, compared with 49 s in the regular case). Not surprisingly, one effect of this is that the number of passengers that have to be accommodated on the platform is a lot higher (regularly reaching 28 passengers). Passengers would be waiting for longer in more crowded conditions.

The average time spent by each bus in serving passengers is the same as in the regular case (11 s), but when we look at the variation of passenger delays (the maximum delay is 21 s) we can see signs of another problem: half the buses take no passengers at all (the first bus of each pair takes all the relevant passengers and the second therefore takes none). As buses have to queue before the bus stop, more time is spent in the queue than in the regular case, resulting in an average queue delay of 47.75 s (0 s in the regular case) and a maximum of almost 96 s. The resulting queue length is up to five buses, meaning that buses could cause an obstruction for more than 60 m before the stop. The danger is that it is possible to think that the bus stop is working because the overall figures look reasonable – a low degree of saturation would normally be a sign that the bus stop had adequate capacity. To try to understand a little better what is happening in this example, we need to look at the period within the simulation in which the buses actually arrive.

Table 4.3 shows the outputs from a simulation run using the same data as those for Table 4.2, but this time only simulating the first 5-minute

Table 4.3   Simulation outcome for an irregular bus service (over a 5-minute period)

Routes using stop	3
Simulation period (min)	5
Average bus flow (buses/h)	72
Entry bus flow (buses/h)	155.17
Boarding demand (passengers/h)	360
Mean passenger waiting time (s)	59.8
Maximum passenger waiting time (s)	279.0
Mean passengers on platform	14.33
Maximum passengers on platform	28
Mean bus delay for passengers (s/bus)	11.1
Maximum bus delay for passengers (s/bus)	21.1
Mean bus delay in queue (s/bus)	47.75
Maximum bus delay in queue (s/bus)	95.5
Mean bus total delay (s/bus)	68.85
Maximum bus total delay (s/bus)	106.6
Berth capacity (buses/h)	170.62
Saturation	0.42
Effective saturation	0.91
Mean bus queue length (buses)	3.44
Maximum bus queue length (buses)	5.00
Exit time deviation (s)	121.18

Table 4.4   Headway statistics at various points in the bus stop

	Arrival at the end of the queue	Entry to the berth	Exit from the berth
Mean headway (s)	46.76	48.11	47.83
Standard deviation (s)	100.578	59.50	67.96

period. We can consider the entry flow first. The entry flow is calculated by taking the sum of the dwell time and the clearance time and dividing the result into 3600 to find the maximum number of buses that could enter the stop under the given conditions. On average, and when calculated over a period of an hour as shown in Table 4.2, the entry flow is about the same as the actual number of buses arriving at the bus stop. Table 4.3 looks at what happens when the buses actually arrive at the stop. In this case, buses enter the bus stop at the higher rate of 155.17 buses/h, giving an effective degree of saturation of 91%. This is because as one bus leaves the next bus is immediately behind it in the queue (except when the last bus of each batch leaves the stop). As noted above, it is this flow that needs to be used in the design calculations when trying to decide how many berths are required for the operation at the stop. We can see that in cases where we have to deal with irregular bus operations we will need to design a bus stop with greater capacity than we might otherwise expect. In general, this means allocating more road space to the bus stop – in this case by constructing more berths. For the operation described in Tables 4.2 and 4.3, we would have to design a bus stop with a capacity of about 260 buses/h (assuming we design for a 60% degree of saturation), which is rather different from the average hourly bus flow of 72 buses/h. The bus stop as modelled in Tables 4.2 and 4.3 would involve passengers in considerable delays, whether they are in the vehicles as they arrive or are waiting to board, not to mention the need to accommodate larger numbers of passengers on the platform so that they can easily find and board their bus. If we were to design the bus stop using the data in Table 4.1, the result would be a bus stop with insufficient capacity for the operation as it really occurs.

We also looked at the effect of allowing passengers to board the second bus in each pair of buses arriving at the stop. This has the effect of evening out the variance in passenger service time, but would have little other effect on the performance of the bus service. It is also useful to compare what happens at each end of the bus stop. Table 4.4 shows the average headways and the standard deviations for each of the situations modelled in Table 4.2 and identifies these statistics at the beginning of the queue, at the entry to the berth and at the exit from the berth. The main feature of this exercise is that it shows that the queue absorbs a large proportion of the variation in headways, which arises because of the pairing of the buses as described earlier. This effect is slightly lost at the exit from the stop because of the difference in dwell time for each of the buses in each pair. The overall outcome is that it appears that the bus stop acts as a regulator in the system in this case. Whether the 'improved' headway distribution at the exit side of the stop would be maintained to the next stop is of course dependent on the traffic conditions between them. In any case, the main problem is how to design the bus stop so that it has sufficient capacity for the operation. In this case, it would appear that more capacity is required at the bus stop.

The way to increase capacity at a bus stop is to increase the number of buses that can enter the bus stop area within a given time period. Generally this means providing more berths. However, it is essential that the additional berths can be reached by the buses without interfering with the operations of other buses at the stop. Simply adding berths does increase capacity, but the resulting difficulty for buses in being able to enter any available berth means that the increase is progressively smaller as the number of berths involved increases. A three-berth bus stop platform would be nearly 40 m long if 12-m buses were being used, but would only add 30% to the capacity of a two-berth stop at the same location. This provides a problem for passengers – the distance they would need to walk before being able to board a bus at the third berth would be a severe disincentive, and the likelihood is that they would wait for the bus to come to them (i.e. to stop again) at the front berth when that is free. This adds to the internal delay at the stop.

Therefore, it is a good idea to split the stops into pairs of berths, leaving a gap between the berths to allow easy access to the front berth. This is necessary to provide the functional independence of the two pairs of berths and thus increase the capacity of the bus stop. The absolute minimum is the distance needed by a bus arriving to use the front berth, except where this is less than the distance needed by the bus in the front berth of the rear pair to clear a bus in the rear berth of the front pair. Table 4.5 shows some summary outputs from simulation runs carried out using IRENE. IRENE is simpler than PASSION in that it does not allow for such sophisticated representation of bus or passenger operation. This is because IRENE was developed for the very high bus flow conditions in Chile, where the performance of individual lines and passengers was not a concern. Unlike the current version of PASSION, however, IRENE can model multiple-berth bus stops and this is useful for the following discussion.

The results in Table 4.5 show the performance characteristics for various designs of bus stop and different operating rules. The examples show outputs for a single-berth stop, a stop with two adjacent berths, a stop with three adjacent berths and a stop with two functionally independent pairs of adjacent berths. Each stop was simulated with 200 buses/h and an average of three boarding and three alighting passengers per bus. The

Table 4.5   Simulation outputs from IRENE showing capacities and performance of various bus stop designs

Bus stop design	Capacity (buses/h)	Saturation (%)	Queue time (s)	Passenger service time (s)	Internal delay time (s)	Average queue (buses)
Single berth	109.5	182.6	1169.74	29.70	NA	83.33
Two berth, multiple stoppings	146.1	136.9	925.21	29.90	1.51	65.48
Two berth, single stopping	139.7	143.2	692.97	29.60	1.57	50.85
Two berth, stop nearest to exit	172.04	116.3	391.40	29.60	2.48	26.56
Two berth, use specialised doors	182.5	109.6	208.36	28.60	1.89	14.06
Three berth, multiple stoppings	173.0	155.6	482.98	30.10	2.79	31.07
Three berth, single stopping	171.3	116.8	178.01	29.73	1.75	13.08
Three berth, stop nearest to exit	224.2	89.2	75.07	22.29	2.95	5.09
Three berth, use specialised doors	237.1	84.4	12.29	28.71	1.57	0.48
Two double berths, stop nearest exit	362.5	55.2	10.49	28.81	0.60	0.19

NA, not applicable

outputs show the capacity of the stop under the given operating rules, the degree of saturation obtained, the time spent by a bus (on average) queuing before the stop, serving the passengers and because of internal delay. Finally, we indicate the average length of the queue during the simulation period (1 h).

In the case of the two and three adjacent-berth designs, we show the effects of making the buses stop only once ('multiple stoppings' means that a bus could stop more than once within the bus stop), making the drivers stop only at the berth nearest to the exit of the stop, and the use of doors dedicated to boarding or alighting. On the evidence of this simulation exercise, only the bus stop with a pair of adjacent double berths performs within the design capacity rule of a degree of saturation of 60%.

Figure 4.3 shows some example layouts with rough estimates of the lengths of kerb space required in each case (see Chapter 5 for the rationale behind these lengths) and the resulting effect on the capacity of the bus stop. Taking the operating conditions included in Table 4.5, we can see that the theoretical capacity of the single-berth bus stop is 109 buses/h. The design flow would be 60% of that (65.4 buses/h). A second berth adjacent to the first would increase the theoretical capacity to between 139 and 182 buses/h (depending on the operating conditions) and the design flow would then be between 83.4 and 109.2 buses/h. A third berth would give a theoretical capacity of between 171 and 237 buses/h (design flow would be between 102.6 and 142.2 buses/h). The two independent pairs of adjacent berths would, under that operating regime, provide a theoretical capacity of 360 buses/h and a design flow of 216 buses/h.

We should re-emphasise the importance of dealing with short-term high bus flows as found in the UK. A glance at the length of time spent in the queue, as shown in Figure 4.1, shows that if bunches of buses catch up with each other at a bus stop, congestion in and around the bus stop would become a serious problem.

Models such as IRENE and PASSION can illustrate the impact of a given stop design on the operation of the buses (and in the case of PASSION, passengers) by estimating the values for each of the time periods described above. This is helpful because it enables the analyst to determine what needs to be incorporated in a bus stop in order for it to work at the appropriate degree of saturation. This is important for accessible bus systems because most aspects of accessible operation will fail if the bus stop does not have sufficient capacity. For example, buses will be unable to reduce the horizontal gap between the bus and platform if they are unable to reach the berth properly and passengers will be subjected to a lot of confusion and congestion at the bus stop if too many buses are trying to serve too many passengers in too small a space.

It may not be possible to design a particular bus stop with sufficient capacity – perhaps because of constraints of space. It could be the case that

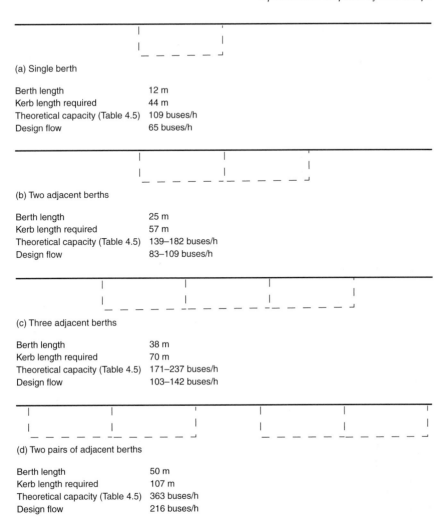

(a) Single berth

Berth length	12 m
Kerb length required	44 m
Theoretical capacity (Table 4.5)	109 buses/h
Design flow	65 buses/h

(b) Two adjacent berths

Berth length	25 m
Kerb length required	57 m
Theoretical capacity (Table 4.5)	139–182 buses/h
Design flow	83–109 buses/h

(c) Three adjacent berths

Berth length	38 m
Kerb length required	70 m
Theoretical capacity (Table 4.5)	171–237 buses/h
Design flow	103–142 buses/h

(d) Two pairs of adjacent berths

Berth length	50 m
Kerb length required	107 m
Theoretical capacity (Table 4.5)	363 buses/h
Design flow	216 buses/h

Fig. 4.3   Bus stop layouts

organising the capacity at a previous stop would deliver more consistent departures and, with appropriate priorities between the two stops, the arrival pattern at the subsequent stop would be smoother, thus requiring a design for a lower capacity. If, for example, the redesign of an upstream stop meant that the bus arrivals considered in Table 4.3 became like those in Table 4.1, the entry rate would fall from 155.17 to 72 buses/h, making the required design capacity about 120 buses/h rather than 260 buses/h (assuming a 60% degree of saturation for the design). However, it is likely that the design could be thought through in such a way as to split the stop into two parts and to allocate the services between the stops to minimise interactions. This would reduce the entry rate to be considered for the design and thus the required capacity would be lower. For example, two adjacent berths would be sufficient in this case. It might also be possible to look at the timetables to see if one of the services could be shifted a little to reduce problems at a critical stop.

The overriding objective is to ensure that the passengers have an accessible bus stop. A major element of this is that the vertical and horizontal gaps between the bus and the bus stop platform are as small as possible. This means that the buses must be able to approach the bus stop platform without being constrained by other buses, parked cars or delivery vans. Ensuring that other buses do not prevent the bus stop from being accessible necessitates making sure that the bus stop has sufficient capacity.

We have mentioned above the need to make the bus arrivals as regular as possible. We also made the point that buses operate within the traffic system. We need to consider the effect of a bus stop on the traffic system so that we do not unwittingly cause problems for buses upstream by creating traffic congestion at downstream bus stops.

Traffic Issues at Bus Stops

General Issues

The way mutual impacts between bus operations and general traffic are treated is an indicator of how society operates at a global level. Going back to the discussion in the beginning of this book about accessibility-enhancing and movement-enhancing objectives, the usual process of selecting design features of bus stops in urban areas reveals a perverse logic. Conventionally, it is considered legitimate to consider that the less a bus stop affects traffic flows the better. The problem is that this is usually the main (and sometimes the only) criterion to define how a stop will be located and built, and the common perception is that the impacts of bus stops on urban traffic in particular are very bad. Even worse, in their extreme simplification, most tools for traffic analysis end up reinforcing these views and in practice prioritising the circulation of cars over the accessibility of bus systems for their potential users.

Buses need sufficient road space near to bus stops so that they can leave and enter the traffic stream and not be obstructed by or obstruct other vehicles. Even in rural areas traffic queues can be a problem at certain times of the day and they are subject to seasonal fluctuation, but interference can be minimised if sufficient space is provided for buses.

Capacity is not the only aspect of bus stop operation that could affect the ability of a bus to reach the platform in the way that we would wish. Bus stops need to be located in such a way that they are not adversely affected by traffic management measures such as junctions or traffic signals, or car parking. As the overriding need is to make bus stops accessible, we have to decide where the priority lies: a bus stop which is inaccessible prevents some people from taking part in activities, and we should only move away from the accessibility requirement in extreme circumstances.

When a bus arrives at a stop it has an impact on any traffic in the vicinity and this must be taken into account when deciding on the location of a bus stop. This is not only an urban problem: the need to minimise impacts on traffic is just as great in rural areas as it is in urban areas, and is arguably more so. Speeds are higher and sightlines less clear in rural areas, so a stopped bus, however rare an event that is, must be safely located in order to reduce accidents. The problem in rural areas is, therefore, one of making suitable arrangements for the buses when they do arrive and ensuring that the design is appropriate for such services as exist.

Sometimes, for example in rural areas, bus stops are informal affairs with little or no infrastructure and the buses operate on a more or less hail-and-ride basis. As noted above, however, accessibility issues mean that there may be a need for the provision of some infrastructure in order to ensure that everyone has a reasonable chance of using the bus system (we shall discuss such infrastructure in Chapter 5). This means that some rural bus stops will have to be fixed and have suitable infrastructure. Suburban areas sometimes also have hail-and-ride services with little or no infrastructure, but here again, in order to provide suitable access to society's activities, infrastructure will need to be provided. As discussed above, the network should become more dense as a result of seeking to ensure that as much of a residential area as possible is within an inclusion zone, and this means that some form of bus stop will need to be installed at points on roads that were not intended for such use. Even with accessible minibuses, this will mean that locations have to be chosen carefully in order to be sure that they will be safe as well as accessible.

Even a simple bus stop can cause problems for traffic, which in turn has an adverse impact on the ability of buses to arrive close enough to the kerb to provide an accessible interface for passengers. Two issues arise when we consider the interactions between buses and traffic:

- buses stopping at a bus stop could obstruct traffic
- buses need to be able to reach the bus stop platform.

It is important to ensure that buses can reach the stops within the traffic system. This can be adversely affected by poor performance at bus stops by earlier buses which cause delays – for example by causing queues. It is enchanting, but too simplistic, to believe that buses can be used as a mobile traffic calming scheme by allowing them to block the traffic at a bus stop. Buses are part of the traffic stream and obstructions to traffic will tend to obstruct buses. We need to control the impacts of bus stops on traffic, and therefore we are concerned about what happens to the interactions between buses and other traffic at and around bus stops. A bus stopping within a traffic lane where overtaking is not possible gives a simple base case which we can use to raise the basic issues. The more complex case where overtaking is possible will be discussed later.

Traffic Queues behind Buses: Simple Case

Unless a bus which has stopped at a bus stop can be accommodated away from the main traffic lanes, a traffic queue will form behind it, and this poses a safety problem. This will occur even where the bus and traffic flows are low. It is not desirable to put a bus stop in a bay away from the main traffic lanes, because it is too difficult for a bus to regain the traffic lane and this adds to the external delay at the bus stop. Therefore, when deciding on the position of a bus stop, it is important to consider not only the point at which the bus is intended to stop (the berth), but also the distance up to the end of the associated queue.

Figure 4.4 illustrates a bus stop located at point A. Figure 4.4(a) shows the situation where a bus is stopped at the bus stop. While the bus is stopped (i.e. during the dwell time) traffic cannot pass the 'stop line' at the back of the bus at point B. The traffic continues to arrive at the mean arrival rate while the bus is stopped, but as it cannot depart a queue is formed. The end of this queue is indicated in Figure 4.4(a) by point C. The distance from B to C is the length of the initial queue. Once the bus leaves the stop, the vehicle(s) at the front of the queue follow, departing from the stop line at the saturation flow. As the front vehicle leaves the stop line, the vehicles at the back of the queue are still stationary and more arrive to increase the length of the queue. The critical point is, therefore, the furthest point from the bus stop that a vehicle can queue before the back of the queue begins to follow the bus past the stop. This is shown as point D in Figure 4.4(b).

Two points should be drawn from this which will be helpful in the subsequent discussion:

- when the bus stops, vehicles continue to arrive but cannot leave, so a queue forms with each vehicle joining at the arrival rate (see Figure 4.4(a))
- when the bus departs, the departure rate is at the saturation flow (which is greater than or equal to the arrival rate), and vehicles continue to join the back of the queue while the queue is dispersing (see Figure 4.4(b)).

There is no way in which the actual maximum length of the queue can be predicted because this depends on the way in which the initial queue

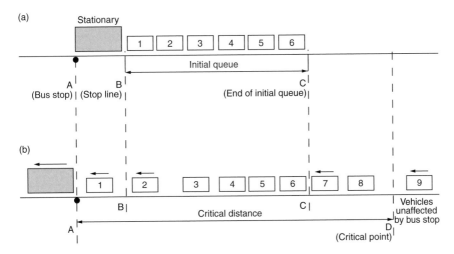

Fig. 4.4 (a) Stationary bus and initial queue. (b) Departing bus, initial queue dispersing and additional vehicles arriving at the end of the initial queue

disperses as the 'new' cars arrive. For the purposes of this problem, the critical point is calculated on the basis of the time needed for the initial queue to clear plus the time needed for the extra vehicles that arrive while the queue is dispersing to clear the stop line. The actual maximum queue length is at some point between the initial queue length and the critical point. The reason for finding the critical point is to establish that the bus stop has enough safe distance upstream of its location – avoiding junctions and other potential conflicts with the traffic and pedestrian environments. Therefore, the whole of this distance needs to be examined in terms of its suitability for queuing traffic.

The relationship between the number of vehicles behind a stationary bus and the amount of time it is stopped can be considered in terms of the arrival rate of the traffic and the saturation flow. Figure 4.5 illustrates the traffic flow behaviour from the time just before the bus stops to some time after the queue has cleared. The vertical axis shows the cumulative number of vehicles arriving at the bus stop during this period. In Figure 4.5, points B, C and D correspond to the points shown in Figure 4.4. The initial queue length is dependent on the arrival rate of vehicles at the bus stop and the dwell time. The maximum queue length is dependent on the arrival rate of the vehicles at the back of the queue and the saturation flow at the front of the queue.

Brown and Tyler (1999) show that the number of vehicles that we have to consider can be calculated using knowledge of the arrival rate of traffic at the stop area, the saturation flow of the traffic and the dwell time for buses at the stop. This can easily be converted to distance using mean

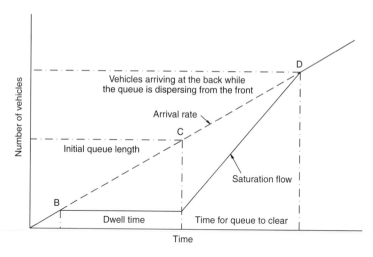

Fig. 4.5   Traffic behaviour around a bus stop

vehicle lengths, and thus the critical distance can be estimated. The number of vehicles can be calculated as:

$$l_1 + y = \frac{sa_r t_s}{s - a_r}$$ (4.4)

where l_1 is the initial queue length (vehicles), y is the number of vehicles arriving at the back while the queue is dispersing from the front, s is the saturation flow for traffic, a_r is the arrival rate for traffic at the bus stop and t_s is the dwell time of buses at the bus stop.

The critical distance d_f is given by:

$$d_f = (l_1 + y)l_v + l_b$$ (4.5)

where l_v is the mean length of a car and l_b is the mean length of a bus. It is important to note that the critical distance can be considerably greater than the initial queue length. Brown and Tyler give an example where, at an arrival rate of 720 vehicles/h and a dwell time of 30 s, the initial queue length is estimated to be six car-lengths (about 30 m), to which must be added the length of a bus, to make about 42 m from the stop. With a standard saturation flow, the critical distance for these values is nearly 60 m. The difference amounts to some 18 m.

Brown and Tyler suggest the following strategy to use this model in the location of bus stops:

(1) *Obtain data* about traffic flows, passenger and bus demand in the area around the proposed bus stop location to obtain a realistic estimate of the arrival rate. Ensure that traffic flow data are suitably adjusted to take account of the grouping effects of traffic behind buses.

(2) *Calculate the saturation flow.* If there is not an acknowledged standard figure for the area this could be calculated using one of the standard models (e.g. Kimber *et al.*, 1986).

(3) *Calculate the dwell times* using equation (4.3) with either equation (4.1) or equation (4.2), taking care to make sure that the correct bus design is incorporated in the calculation.

(4) *Calculate the critical distance* using equation (4.5) or look it up in the appropriate table.

(5) *Visit the site* with representatives of the highway authority, bus company, police, etc., to make an inventory of the characteristics of the infrastructure over the entire critical distance. Obtain the views of residents and other local people about the location. It is also important to obtain the views of bus users, especially those who use the bus stop in question for alighting or boarding, but who do not live or work near the stop.

(6) *Find the most accessible position* for the bus stop at the location.

(7) *Decide on provision of accessible platform, shelter, etc.,* to accommodate expected demand.

(8) *Check sightlines, overtaking restrictions, other restrictions (e.g. bends, junctions, etc.) over the critical distance.* This might influence a decision to install a bus bay or to move the stop. If it is necessary to move the stop, go back to step (5).

(9) *Design the bus stop infrastructure,* including details of platforms, shelters and approach paths for passengers and buses.

(10) *Locate sites for warning signs (if necessary)* at a suitable distance before the critical point.

Having explored the issues in this simple case, we turn to the more complicated one where the interactions between buses and traffic can be more varied.

Traffic Queues behind Buses: Complex Case

The simple case just described assumes of course that traffic is always obstructed by a bus while it is stationary at the bus stop. However, it is not clear that this approach will provide a good analytical tool when the traffic is only partially obstructed by a bus at a bus stop. This occurs when traffic manages to find a way around the stationary bus, thus potentially incurring little or no delay. Silva (2001) studied this problem using a microscopic traffic simulation model (SIGSIM, Silcock and Crosta (1995)) as a tool to help us understand the dynamics of the interactions between buses and traffic at bus stops.

Different bus stop layouts can be expected to cause different delays in traffic, both for buses and other vehicles. Generally speaking, *in-line bus stops* are expected to cause more obstruction to general traffic than *off-line stops*. Thus, other conditions being equal, delays for vehicles other than buses are expected to be larger in areas with in-line bus stops than in areas with off-line stops. On the other hand, the further buses pull into stops (i.e. the more they displace laterally from their original path) the larger is their expected delay before pulling out.

A solution usually adopted by conventional models such as SIGSIM to represent bus stops in urban areas is based on the same assumption used earlier in this chapter. That is, a stopped bus will block the lane, and vehicles travelling behind the bus must stop until the bus leaves the stop and the queue dissipates. This is adequate to study bus stops in single-carriageway rural roads, where the main issue is the location of the stop and the critical condition is that in which no vehicle manages to overtake the stopped bus. In this case, the assumption considers the worst case in order to avoid the situation where queued vehicles reach critical upstream points such as junctions or blind spots.

Urban environments are different. The traffic volumes tend to be higher and the space more scarce than in rural areas. Also, in a typical journey a vehicle tends to make more stops and the length of passenger journeys is shorter, so delays tend to account for larger proportions of total travel times than in rural environments. In this case, the criterion of 'protecting the back of the maximum queue' to locate the stop is an insufficient approach, because:

- these maximum queues in busy areas would probably be too long to fit into actual available spaces
- in real situations drivers manage to find their way around stopped buses, so the maximum queues tend to be a rare phenomenon anyway.

We have developed a microscopic simulation model to address this problem and we now explain what happens in these cases and how the model helps us to understand and resolve the problems. The model is called BusSIGSIM (Silva, 2001), because its starting point is the previously existing model SIGSIM (Silcock, 1993; Crosta, 1999). Of all the potential interactions between buses and traffic that take place at and near bus stops, BusSIGSIM considers three sets of elements: the stopping buses and bus stops, the vehicles that might try to overtake the buses, and the vehicles travelling in the adjacent lanes, of whom action might be required to allow the overtaking manoeuvres to happen. BusSIGSIM reproduces the behaviour of each of the three elements realistically, reacting to the actual circumstances found and considering the behaviour of the other elements.

The main reason why we decided to develop BusSIGSIM is that most computational tools for traffic analysis treat the operations involving buses

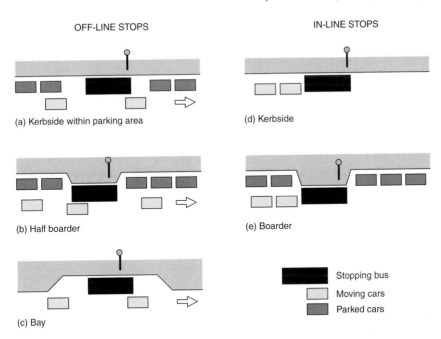

OFF-LINE STOPS

IN-LINE STOPS

(a) Kerbside within parking area

(d) Kerbside

(b) Half boarder

(e) Boarder

(c) Bay

Stopping bus
Moving cars
Parked cars

Fig. 4.6   Schematic layout of different types of bus stops

in a simplistic way, disregarding the real nature of the corresponding manoeuvres. BusSIGSIM was designed to estimate the effects of urban bus stops, employing a stochastic approach to explore the vehicular interactions. As a consequence of this, solutions to bus stop design can be tested taking into account the real behaviour of drivers and their vehicles. We will now focus on the elements considered in BusSIGSIM and the way they behave, in order to understand how the operation of urban bus stops can affect general traffic.

Buses and stops
A useful way to classify bus stop layouts is to split them into the in-line and off-line types, as shown in Figure 4.6. The difference is generally assumed to be that buses stop in line with the traffic stream in the first type and move sideways to leave the traffic lane unimpeded in the second. Most traffic simulation models assume that buses completely block the kerbside lane during their dwell time at in-line stops. Conversely, at off-line stops, buses are allowed to pull out of the lane, ensuring that the remaining traffic flows normally during the service time (small delays can occur, but only when the bus is pulling in or out of the stop area). In practice, buses move towards the nearside to approach the kerb at any type of stop, some layouts requiring larger displacements than others. Therefore, BusSIGSIM assumes that all the known layouts can be described following the

diagram given in Figure 4.7, where critical dimensions (e.g. depth of the bay and distances between the stop point and obstacles) assume the appropriate values, as described below.

Figures 4.8 and 4.9 show the scheme adopted to identify such dimensions in BusSIGSIM. The distances l_{in} from the obstacle at the entry to the stop point and l_{out} from the stop point to the obstacle at the exit, are meaningless when the depth d is equal to zero, as in a parking-free kerbside stop, for instance. For stops with multiple berths, the model allows a spacing s_i to be defined for each pair of berths $[(i-1), i]$, so that there is no need to constrain stop layouts by forcing berths to be equally spaced.

The model is able to reproduce with satisfactory accuracy the lateral position of buses operating in a wide range of stop types, and the paths they take to reach their stopping points and to pull out back to their trajectories.

The vehicle overtaking the bus

The conceptual overtaking manoeuvre used in the model is based on that defined by the Association of State Highway and Transportation Officials (AASHTO, 1990): it begins at the moment when the vehicle performing the manoeuvre (the *overtaking vehicle*) starts accelerating before changing its trajectory. In terms of a car-following model, this is equivalent to saying that the overtaking manoeuvre starts when the follower stops following the leader (i.e. stops using its leader's behaviour to adjust its own speed). The manoeuvre ends when the overtaking vehicle moves back to its original lateral position in lane.

In the case under consideration here, vehicles usually make their way around the bus at the first opportunity, using every available space, and come back to their original lateral position in lane as soon as possible. Evidence of this behaviour can be seen in Figures 4.10 and 4.12, which display sequences of frames taken from a video recorded at East Ham

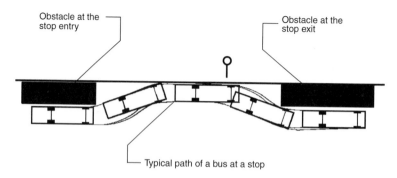

Fig. 4.7   Generic representation of bus stop layouts

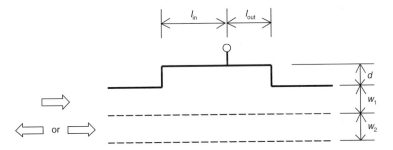

Fig. 4.8   Dimensions of single-berth bus stops in BusSIGSIM

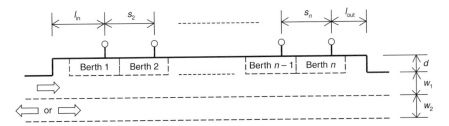

Fig. 4.9   Dimensions of multiple-berth bus stops in BusSIGSIM

Station bus stop in East London. Figure 4.10 shows vehicles queuing behind a stopped bus until a suitable gap appears in the opposite traffic stream, and then overtaking the bus using the opposite lane.

If there is no suitable gap, or if the street has only one lane, the vehicle assesses the possibility of disregarding the strict lane discipline in order to avoid stopping. In this book, this behaviour is called *squeeze*. Squeeze is the use of temporary *de facto* lanes, narrower than the existing lanes, in order to accommodate the traffic streams in the available street width and avoid stopping behind an obstacle (e.g. a stopped bus). Once the obstacle has gone, the *de facto* lane disappears and traffic continues to follow the normal lane discipline. This is represented schematically in Figure 4.11.

The sequence of pictures in Figure 4.12 shows a real case of vehicles overtaking a stopped bus by squeezing between the bus and a queue that is being formed in the opposite lane. The overtaking vehicles make this manoeuvre partially using both lanes. Vehicles that join the queue in the opposite lane during the sequence of pictures stop closer to the nearside than do vehicles already in the queue at the start of the sequence.

Two aspects need to be stressed at this point. First, it is not always necessary that vehicles in the opposite lane change their trajectories to make room for the overtaking manoeuvres: if the effectively available width of the street is sufficient, the overtaking manoeuvres may take place without the help of vehicles in the opposite lane. Secondly, the same basic

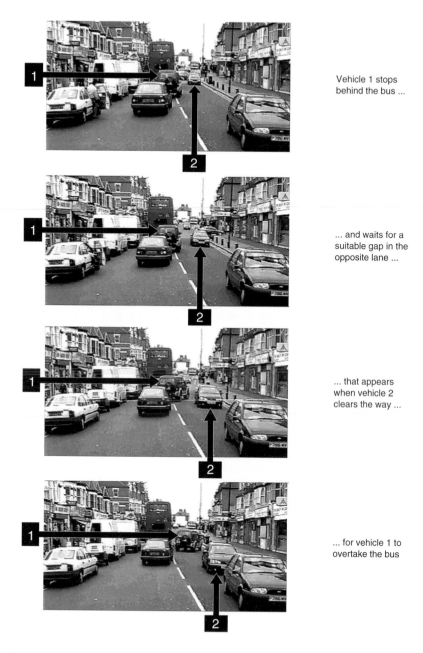

Vehicle 1 stops
behind the bus ...

... and waits for a
suitable gap in the
opposite lane ...

... that appears
when vehicle 2
clears the way ...

... for vehicle 1 to
overtake the bus

Fig. 4.10   Vehicles overtaking a stopped bus using a gap in opposite traffic

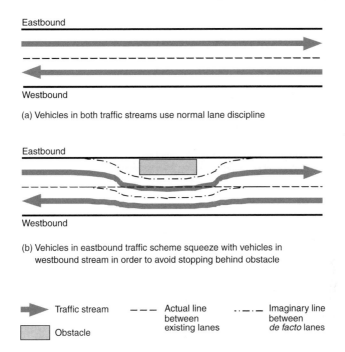

Eastbound

(a) Vehicles in both traffic streams use normal lane discipline

Eastbound

Westbound

(b) Vehicles in eastbound traffic scheme squeeze with vehicles in
    westbound stream in order to avoid stopping behind obstacle

Fig. 4.11   Schematic representation of a traffic stream squeezing to avoid an obstacle

characterisation of overtaking manoeuvres (using gaps or squeezing) in two-way streets with one lane per direction can be used to describe overtaking manoeuvres in streets with multiple lanes per direction.

The vehicles in the adjacent lane

Whereas the gap acceptance depends only on the driver of the overtaking vehicle, the squeeze is a manoeuvre that may require some action from the vehicles travelling in the adjacent lane. If the overtaking vehicle needs more space to perform the manoeuvre than that available in the nearside lane, then two conditions are necessary for the squeeze to happen:

- space can be created by traffic streams rearranging within the available width in the nearside and adjacent lanes
- the driver of the vehicle in the position to give way is polite enough to move sideways to allow the manoeuvre to happen.

If both conditions are satisfied, the latter vehicle will start to move towards its nearside (if travelling in the opposite direction) or offside (if in the same direction). All this is considered in the mechanism adopted in BusSIGSIM to represent the squeeze.

Vehicles approach
a stopped bus ...

... when a queue in
the opposite lane
offers no gap

But vehicles joining
the queue leave a
space ...

... that is used by
vehicles to overtake
the stopped bus

Fig. 4.12   Vehicles squeezing with opposite traffic to overtake a stopped bus

Simulating bus stops

Two tests were performed to analyse the sensitivity of BusSIGSIM to changes in the bus stop layouts. They were designed to analyse the model's predictions of traffic delays and horizontal gaps between stopped buses and stop kerbs.

The first experiment was designed to investigate the effects of changes in bus stop layouts on the BusSIGSIM predictions of delays in journeys (of both buses and non-buses). Comparisons are made between delays predicted by BusSIGSIM for a number of layouts and delays predicted by SIGSIM for the ordinary representation of bus stops originally provided.

The delay suffered by a vehicle is estimated as the difference between the total time that it actually spends to complete the route and the time it would have spent if it could have travelled at its desired speed all the way. Thus it includes delays at traffic signals, delays due to slow vehicles travelling ahead, buses' dwell times at stops, etc. For this sensitivity analysis it is assumed that, keeping all input data unchanged except the bus stop layout, the changes in delay for the routes using the stretch where the stop is located are due only to the differences in the stop layout. Even for the stopping buses, the dwell times would change because of the manoeuvre to pull out of the stop, not because of the passenger service time.

The second aspect analysed is the horizontal gap between the bus and the platform when the bus is stopped to pick up and set down passengers at a bus stop. The average gap used in this analysis is calculated from the mean value of stopped buses' lateral positions for each of a number of different stop layouts.

Traffic delays

We considered the average delay (in seconds per vehicle) in two different types of route (buses and other vehicles) associated with a number of bus stop configurations. For each bus stop, the values to be compared are the differences between the average delays estimated by BusSIGSIM for each stop layout and those estimated for the stop as represented by SIGSIM (in-line, fully blocking the lane). Table 4.6 displays these differences for routes using a street with one lane per direction, and Table 4.7 displays the differences for a street with two lanes per direction.

Four layouts were chosen for each case: three arrangements of off-line stops and the simplest in-line type (the kerbside stop located in an area free of parked vehicles). In both cases, the first off-line layouts describe the situations existing in Ruskin Avenue (East London) and Manor House (North London) bus stops in the year 2000. These stops are located in streets with one and two lanes per direction, respectively. The remaining off-line layouts for the one-lane stop correspond approximately to the recommended dimensions in force in London (London Bus Initiative, 2000), with some variations found in practice.

The figures in Tables 4.6 and 4.7 suggest that what BusSIGSIM predicts is in accordance with what would be expected from the impacts of these bus stop layouts. Where buses pull further into the stop it is harder for them to pull out. Therefore, delays tend to be longer in these situations. The estimates obtained using BusSIGSIM correspond to these expectations.

It is noted also that the SIGSIM representation of bus stops produces no internal or external delay for stopping buses, as buses never need to wait for an adequate gap to leave the stop in this model. This means that any representation of such delays would produce positive numbers in the 'Buses' columns in Tables 4.6 and 4.7. The average delays for buses simulated by BusSIGSIM are consistently larger than those simulated by original SIGSIM. The exceptions, both in Table 4.7, relate to situations in which the buses did not need to negotiate with other traffic streams to pull out of the stop. The bus open-ended bay and the in-line kerbside layouts should in fact present bus performances similar to the representation by the original SIGSIM. Theoretically, in these cases the delays estimated by SIGSIM and BusSIGSIM should be the same. In effect, the differences in delay are too low to be considered relevant.

As for the remaining vehicles, their delays, as calculated by BusSIGSIM, are smaller than those calculated by SIGSIM for all cases. The difference is generally more significant in the case of the street with one lane, as opposed to two lanes, per direction. This is consistent with the fact that SIGSIM does not allow any overtaking manoeuvre to take place in the

Table 4.6 Difference in average delay (s/vehicle) between the SIGSIM and BusSIGSIM representations, for a street with one lane per direction

Stop layout	Buses	Other vehicles
Off-line (23-m clear kerbside in parking area)	+2.67	−6.28
Off-line (40-m clear kerbside in parking area)	+4.20	−6.81
Off-line (27-m clear, 0.8-m deep half boarder)	+2.24	−5.84
In-line (parking-free kerbside)	+1.27	−2.76

Table 4.7 Difference in the average delay (s/vehicle), between the SIGSIM and BusSIGSIM representations, for a street with two lanes per direction

Stop layout	Buses	Other vehicles
Off-line (90-m long bus bay)	−0.13	−3.27
Off-line (53-m long bus bay)	+4.07	−3.08
Off-line (40-m long bus bay)	+6.95	−2.65
In-line (parking-free kerbside)	−0.51	−1.12

Table 4.8   The average horizontal gap between a stopped bus and the platform, for a street with one lane per direction

Stop layout	Gap (mm)
Off-line (23-m clear kerbside in parking area)	652
Off-line (40-m clear kerbside in parking area)	346
Off-line (27-m clear, 1.0-m wide half boarder)	532
In-line (parking-free kerbside)	323

Table 4.9   The average horizontal gap between a stopped bus and the platform, for a street with two lanes per direction

Stop layout	Gap (mm)
Off-line (90-m long bus bay)	328
Off-line (53-m long bus bay)	355
Off-line (40-m long bus bay)	462
In-line (parking-free kerbside)	329

former case, whereas lane changes are possible in the latter. One can observe also that the gains in travel time for other vehicles are larger when the stop layout allows the bus to pull in further.

Horizontal gaps

We discuss the access of passengers to the vehicle in some detail in Chapter 5. The sensitivity analysis as discussed so far deals with the impacts of bus stop layouts on the traffic. In doing so, the focus has been on how far out of its bay the stopping bus is (and therefore the extent to which it blocks traffic) during its dwell time. The accessibility viewpoint also considers the lateral position of stopping buses, but focuses on how close it is to the bus stop platform.

In the light of our practical experience, it is expected that shorter and deeper bays result in wider gaps than do longer and shallower bays. The values estimated for these gaps using BusSIGSIM with the same configurations as used in the delay estimation are shown in Tables 4.8 (for a street with one lane per direction) and 4.9 (two lanes per direction). As noted above, there is no reference here to the original simulation by SIGSIM because the model does not represent vehicles' lateral movements.

The figures in the tables confirm the expected tendency. Table 4.8 shows that the 40-m *sterile length* (i.e. the length of the kerbside lane without parked vehicles) allows the bus to get almost as close to the stop platform as is possible in the case of the parking-free kerbside stop. Shorter sterile lengths cause wider horizontal gaps, even in the case of the half boarder layout (third line in the table). This is compatible with the late start in the steering because of the blind spot obscuring the obstacle at the entry of the stop, as discussed in Chapter 5. Table 4.9 shows the same sort of relationship between horizontal gaps and sterile lengths.

A comparison between the two tables reveals another interesting aspect. As can be seen in Figure 4.6, in-line stops have no obstacles to prevent buses from getting close to the kerb. The values obtained for the in-line layouts (the last line in Tables 4.8 and 4.9) suggest that, for the parameters used in the simulation, the closest the bus gets to the stop platform is approximately 320–330 mm. The open-ended bus bay (90-m long in the representation) is the only other layout to allow a horizontal gap in this range.

In the surroundings of a bus stop, bus operations may affect the movement of some users (private car users in particular), but only passengers boarding or alighting buses at that stop have their accessibility affected. Besides, unless very high flows are observed, the impact of a bus stop on traffic can be much smaller than is commonly thought. In many cases, drivers can easily cope with stopped buses, performing various kinds of manoeuvres to overtake them. The real delay experienced by these drivers can be very close to zero.

Apart from showing that BusSIGSIM is capable of differentiating between the effects caused by different configurations of stops, the tests performed to analyse the model's sensitivity also show that it is possible to evaluate traffic performance and to design bus stops based on realistic estimates of their impacts. This is an important step towards an approach to traffic design that seeks the accommodation of interests rather than the prioritisation of categories of vehicles or users.

When we assume that bus stops cause impacts that they actually do not cause, we can reject good solutions which are good for potential bus users. What we are doing in such cases is to reduce the accessibility for worse-off people in order to keep the level of service of movement for those with access to a car. On the contrary, when we assume that drivers find creative ways to minimise the delays in their journeys, we can count on this to work out solutions that can improve accessibility and will not make anybody worse off. Figure 4.13 illustrates an example of this point. It shows the same East Ham Station bus stop where the films shown in Figures 4.10 and 4.12 were recorded. The picture reproduced in Figure 4.13 was taken in December 2000, after the implementation of changes to the design of the stop (see Chapter 5). As part of these changes, a new line was painted between the lanes, making visible the imaginary line between *de facto* lanes, as shown in Figure 4.11. The new line is there to make the squeeze easier. Drivers in the lane opposite the stop are now induced to

New line

Fig. 4.13   East Ham bus stop

make room for drivers behind the stopped bus to overtake it. The latter are less dependent on the politeness of the former now than when the film shown in Figure 4.12 was made. The studies to analyse changes in operations and accessibility before and after the alterations in this stop are still underway, but we are confident that the delays are shorter now, even with a more accessible bus stop.

Conclusions

The discussion in this chapter suggests a number of issues that need to be addressed before we can begin to design a bus stop to allow greater accessibility to the bus system. It seems clear that a bus stop with insufficient capacity will be unable to deliver an accessible interface for passengers with locomotory difficulties. Therefore, it is an essential prerequisite that bus stops are constructed so that they can accommodate the number of passengers and buses that will be using the bus stop. This cannot be overemphasised – not only does bus stop capacity affect the accessibility at the bus stop, it also affects where it is feasible to put bus stops, thus contributing to the consideration of the design of the network. As considered in Chapter 3, this is a major element of the accessibility to the bus system because of the impact on the distance it is necessary to travel to reach the bus system.

For bus stops to work properly, it is important that they are designed to accommodate the required number of passengers. This is rather more sophisticated than the usual approach of providing a standard bus shelter and seating irrespective of the demand at the bus stop. If the bus stop platform cannot accommodate all the passengers needing to use it, there will be confusion and congestion between the passengers, thus reducing accessibility to the buses, which will incur increased delay at the bus stops. It is necessary to establish how many passengers will be waiting, including consideration of their arrival patterns, need for interchange and the bus lines they wish to use. It is also essential to include in this analysis the accessibility needs of the passengers so that neither people nor objects act as unwitting obstacles to other passengers. This information will feed into the design requirements for the infrastructure that will be considered in Chapter 5.

The analysis of bus stop capacity, both for passengers and buses, requires the use of specialised microscopic simulation models. These models must incorporate the possibility of allowing exact arrival and departure data for both buses and passengers so that different bus stop designs can be tested against real and repeatable situations. Careful analysis of the output is required in order to detect inherent problems at the bus stops. We have given one example of the importance of detailed analysis of short time periods in order to detect and analyse an underlying problem caused by irregular bus arrivals. It is important not to underestimate the real bus flows in the bus stop – designing for a regular bus service will be insufficient if the reality is different.

The theoretical capacity of a bus stop can be established using microscopic simulation models, but the design flows that a bus stop can actually work with are much lower. We consider that a reasonable rule of thumb is to design for a degree of saturation of 60% for the design bus flow. However, such advice should be treated with caution – it could be appropriate to design for an even lower degree of saturation in some circumstances. It may not always be possible to construct a bus stop which is adequate for the appropriate bus flow, in which case the modelling approach should be used to investigate alternatives – for example, separating bus stops for different bus lines, and altering routes and service patterns to reduce the level and variation of arrival flows (of both buses and passengers).

It is important to deal with traffic at and around bus stops and to have a realistic view about the real effects of bus stops within the traffic stream. We have shown how in the simple case of traffic queuing behind a stopped bus the resulting queue length needs to be estimated so that bus stops can be positioned to avoid problems with obstacles, junctions or blind spots. However, this is only the simple case where traffic cannot pass the bus. We have also shown a way of modelling the impacts on traffic if it were able to squeeze past the bus. In this case it is important to estimate the resulting effects on the traffic stream and what, if anything, is required in terms of traffic management to encourage this. We have shown how just moving the centre line of a road could have remarkable effects on the ability of traffic to pass a stopped bus and thus enable us to construct a more accessible bus platform than would otherwise have been the case.

Having discussed the ephemeral issues of capacity and queues, the next chapter considers how accessibility could be incorporated in the design and construction of the infrastructure at the bus stop.

References

AASHTO (1990). *A Policy on Geometric Design of Highways and Streets*. Washington, DC: American Association of State Highway and Transportation Officials.

BAEZA, I. (1989). Estimación de la capacidad de paraderos de buses. Ceng Thesis, Universidad de Chile.

BROWN, N. L. C. K. and TYLER, N. A. (1999). 'Catch me if you can: traffic management for accessible rural bus stops'. *Traffic Engineering and Control*, Vol. 40, No. 10, pp. 487–491.

CROSTA, D. A. (1999). *Parallel SIGSIM: Version 3.0 User Guide*. Working paper. London: University of London Centre for Transport Studies.

FERNANDEZ, R. E. (2001). Modelling bus stop interactions. PhD Thesis, University of London.

GIBSON, J., BAEZA, I. and WILLUMSEN, L. G. (1989). 'Bus stops, congestion and congested bus stops'. *Traffic Engineering and Control*, Vol. 30, No. 6, pp. 291–302.

KIMBER, R. M., MCDONALD, M. and HOWNSELL, N. B. (1986). *The Prediction of Saturation Flows for Road Junctions Controlled by Traffic Signals*. Research Report 67. Crowthorne: Transport and Road Research Laboratory.

LONDON BUS INITIATIVE (2000). *Bus Stop Layouts for Low Floor Bus Accessibility*. London: Transport for London.

SILCOCK, J. P. (1993). *SIGSIM Version 1.0 Users Guide*. Working paper. London: University of London Centre for transport Studies.

SILCOCK, J. P. and CROSTA, D. A. (1995). 'SCOOT control of a simulated road network'. *4th International Conference on Applications of Advanced Technologies in Transportation Engineering*, Capri.

SILVA, P. C. M. (2001). Modelling of interactions between bus operators and traffic flow. PhD thesis, University of London.

Chapter 5

Bus Stop Infrastructure

M. Caiafa, N. Tyler and I. Brown

Introduction

Having considered the planning and capacity issues surrounding the bus system, the next step is to consider the design of the bus stop infrastructure. Several attempts have been made to formalise bus stop design in recent years. London Transport (1997) has published guidelines on bus stop and bus bay design as part of the London Bus Priority Network Scheme. This work was updated in 2000 with the publication of the guidelines for accessible stops published by Transport for London's London Bus Initiative (London Bus Initiative, 2000). Barham *et al.* (1994) have also published guidelines for bus stations and other public-transport-related infrastructure. Parallel work in France has also begun to identify the space required for bus stops (Uster *et al.*, 1997) and has resulted in guidance on the design of accessible bus stops (CERTU, 2001). COST 322 (European Commission, 1995) has included aspects of stop design as it relates to the design of low-floor, wheelchair accessible buses. Rogat *et al.* (1993) discuss various approaches to kerb design for bus stops. Tebb (1997) proposed a 'unistop' concept in which stops are standardised with higher 'bus-friendly' kerbs, using guide wheels to help align the buses with the platform. From empirical tests, Caiaffa and Tyler (1999b) explain how much space before and after the bus stop is required to achieve an accessible service at the stop. Typical outputs from this body of work include the design of bus stop platforms and layouts to accommodate buses within the traffic systems often encountered in town centres. In all cases, the emphasis is on providing solutions to the problem of the interface between the vehicle and infrastructure.

User-centred Approach to Design

We are concerned with the accessibility at bus stops from the users' point of view and between the bus stop and buses. We have therefore explored bus stop design from a slightly different perspective. What do we expect a bus stop to be? The answer to this question changes according to the respondent's point of view.

Users of the bus stop like a place:

- where they can wait comfortably and safely for a bus service to which they will have easy access, that will arrive within a time that is reasonable enough to wait and that is going to take them where they want to go
- which they can identify easily
- where they can find out about the bus service (arrival and departure times, destinations and other information)
- where they can find out about the area around the bus stop so that, on alighting from a bus, they can find their way from the bus stop to their destination.

Bus drivers want a place:

- that is easy to identify in the street space
- that is easy to stop at
- that is devoid of parking and delivery-vehicle problems
- where passengers can board and alight as quickly as possible
- that has no obstacles that can be struck by the bus on arriving or leaving the stop
- that is consistent in its design so that all bus stops feel the same
- that is easy to leave and re-enter the traffic stream
- where it is easy to see passengers boarding and alighting from the bus.

Bus operators want a place:

- where the bus can stop without problems
- where the bus can re-enter the traffic stream as easily as possible
- which imposes the least possible delay on buses.

Traffic planners want a place:

- that is safe for buses to stop with a minimum disturbance to traffic
- that is cheap to install and maintain
- that will incur minimal opposition from users, nearby residents and businesses and bus operators.

People living near to bus stops like a place:

- that is not too far from their home

- that is not outside their home
- that is not unsightly.

Traders based near to a bus stop like a place:

- that is close to their business (if they believe that bus users are core customers)
- that is far away from their business (if they believe that bus users are not core customers)
- that does not obstruct views of their premises
- that does not obstruct access for delivery vehicles and customers.

Pedestrians want a place:

- that does not obstruct their use of the footway
- that does not make them feel insecure.

Car drivers want a place:

- that does not interfere with the traffic system in any way
- that does not eliminate or reduce parking.

Needless to say, many of these wishes are mutually incompatible, and the task of the bus stop designer is to achieve a compromise that will satisfy as many of these desires as possible.

Bus users and bus drivers should be accommodated first because they are the prime users of the interfaces provided by the bus stop. Next we include the local authority planners and highway engineers, who have to accommodate these needs within the context of the maintenance of the local environment, public transport and traffic engineering constraints. We also have 'non-bus-users' (e.g. pedestrians and people not using buses), and 'non-bus-drivers' (drivers of vehicles other than buses, who experience the problems and benefits of bus operations within the traffic system). Non-bus-users express their interests directly to planners (e.g. about the location of a bus stop). Non-bus-drivers express their views to planners and highway engineers about the removal of parking or the restriction of road space resulting from the installation of a bus stop or bus lane. There are overlaps between these groups in terms of the actual people concerned (e.g. a person could be a bus user at one time and a non-bus-user at another), but we are interested here only in their function. Finally, due account should be taken of the ways in which our response to all of these needs affects people who do not use the bus system.

When taking the needs of potential users into account in the design of a bus stop, it is important to establish which groups should be formalised inside the decision process and how this involvement should work. Conversely, it needs to be quite clear who might be partially or fully excluded from the process. This check is important to make sure that no relevant people are excluded and that any excluded group has no relevance to the decisions. Finally, it is necessary to identify how the relationships would work: who has access to whom. Only once these questions have been answered can a suitably participative system be set up.

Figure 5.1 shows a typical arrangement of the potential participants in the bus stop design process, together with their paths of communication. Figure 5.2 shows how the same groups would be involved in a more participative structure, including the associated communication routes. Such a decision process is discussed in more detail in Chapter 7.

The relationships we have been discussing provide the means by which the inputs to the design process should be brought to the attention of the bus stop designer. As can be seen from Figure 5.2 the sources of the inputs

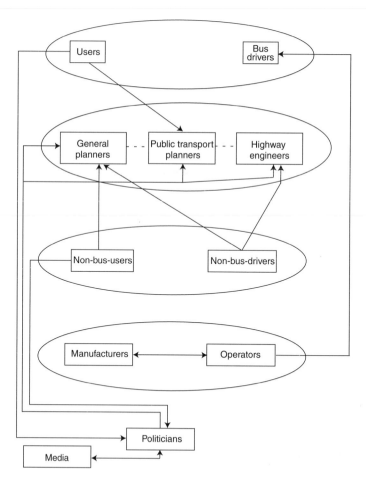

Fig. 5.1   Current participation in the bus stop design process

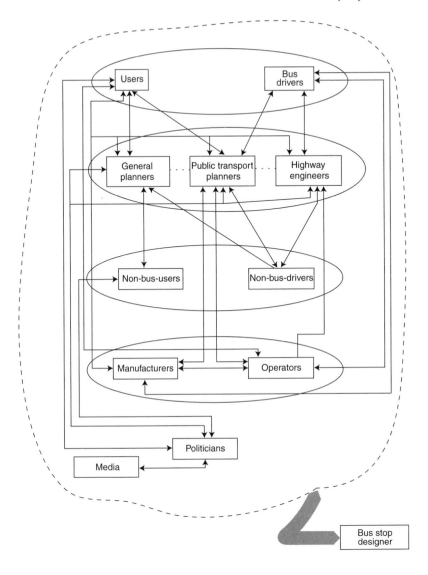

Fig. 5.2   Participative approach to the bus stop design process

are varied and come from agents with very different priorities. The bus
stop designer has the difficult and important task of taking these inputs
and generating a design that seeks to minimise the conflicts between the
differing priorities. Bus stop designers need a high level of knowledge of
the techniques and opportunities available to them as well as a good

knowledge of accessibility needs to enable them to make good decisions about the inevitable compromises that have to be handled.

Elements to Promote Accessibility

There are five basic elements to be considered in the design of bus stop infrastructure: vehicle characteristics, platform characteristics, the static and dynamic interfaces between them (gaps and manoeuvres), and the bus stop layout. The needs listed above have to be brought to bear on these elements in order to obtain a design that is user-friendly and that minimises conflicts within the bus stop environment.

These elements are summarised in Figure 5.3. As Figure 5.3 shows, the elements can be divided into two groups: those of interest and concern to the highway and traffic engineers of a locality and those that concern the bus drivers. A specification for either the vehicle or the infrastructure that does not take the other element into account will fail to yield an accessible bus stop. Nevertheless, the main objective of the two groups has to be to improve accessibility to users. Each group needs to study the set of elements and work with the other group to make reasonable improvements in order to guarantee access throughout the accessible journey chain (Box 5.1).

Vehicle characteristics	Platform characteristics		Bus stop layout		
• Type • Overall length • Front overhang • Lateral overhang • Wheelbase • Ground clearance (ride height and lowered) • Door positions	• Length • Width • Height • Crossfall • Kerb profile • Connection to footway • Drainage system		• Kerbside • Full boarder • Half boarder • Bay • Single berth • Multiple berth • Parking/traffic implications		**Interests of highway and traffic engineers**
	Interface: gaps	**Interface: manoeuvres**			
	• Vertical gap • Horizontal gap	• Approach • Alignment • Stopping • Exit			**Interests of bus drivers**
Vehicle	**Vehicle–platform interface**	**Platform**	**Vehicle–bus stop layout interface**	**Bus stop layout**	
• Comfort • Security • Cleanness	• Safety • Easy access	• Width • Crossfall • Even • Consistent	• Any, as long as it is accessible	• Shelter • Information	**Interests of the users**

Fig. 5.3 The elements of a bus stop and their interactions

Box 5.1 The elements of a bus stop and user groups

Users are interested in elements such as available space, easy access to the bus and the connection between the bus stop and the rest of the footway. They are less interested in whether this is achieved with a kerbside or a full boarder or in the exact length or height of the platform. Drivers are concerned about ground clearance and platform height, the bus stop layouts and any guidance system that is provided. Operators are looking for low operating costs and the right price for their vehicles, and so are interested in the vehicle type, length and wheelbase. Other elements concern two or more groups (e.g. the door position is of interest to users, drivers and operators), for different reasons and with different priorities.

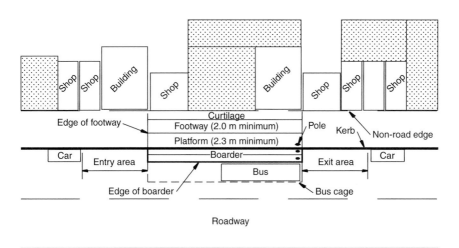

Fig. 5.4 Glossary of terms for an accessible bus stop (plan view)

Before discussing the various elements of an accessible bus stop it is useful to be clear about the terminology we shall be using. Figure 5.4 shows a conceptual bus stop, indicating the various terms we shall be using. The *edge of the footway* is usually delineated by a kerb in an urban area, but this may not be the case in a rural area (if there is a footway at all). The edge of the footway is therefore the boundary between the *footway* (the space used by pedestrians) and the *roadway* used by traffic or the bus stop *platform*. The platform might be indistinguishable in physical terms from the footway in many cases, but we need to design it specifically to be part of the accessible interface between the buses and the pedestrian space on the footway. Every bus stop has a platform, even where it is not identifiable as a physically separate infrastructure: the platform constitutes the area in which passengers wait, from which they board buses and at which they arrive when alighting buses.

The *entry area* is the space defined by the distance required by a bus to move from the driving line (the line it follows along the roadway in normal driving conditions) to the kerb. This depends on the approach angle required to reach the bus stop.

A *boarder* is a platform that has been constructed into the roadway. These can be either full boarders (extended into the road by at least 2 m) or half boarders (extended by about 1 m).

The *exit area* is the space defined by the distance required by a bus to move safely from the stopping position to the driving line.

The *non-road edge* is the physical limit of the space between the roadway and the building line, fencing or other boundary of the street space.

The *curtilage* is the space between the non-road edge and the legal limit of the public footway. The boundary between the curtilage and the non-road edge marks the edge of the part of the footway that is under the control of the highway authority and may be coincident with the non-road edge. The curtilage may be owned by a building owner and, as such, is not technically part of the footway. This is important if it is necessary to make changes to the footway in order to make the bus stop accessible as the owner of the curtilage would need to be consulted and involved in the scheme.

A *bus cage* is the set of markings on the roadway that delimit the bus stop area.

In addition, there are some other terms that will be used in our discussion of bus stop design

- The *vertical gap* is the distance between the surface of the platform and the floor level of the bus door when the bus is ready for boarding and alighting passengers (i.e. with the suspension system lowered).
- The *horizontal gap* is the lateral distance between the kerb edge and the outside edge of the bus floor at the doorway(s) when the bus has stopped correctly.
- The *ground clearance* is the vertical distance between the roadway and the lowest point of the bus overhang areas.
- The *front overhang* is the area of the bus in front of the front wheels that could overhang the platform as the bus approaches the kerb.
- The *lateral overhang* is the gap between the side of the bus body and the outside surface of the tyre.
- The *rear overhang* is the area of the bus behind the rear wheels that could overhang the platform as the bus leaves the kerb.
- The *skirt* is the lower body panel along the nearside of the bus between the wheels.

Bus Stop Design: Thinking from the Passenger's Perspective

If we really want public transport to be fully accessible, we must learn how to design all the elements of the system in an accessible way. This means placing the users' needs at the forefront of the design process. Too often, current design processes satisfy the engineering and commercial requirements and the users are only considered afterwards. Accessibility requires that we work the other way round: the engineering and commercial decisions should really be about how to meet the users' needs. Our approach is to learn what users need in order to use the bus system and then to work out how to ensure that a bus stop can be designed to play its part in reducing barriers to travel.

We need to plan to meet all users' needs first. Then we need to adjust the project according to technical and economic restrictions, bearing in mind that each element that is removed will affect group(s) of people and might exclude them from the public transport system. With this process, decision-makers know what they can offer and who will suffer as a result. Where they cannot offer suitable accessibility within their project, decision-makers must know what alternatives they will have to provide so that genuine access is available to everyone.

Converting users' needs into bus stop design requires detailed consideration of three groups of interactions:

- between users and the vehicle
- between the users and the bus stop
- between the vehicle and the bus stop.

It is important to include all three in the design of a fully accessible bus stop as the exclusion of one could negate the benefits from the others.

The EXCALIBUR project was set up to investigate what was required of bus stop infrastructure in order to enable a greater number of disabled people to use the bus system. We started by exploring the interfaces between users, bus stop and vehicle, and converting these into a specification for the design of an accessible bus stop. The following three basic areas of study were identified.

- Physical access to the vehicle:
  - to ensure consistent ease of access for passengers between buses and bus stop platforms
  - to avoid the need for specialised equipment to enable boarding and alighting from buses
  - to enable buses to reach the bus stop platforms at all times.

147

- Use of space at the platform:
  - to have adequate shelter, seats and space for passengers at bus stops
  - to promote comfort, security and safety.
- Information provision:
  - to provide clear, understandable and appropriate information to bus passengers.

We carried out a number of experiments on a specially constructed site in the Royal Docks in London to help us to determine ways of addressing these problems in a controlled environment before adding the complications of in-service operation on-street.

Interface between Users and the Vehicle

The key objective for the interface between users and the vehicle is to ensure consistent ease of access for passengers between buses and bus stop platforms.

Problem

Passengers have problems when the gap between the bus and the platform is too big. There are two gaps to consider: vertical and horizontal. There is a relationship between horizontal and vertical gaps, which is illustrated in Figure 5.5.

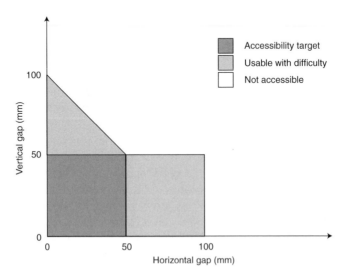

Fig. 5.5 Gap dimensions recommended by the Federal Ministry of Transport in Germany (Bundesministerium für Verkehr, 1997)

Box 5.2   Wheelchair design

As more people who use wheelchairs become more familiar with going out, we can expect to find more types of wheelchair being used. It is important to remember that the 'basic' wheelchair was designed to enable people to be manoeuvred around institutions rather than to go on buses. Newer wheelchairs are being designed to facilitate all sorts of activities never envisaged a hundred years ago. Some sports, such as basketball, require a lot of very fast movement in tight corners and wheelchairs have been designed to facilitate this type of activity. However, there is a case for paying more attention to the design of wheelchairs for everyday use (e.g. going to the shops or boarding and alighting public transport). Wheelchair design and prescription need to move forward to take account of the fact that people now want to be able to go out to take a full part in society and that this includes the use of public transport. There is no doubt that some designs are easier to use on public transport than others and, as with other aspects of user needs, due account should be taken of the resulting requirements when choosing a wheelchair. The Public Service Vehicles Accessibility Regulations (2000) (updated by the Public Service Vehicles Accessibility (Amendment) Regulations (2000)) specify a reference wheelchair for which all public transport vehicles will have to be designed. This means that a user should know that if their wheelchair is constructed within the reference dimensions they should be able to use buses, trains and taxis. However, these regulations only specify dimensions such as length, width and height. They do not specify other details that are important for access to public transport vehicles, such as the diameter of wheels or the overall balance of the wheelchair (e.g. when travelling up a slope).

Figure 5.5 shows that there is some tolerance towards the vertical gap if the horizontal gap is smaller. Thus, a vertical gap of 75 mm could be tolerated if the horizontal gap were 25 mm. However, if the horizontal gap is more than 50 mm, the vertical gap can be no more than 50 mm. In no case should either gap be more than 100 mm. Our findings broadly support this view.

A number of problems were identified during our experiments, mostly because of variations in the design of buses. There are many different bus designs, and the bus stops must be able to accommodate those designs that are expected to use them. We experienced problems with the different floor heights found on different vehicles (at both ride height and when the vehicle was lowered). We also found that the wheels were in different positions with respect to the bus body, meaning that the drivers of different buses would need to position the bus differently in order to maintain a consistent horizontal gap for passengers. The need to ensure that the bus stop design 'fits' the design of the buses using it was also identified.

Another issue for many passengers is the location of the door of the bus when it arrives. Uncertainty about this changes people's perceptions of where to wait to be ready to board the bus. This is a particular barrier to people who need to prepare more carefully to board the bus (e.g. wheelchair users, see Box 5.2) or for whom the doorway is less obvious (e.g. people with low vision).

As buses become longer and have more doors for the driver to oversee, the rear-view mirrors need to be larger and positioned further away from the vehicle body. Figure 5.6 shows the mirror cluster on a bus in Kassel, Germany. Three mirrors are provided to assist the driver in positioning the bus. The main mirror is the standard rear-view mirror used for locating the rear corner of the bus. A second mirror enables the driver to check the position of the side of the bus relative to the platform so that it is easier to see how well the centre and rear doors are aligned with the platform. Finally, the third mirror allows the driver to see exactly the position of the front door relative to the platform. However, the cluster, and in particular the large rear-view mirror, is quite large and presents a potential obstacle. Figure 5.6 shows the position of the cluster relative to the height of a passenger standing on the platform.

Fig. 5.6   The mirror cluster used in Kassel, Germany

Box 5.3   Bus design issues for bus stops

Buses are designed to suit operators – maximising seating capacity, complying with regulations and to contribute towards reducing operating costs – rather than to suit passengers. The concept of thinking about how to make the vehicle work with its operating infrastructure is not yet a common feature in bus design. One reason for this is that bus stops do not yet have common features with which design features of buses could be matched. The EXCALIBUR project, in establishing a basic design for a bus stop, has made a useful contribution by identifying those parts of bus design that could be changed to make them more accessible to people – and easier for drivers to operate – at bus stops. These features include door position, wheel design, wing mirror design and lateral overhang.

Wheel design is another issue – the wheel nuts could cause injury if they were to catch a person waiting near the platform edge.

With each of these issues, the basic problem is made a lot worse by the lack of consistency between different vehicles, drivers and operating practices (Box 5.3).

EXCALIBUR recommendations

The vertical gap is a design issue related to the design of buses and platforms and, as indicated in Figure 5.3, is an issue of concern both to highway engineers and the bus operators who purchase the vehicles. One way to tackle this is to raise the platform level so that it is nearer to the height of the bus floor at the doorway. If the platform is raised above the 'standard' kerb height, the stop must be designed so that the bus can always reach the kerb with a small horizontal gap. If a passenger has to step down to the road level in order to walk to the bus, the higher kerbs will make this harder rather than easier than would be the case with the current kerb heights. However, increasing the kerb height could cause problems for buses as they approach the stop, and therefore we have to be careful to design the bus stop infrastructure to eliminate any such problem. Simply increasing the kerb and platform height by raising a standard kerb is not an option, as this will cause problems for both buses and drivers (we will consider the bus–kerb interface in more detail below). At this point, however, we are considering the effects on the passenger side of the bus stop, including the effects on footway design and construction.

In order to reduce the horizontal gap, it is necessary to be able to bring the bus very close to the kerb. It is important to recognise that the position of the bus when it is stopped at a bus stop is the end result of a series of actions taken by the bus driver, starting many metres upstream of the bus stop. A difference in the driving line before the bus stop, the approach angle or the point at which the driver begins to turn towards the kerb determines a difference in the horizontal gap and longitudinal position of the bus when it stops. The horizontal gap, as indicated in Figure 5.3, is a design issue for bus drivers and involves the detailed design of the kerbs and the approach to the bus stop. Apart from being a matter of infrastructure design it should also be a major element of drivers' training programmes. In our experiments, we were looking for consistent stopping positions and small horizontal gaps, and therefore we had to find ways of making the bus approach path more consistent.

A major part of the experiments was therefore to make sure that the bus could approach the stop easily and stop at a given stopping point with a consistent horizontal gap. We found that this was largely a matter of obtaining a correct approach to the stop. To obtain this consistency we have to ensure that the bus drivers can stop their buses in such a way that the access door is always at the same place in relation to the bus stop, irrespective of the vehicle design. This would be a lot easier if all buses had doors in the same place, but this is unlikely to occur in practice. The solution is to provide the driver with an easy way of making sure that (at least) one door is presented to the passengers consistently at the right place. This might mean providing different stopping markers for different buses. These would be similar in nature to the indications at railway stations or airport terminals which show the correct position for the vehicle to stop, depending on its type or length.

Mirrors and wheels are a matter for vehicle design, but some thought could be given to encouraging passengers to wait away from the kerb edge. This would also help to encourage drivers to make a closer approach to the kerb. Other issues of bus design that could influence accessibility at bus stops are described in Box 5.4.

Interface between Users and the Bus Stop

Problem

People need to know where the bus stop is and be able to recognise a consistency in the appearance of bus stops so that they know how to recognise them. However, bus stops will always look different from each other, even if the basic design is standardised so that their appearance is consistent. In the UK, it is fairly common (but not universal) practice to indicate bus stops by means of a pole with an indication that it is a bus stop (usually called a 'flag'). Leipzig, Rouen and many other cities have adopted a contrasting paver with a roughened surface which is detectable by a long cane (Figure 5.7) as a mean of marking the bus stop area. Another indication is the shelter. Whatever the means of displaying the presence of

Box 5.4   Other issues of bus design that could influence accessibility at bus stops

---

Several other aspects of the vehicle will affect the design of a bus stop because of their interactions with the users:

- The positioning of handrails, for example, could preclude the use of a door by people in a wheelchair. People who experience difficulties stretching their arms could find the wider doors difficult to use.
- Many ambulant disabled people find ramps and inclines uncomfortable to use because of the strain on ankle and knee joints.
- The choice of ticketing system can be quite exclusive: the need to enter a bus by a particular door in order to show a pass or buy a ticket from the driver precludes the possibility of choosing to use a more comfortable door arrangement. As more of the bus becomes low floor, this becomes increasingly important. The CIVIS bus in France has a completely flat low floor for its entire 18-m length, and thus consistent access is available along the entire vehicle. To take full advantage of this, the ticketing system would need to function whichever door is used to enter the bus.
- Driver training is crucial to the whole process, not only insofar as manoeuvring the bus is concerned, but also in deciding what to do if for some reason the bus stop is unreachable. Drivers should also be aware that some people may still have difficulty in identifying a route number or destination, and will therefore stop a bus on the off-chance that it is the correct one and then ask the driver to confirm the route and destination. Such requests should be treated sympathetically, however much it might seem that the question is strange.
- Information displayed outside the vehicle also has an effect on the design of the bus stop: How easy is it to see the route number and destination of an on-coming bus? To what extent should routes be indicated as a single destination (i.e. without intermediate termini) so that the need to check the destination as well as the service number is reduced? Advertising features on the vehicle can sometimes obscure route and destination information.

---

a bus stop, it will be necessary to ensure that the same method applies to every bus stop. Whether the indication is a pole or the shelter or markings on the footway surface, the indication must take account of the fact that if the bus stop were a boarder the indicator would still have to be identifiable from the footway. A simple example of this problem would be that a person would know when they had reached a kerbside bus stop because of the presence of the shelter within the footway. However, if the stop were a bus boarder, the shelter would be located towards the edge of the footway, almost at the 'normal' kerb line. Such a bus stop could easily be missed by someone looking for shelters in the footway.

The bus stop shown in Figure 5.8 is an example of the confusion that can arise when it is not clear where a bus stop is actually located. In the photograph, the bus has stopped at the bus stop pole, at the end of the half boarder platform where the elderly man is sitting on the bollard. The bus stop pole is obscured from pedestrians and passengers by the telephone box. The shelter is located several metres downstream from the boarder – a long way away from the bus stop – yet you can see passengers waiting in the shelter. The confusion is increased because the bus stop cage markings in the road continue to the end of the kerb line in front of the shelter. Passengers are confused by the arrangement and bus drivers have a real problem in deciding whether to stop at the bus stop or at the shelter where the passengers are.

A bus stop is a place at which a pedestrian changes into a passenger, and vice versa. These changes take time. The whole bus stop area is a place where many different people undertake many different actions. People need to negotiate the horizontal and vertical gaps, they have to rearrange their bags, cases and pushchairs in order to board the bus, to look for information, and to find their money or ticket to pay or show to the driver on entry. A similar process occurs when a passenger leaves the

Fig. 5.7   Footway markings for a bus stop in Leipzig

Fig. 5.8   A confusing bus stop: neither passengers nor bus drivers know where the bus should stop

bus: they have to change from being a passenger to being a pedestrian. People, after alighting from a bus, commonly take one or two steps and then stop to rearrange their bags, pushchair, etc., before proceeding along the footway as a pedestrian. This can cause delays to other alighting (and sometimes boarding) passengers. One purpose of infrastructure such as a bus stop is to organise time for these processes by providing them with a convenient space. A bus stop is not just a place where people wait to catch a bus – we have also to design the physical space to facilitate their arrival at, and departure from, the bus stop as pedestrians. It is therefore important to include this space in the overall dimensions of a bus stop in such a way that it does not interfere with the continuing activities along the footway.

The bus stop design must ensure sufficient space to make sure that accessibility is maintained in the bus stop area. The main – but, as we shall see, not the only – basis for measurement for this is the manoeuvrability of a wheelchair. This is because a wheelchair needs a continuous and smooth surface in order to move on its wheels and is constrained by the space needed for turning with the wheels remaining in contact with the ground. A wheelchair user should be able to leave the bus and move away from the stop, enter the shelter and gain access from the shelter to the bus. The space required for these manoeuvres determines how much space should be made available for the bus stop area as a whole. This provides one of the conditions under which a boarder might need to be considered, as this would relieve the constraint where the footway is narrow. The space available for a bus stop will also influence the choice of shelter.

EXCALIBUR recommendations

The means of identifying a bus stop should be clear and consistent, including information about the services that call at the stops. This is often done using a bus stop pole and flag. Some places have done away with the bus stop pole and flag to indicate the location of a bus stop, preferring instead to place the flag on the shelter (Figure 5.9). The main usefulness of the pole is to help passengers identify the location of a bus stop from a distance. However, the size of the service numbers on the bus stop shown in Figure 5.9 is far too small and requires passengers to approach too close to the stop when attempting to find out if their bus calls there. Consistency is extremely important: whatever means are used to identify a bus stop, they should always be in the same place with respect to the boarding point for the buses. This will be helpful to both passengers and drivers, by indicating where the main part of the activity will be when the bus arrives. Identifying such a point within the bus stop environment provides a location from which other elements of the bus stop can be measured (e.g. for legal reasons). However, this alone should not determine where the bus stop pole is located.

The bus stop pole can be a good way of telling the driver where to stop the bus. By common consent, this was felt by drivers to be easier if they were required to stop the bus with the front of the bus level with the pole. The pole should therefore be set so that the bus doors will be aligned with the access point when the front of the bus is aligned with the pole. Placing the bus stop pole anywhere further along the platform will obstruct passengers trying to board the bus.

Fig. 5.9   A bus stop flag incorporated in a bus stop shelter

Fig. 5.10   Obstacles at a bus stop make it difficult for passengers as well as the driver

Another objective of the EXCALIBUR experiments was to establish exactly how much space is required at bus stops in order to enable people with mobility difficulties to use the stop in comfort. This enabled us to work out how much space should be reserved for passengers at a bus stop and where obstacles and street furniture would need to be excluded in order not to disable people. We also looked at the needs for shelter design, given the interaction between the bus and the bus stop and the needs with respect to the provision of seating. We also investigated information needs at bus stops and the extent to which these affected bus stop design.

The first issue is to have enough uncluttered space. The passenger area of the bus stop should be kept free of all obstructions so that passengers are free to move easily onto and off the bus and to enter or leave the bus stop area without undue hindrance. The obstacles make it extremely difficult for passengers to find their way around the area, but also make it difficult for the drivers. We have commented on this above (see Figure 5.8). Another example is shown in Figure 5.10 where the bus driver finds it difficult to locate the front door near to the bus stop without obstructing it at the shelter and the rear door being obstructed by the litter bin. Figure 5.11 shows the bus stop illustrated in Figure 5.8 after it had been redesigned to make it more accessible. Comparing Figures 5.8 and 5.11, you can see the difference between the original cluttered and confusing bus stop and the new arrangement installed as part of the EXCALIBUR project.

It is very useful for boarding passengers to know where to expect the bus entrance doorway to be when the bus arrives. This enables them to form a queue or group so that they are ready to board the bus when it

Fig. 5.11 The obstacles have been cleared away to make the bus stop more accessible

arrives. Where different types of bus arrive at a bus stop, and where some of these have doors at different positions (e.g. some at the front and some at the rear), it is important to make sure that in every case the doorway appears at the same place at the bus stop. This avoids confusion among the passengers and helps to speed the boarding and alighting process.

Where alighting passengers are concerned, it is important that they can leave the bus stop area as quickly as possible. If boarding passengers are milling around the entrance door, the alighting passengers should be able to leave the bus stop, either by turning towards the rear of the bus, or by walking around the boarding passengers towards the front of the bus. The bus stop shown in Figure 5.11 leaves ample space for passengers to leave the bus stop area and disperse along the footway. This is made a lot easier because the platform length ensures that the platform width is maintained towards the rear of the stop, and thus the dispersal from the bus stop onto the footway can take place over a reasonable distance. The platform length also helps to draw alighting passengers towards the less congested space towards the rear of the bus, and therefore away from boarding passengers. If the platform is too short, this cannot happen and the result is congestion on both the platform and the footway, which can prevent passengers from alighting in some cases.

Where buses have more than one door, it is usual in the UK to require passengers to board through the front door and to alight through the other door(s). In such cases, in addition to the identification of the entry door position, it is useful to identify the area where alighting passengers could be expected to step onto the platform. This helps to keep the area clear so that they can leave the stop quickly and without obstructing boarding passengers. This is even more important where wheelchair users are required to use the rear door of the buses: they need to know where to wait in order to have an easy route to the bus when it arrives.

There is also an issue about the way in which people wait for buses at a bus stop. Historically, people have been expected to queue ahead of the bus stop so that they can face the bus as it arrives at the stop, and this has dictated the location of the shelter (e.g. see Figure 5.8). However, such queuing practice is now very rare. This means that access to the entrance door of the bus is from all directions – upstream, downstream and straight in front of the door. The group of people attempting to board the bus must sort out who goes first, and how people with wheelchairs, buggies, shopping or young children are accommodated. The resulting approach to boarding the bus can have a substantial effect on the dwell time. Obstacles anywhere near the expected location of the bus doorway will obstruct passengers and should be removed.

Often people wait away from the bus stop area and only come towards the bus as it arrives. This means that they are likely to be obstructing the footway area, including entrances to shops, while they wait. The reason for this behaviour is not known, but it is quite likely to be because people feel that the bus stop area is not large enough or not as interesting as the shop fronts that they could be looking at while they wait, or there could be some other reason (possibly because it is more comfortable to lean against a shop window than to wait at the bus stop). Apart from its effect on the footway, this behaviour will not help the bus operation at the bus stop as these 'lurkers' will become latecomers joining the group of passengers who have been waiting nearer to the bus stop. They will therefore have had less opportunity to sort out the approach to boarding the bus described earlier. They are also quite likely to obstruct alighting passengers as they attempt to leave the stop area. We should try to design bus stops to reduce the difficulties caused by this sort of activity, although it is unlikely that it would be possible, or even desirable, to eliminate it altogether.

People need to feel comfortable while waiting for the bus. Many elderly people and some with spinal problems cannot wait for the bus without sitting down. The amount of waiting time depends on the frequency and reliability of the buses. However, there are upper limits to an acceptable wait. We have found that among people with arthritis, for example, 10 minutes is the most they can tolerate in one position. Appropriate shelter and seating is therefore essential. The shelter needs to be large enough to accommodate the likely number of waiting passengers, including wheelchairs, pushchairs and shopping. However, a suitably sized bus stop shelter can be yet another obstacle on the footway. The shelter should also be located far enough away from the kerb line that people leaving the bus can vacate the stop area quickly and easily. Bus stop shelters should be highlighted so that they do not cause problems for visually impaired people.

People need different seat heights – we concluded that three heights would accommodate most needs, and two would be better than one. Seats should be placed in the shelter so that people sitting on them can see arriving buses and do not obscure information panels. Some people find it difficult to sit down – for example, people with arthritis or sciatica (remember that there are some 7.5 million of them in the UK). Their difficulty is that it is painful to stand for any time and it is very painful to get up from a seat. A novel approach to this has been adopted in Buenos Aires. Their 'sciatica seat' (Figures 5.12 and 5.13) allows a person to lean against the structure rather than sit on it. This was designed after considerable ergonomic research with sciatica sufferers, and the dimensions are set very precisely. It would be interesting to see what adjustments might need to be made if it were to be introduced to the UK. Other examples of seats which are designed to make resting, rather than sitting, easier are shown in Figures 5.14 and 5.15, where more of a profile has been incorporated in the design than in the Buenos Aires example.

Information needs to be presented in different formats so that people with vision and hearing difficulties are not disadvantaged. Audible announcements must be produced to match any information provided visually and should take into account the background noise expected at the bus stop. As will be discussed in Chapter 8, audible information cannot be just a verbal copy of the visual information: information must be reformulated in order to ensure that it is received and understood by the users.

The obvious information to have at a bus stop is a timetable. However, although a timetable is necessary, it is not sufficient to act as the only available information at a bus stop. It is essential that the timetable is printed clearly and shows times for all buses calling at the stop. However, people also want other information at bus stops. A large-scale map of the surrounding area, including where other bus stops and other means of transport (railway stations, taxis, etc.) are located, is helpful. The bus stop name should be readable from inside the bus. This could be addressed by ensuring that the name of the bus stop is shown on the shelter in print that is large enough to be seen from inside the bus. The identity of the bus services using the stop should also be displayed clearly, large enough to be seen easily and in a consistent location at the stop. This information should be repeated in tactile writing (including, but not only, Braille) for visually impaired people on the footway and on the platform. Real-time bus information can also be provided – this reassures passengers that a bus might be coming (although it would be even better if the buses could run to the published schedule!).

Fig. 5.12   The 'sciatica seat' in Buenos Aires, Argentina

Fig. 5.13   The 'sciatica seat', side view

Fig. 5.14   *The leaning seat in Kassel, Germany*

Fig. 5.15   *The leaning seat in Leipzig, Germany*

Pedestrians are also important actors in the bus stop environment. Ensuring that pedestrian activity is available to everyone means that footways must be clear of obstacles and sufficiently wide. Footways should have an uncluttered minimum width of 2 m. At pinch points this could be reduced to about 1 m, but this should be treated as an exception to the general rule. As with other aspects of accessible design, any reduction from these minimum dimensions results in a reduction in accessibility and should be avoided.

Bus stops have to be made fully accessible, and this means responding to the needs of the people using them. The engineering aspects of the design must be based on an approach directed to satisfying these needs as far as possible and working with the public on the compromises that are sometimes required. Many of the features that are necessary to deliver accessibility are very detailed: it is essential that attention is paid to these details, or the ability of the design to deliver accessibility will be compromised.

Interface between Vehicles and the Bus Stop

Problem

The vehicle using a bus stop has to have a floor height that is sufficiently low in order to obtain a satisfactory vertical gap. It also needs the ground clearance to be high enough to pass over the kerb without causing damage to either the kerb or the vehicle. The most satisfactory results will be attained when the floor height and platform height are set to produce a vertical gap within the limits indicated in Figure 5.5. However, this requires a degree of co-operation between the purchaser (and manufacturers) of the vehicles and the designers (and manufacturers) of the infrastructure that has hitherto been all too rare.

The need for a small horizontal gap means that the driver has to bring the bus close to the kerb without damaging either the vehicle or the kerb. Drivers are normally trained to stay away from kerbs because of the damage that can arise as a result of a moving steel object striking a stationary concrete one. In addition to designing the infrastructure (and vehicle) to ensure that no damage occurs, it is necessary to counteract many years of experience and habit before a driver will feel confident about bringing a bus so close to the kerb. It is also essential to bring the bus parallel to the kerb. This requires a platform length which is rather longer than has hitherto been expected at a bus stop.

We also found in the EXCALIBUR experiments that the approach to the bus stop was highly critical and needed to be determined several metres upstream of the stop. This supported the findings of the research done in France by Uster *et al.* (1997). The special kerbs used to help the driver align the bus required a very specific approach angle to work properly, and this proved difficult for the drivers to maintain without some form of guidance.

EXCALIBUR recommendations

The Public Service Vehicles Accessibility Regulations (2000) stipulate that the entry floor height of a bus should be 250 mm above ground level, but this does not take into account the need for a small vertical gap and the consequent constraint on platform height. The vertical gap can be reduced by using a lowering mechanism within the suspension system. This mechanism allows the bus to have a relatively high floor height while travelling, and can lower the bus to provide a floor height which will provide a better interface with the platform. Thus the platform height can be increased, while still allowing the ground clearance to be practical for buses under driving conditions. Modern lowering and raising systems take a very short time to operate and do not materially affect the dwell time. Many drivers lower the bus at every stop because they feel that this speeds boarding.

One issue that arose during our EXCALIBUR experiments was the variability of the ground clearance between different vehicles and even for the same vehicle over the course of a day. Accessibility requirements now make it necessary to keep this issue under constant review. This could be done by moving the control of the regulator valve to the driver's cabin and ensuring that the appropriate height is set before starting on each journey.

Whereas reducing the vertical gap is an issue of infrastructure and vehicle design, the reduction in the horizontal gap is largely a matter of enhancing driving skills. Nevertheless, it is possible to assist the driver with the help of a number of aspects of the design of the infrastructure. The most obvious of these is the kerb profile, which needs to be able to accommodate the tyre or wheel of the bus in such a way that the vehicle is always able to stop at the same point relative to the kerb edge. Co-operation between vehicle manufacturers and infrastructure designers would enable the kerb to be designed so that it can accommodate the tyre at road level and the bodywork of the vehicle at platform level. We discuss these profiles in more detail below.

Sufficient platform length is necessary. It has been found that reductions in platform length beyond a certain threshold result in poor and inconsistent performance in terms of being close and parallel to the kerb.

The accuracy of the approach can be improved dramatically if a guidance system is incorporated in the design of the bus stop.

One of the features of accessible bus transport is that it makes greater and more detailed calls on the manufacturers of both vehicle and infrastructure to produce designs geared to work with the detailed requirements of the interface between the vehicle and platform. We have already made some comments with respect to the suspension height. Another essential change is to regularise the lateral overhang so that the infrastructure which guides the wheels or tyres always delivers the bodywork (and thus the horizontal gap) to the same place with respect to the kerb edge, whatever the type or manufacturer of the bus.

Vertical and horizontal gaps can be bridged by means of a boarding device. The Public Service Vehicles Accessibility Regulations (2000) specify that buses should be installed with a boarding device such as a lift or a ramp. If the bus stops are well designed and the drivers well trained, these should only need to be used *in extremis* (e.g. when the kerb cannot be reached properly for some reason, or if a wheelchair user has a particular difficulty at the stop in question). Ideally, the design of the bus stop should be geared towards providing the best assistance to the driver and the wheelchair users to be able to achieve fully accessible operation without the need of a ramp. This is better for everyone, as it is less stigmatising for the users and reduces the dwell time. Nevertheless, designers also need to check the likely distance of the bus from the kerb. Ramps are easier and quicker to deploy than lifts, especially if they are organised so that the driver can operate them without having to leave the cab. Even so, a powered ramp takes some 15 s to extend or retract once activated by the driver. In addition and prior to starting the ramp, the driver has to ensure that no obstacle or person could obstruct the ramp movement and that the operation will be safe. This is a lot easier (and quicker) if the ramp is situated at the front door of the vehicle, because the driver has a clear view of the ramp, its operation and use. Even so, use of the ramp could easily add 30–60 s to the dwell time at the bus stop. Some wheelchair users prefer to enter and leave the bus by the centre door because this means that they do not have to negotiate the space between the front wheels on their way to the wheelchair space in the bus. This is more difficult for the driver to manage and places the ramp mechanism in one of the most damage-prone parts of the vehicle. There is no easy solution to this issue: the important point is to make sure that whatever is done is consistent so that people understand how they are expected to enter and leave the bus when it arrives at the stop.

A ramp to cover a vertical gap of 125 mm at 7° (12.5%) needs to extend about 1 m from the bus. As noted above, the key constraint here is the need to accommodate a wheelchair user leaving the bus. A wheelchair user cannot begin to turn the chair until all its wheels are free of the ramp, so there needs to be a distance of at least 1.5 m (ideally 2.3 m) beyond the end of the ramp before any obstacle (e.g. the back of the shelter, a wall, passengers' feet, shopping) is encountered in front of the wheelchair. The amount of space required on the platform as a result of this depends on

Table 5.1   Ramp lengths (mm) given selected gradients for different vertical gaps

Vertical gap (mm)	Gradient of ramp[*]			
	5%	8%	12.5%	14%
50	1000	625.0	400	355.8
75	1500	937.5	600	533.7
100	2000	1250.0	800	711.5
125	2500	1562.5	1000	889.4
140	2800	1750.0	1120	996.2
150	3000	1875.0	1200	1067.3
160	3200	2000.0	1280	1138.5
175	3500	2187.5	1400	1245.2
180	3600	2250.0	1440	1280.8
200	4000	2500.0	1600	1423.1
220	4400	2750.0	1760	1565.4

[*]5% = 1 in 20 = 2.86°; 8% = 1 in 12 = 4.6°; 12.5% = 1 in 8 = 7.13°; 14% = 1 in 7 = 8°

the size of the horizontal gap. To cover all eventualities, we should assume that the bus has pulled up with a horizontal gap of 0 mm, and therefore we need to allow for the full extension of the ramp from the expected floor height to the platform height at the correct gradient. Example ramp lengths for a variety of vertical gaps and ramp gradients are given in Table 5.1.

Ramp angles are a problematic issue: many wheelchair users would like to have smaller gradients, but, as Table 5.1 shows, the resulting ramps would often be very long. It should also be noted that the balance of a wheelchair can be quite eccentric: the weight distribution is often thought about only with respect to travelling along a reasonably flat surface. Moving up an incline can make the wheelchair unstable, a condition that is made worse if additional weight (e.g. shopping) is placed at the rear of the chair. As with the buses, there is an urgent need to review wheelchair design, taking into account the conditions in which people wish to use them to go about their daily lives, including the use of public transport.

It might be tempting to think that a ramp (or other boarding device) reduces the need to bring the bus close to the kerb: after all, the ramp could be deployed to bridge quite a large gap. However, it should be remembered that there are many people who find it very difficult to negotiate a ramp, especially one as steep as 12.5% or 14%. This applies to many elderly people and those using sticks or other walking aids in order to walk. For these people there is no alternative to a small horizontal gap.

Thus, even with ramps available on the bus, there is still a requirement to bring the bus close to the kerb in order to make the service accessible.

We have briefly reviewed some of the problems encountered when trying to improve accessibility at bus stops and have indicated some of the possible ways in which these difficulties might be countered. We now discuss how the design of the bus stops can incorporate a lot of these requirements and features so that accessibility can be enhanced at this point in the accessible journey chain.

Design of Accessible Bus Stops: Approaching Practice

The design of a bus stop to achieve all the points raised above is always going to be difficult in the real world. However, we have considered some fundamental issues which have led to basic designs as part of the EXCALIBUR project and these can be used as a starting point for the design of an accessible bus stop.

Every bus stop site is different and, therefore, the basic design might need to be altered in almost every case. It is therefore important to understand why the basic design is the way it is so that the inevitable compromises can be made with a minimal loss to the accessibility and functionality of the bus stop. Another reason why a clear understanding of the principles underlying the basic design is necessary is that this will help to identify those people who will be excluded from the service as a result of any compromise to the design. This will highlight the difficulties that would be caused by a change to the design and make it easier to determine suitable alternative arrangements in the unfortunate cases where such exclusion is unavoidable.

The basic designs provide the ideal (i.e. what is theoretically necessary to obtain an accessible bus stop), and it must be remembered that any diminution of these fundamental principles means a reduction in the amount of accessibility on offer. This would result in some people being excluded from the bus service and thus from the activities they wish to pursue. Each reduction in accessibility must be considered in the light of how it can be compensated for through other measures (and the associated costs and problems that might result).

The following discussion concentrates on the analysis of the decisive elements and steps that will define an accessible bus stop. They are:

- dealing with the vertical gap
- dealing with the horizontal gap
- balancing the crossfall
- setting the design the surface and passenger area
- helping the driver with a guidance system.

The background for these analyses was put together with users as described above, and included consideration of the interfaces between users, vehicles and the bus stop area.

Dealing with the Vertical Gap: Choice of Kerb Height

The height of the platform above road level affects the vertical gap between the platform surface and the floor of the bus at the entrance and/or exit door(s). One of the most useful things to do with a bus stop is to increase the height of the kerb so that the vertical gap can be reduced. There are a few kerbs available that are higher than normal kerbs but that have been designed to allow buses to approach them without damaging the tyres or bodywork.

At the moment there are three kerb types in the UK. The original kerb design was produced in Germany and is now universally known as the *Kassel kerb*. This is designed with a 75 mm radius curve at the interface with the road level to match the tyre profile and a face set at 75° to the horizontal so that the kerb can 'steer' the bus along the platform without

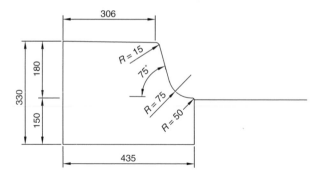

Fig. 5.16   *The profile of the Kassel kerb (dimensions in mm; R, radius)*

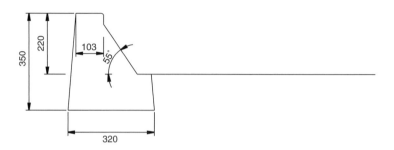

Fig. 5.17   *The profile of the Charcon access kerb (dimensions in mm)*

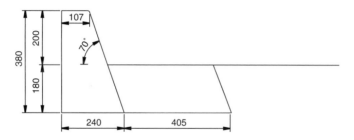

Fig. 5.18   The profile of the Marshall bus stop kerb (dimensions in mm)

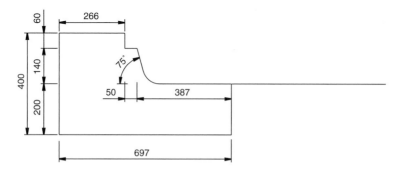

Fig. 5.19   The profile of the Dresden kerb (dimensions in mm)

damaging the tyre. Kassel kerbs are available in two heights (160 and 180 mm) in the UK, although they have been used in Grenoble, France, with a height of 210 mm. The Kassel kerb profile is shown in Figure 5.16.

The second design was developed in the UK. This uses a straight profile, angled so that the upper edge of the kerb does not damage the bodywork when the wheel is placed at the interface between the kerb and the road level. This is known as the *access kerb* and is available in two heights (160 and 220 mm). The face is set at 55° to the horizontal, with a straight edge between the face and the road level. The profile of the access kerb is shown in Figure 5.17.

We also tested a third design called the *bus stop kerb*, which is made in two parts so that the height can be adjusted on site and can be laid up to 200 mm above the road level. The face is angled at 70° to the horizontal, with a straight edge to the road level. We were supplied with a version with 15-mm blisters on the surface of the flat piece (these were designed to advise the driver of the proximity of the kerb). The profile of the bus stop kerb is shown in Figure 5.18.

There are other designs in use in Germany – for example, the Aachen kerb, 180 mm high and a 65° face with a straight edge at road level; the

Fig. 5.20   The profile of the Rouen bus stop kerb, for use with optically controlled buses in Rouen, France

Herten kerb, which is 165 mm high, with a 65° face with a small (15 mm radius) curve at the bottom; and the Dresden kerb, designed for use with bus or tram stops, which has a cut-out at the top to allow for the different body-width characteristics of the two vehicle types (Figure 5.19). A recent development in France is a stepped kerb for use with optically controlled buses, as shown in Figure 5.20.

When the vehicle eventually stops to collect passengers, the vertical gap can be reduced by lowering the bus. This can reduce the floor height of the bus door from its 'drive height' to a 'knelt height' of about 250 mm above the road level, although we have found that this could be as low as 200 mm in older buses (where the suspension has settled over time). The ground clearance is typically about 80–90 mm less than the floor height (i.e. by the thickness of the floor and any chassis parts underneath the front quarter of the bus as indicated in Figure 5.27). At present, the difference between ride height and boarding height seems to be of the order of about 80–100 mm. Thus a bus purchased to deliver the Public Service Vehicles Accessibility Regulations (2000) 250 mm floor height, may have a ground clearance of 160 mm when knelt and 240 mm at drive height.

The profile, another important feature of the special kerbs, affects the horizontal gap. The horizontal gap, on the other hand, is a result of the way drivers approach the bus stop area, this is considered in detail in the following section. To make a good decision about which kerb to use we should consider what happens in the dynamic situation (i.e. when the bus is moving towards and against the kerb).

Dealing with the Horizontal Gap

The delivery of a small horizontal gap depends strongly on the driver's ability to bring the bus close and parallel to the kerb. In looking for a small horizontal gap, we are asking the driver to bring a rigid object 12 m long and 2.55 m wide within a few millimetres of a concrete platform. The driver's view of the bus stop is limited to what can be seen from this position. In practice, this is restricted by a number of factors. The nearest point on the road surface that can be seen from the driving position is about 4.5 m in front of the vehicle. The nearside is obstructed by the corner pillar of the vehicle. Often the front doors have a curtain about 30 cm high at the bottom. Perhaps the most important outcome of all this is that the driver cannot see the kerb near to the bus (i.e. less than 4.5 m from the front of the vehicle) from the driving position. The colour of the road and footway surfaces, which are often in various forms of grey, gives the result that once the nearside of the vehicle is within about 500 mm of the kerb, the driver has no feedback to advise where the vehicle is with respect to the kerb. Thus the driver is unsure whether the vehicle is about to mount the kerb or if it is half a metre away from it.

The driver's view of the rear of the vehicle is restricted to what can be seen in the rear-view mirrors. The rear steering pivot of the vehicle is the rear axle, which could be located some 6 m behind the driver. This means that steering the bus towards the kerb cannot be done until that point is clearly past any obstruction (e.g. a parked car) on the nearside. Asking a driver to position the vehicle with the level of accuracy required for the accessible operation of a bus stop means expecting him or her to achieve a highly skilled and precise control over the vehicle in extremely difficult circumstances.

Meeting the users' need for a small horizontal gap is therefore concerned with helping the driver overcome these difficulties. This requires an understanding of how the vehicle interacts with the infrastructure, and we need to think about the characteristics of the vehicles which might affect this interaction.

Vehicles

As mentioned above, we found a wide variation between buses in relation to ground clearance. The difference between ground clearance and the vertical gap depends on three factors:

- the kerb height
- the difference between the ride height and the boarding height of the bus
- the depth of the floor on the bus.

It is essential that bus operators, bus manufacturers and bus stop designers agree on these aspects of bus design and kerb height. Generally speaking, the higher the kerbs, the more difficult the problem is to resolve. The greater the difference between ride and knelt heights, the longer it takes to kneel and raise the bus at a bus stop, and this could eventually impose an increase in the dwell time. At present, however, the time taken to lower or raise a bus 80 mm or so is about 2–3 s.

Bus manufacturers can help by thinking hard about the area concerned (see Figure 5.27) and what they can do to increase the ground clearance without increasing the vertical gap. On examining the buses, we found a number of parts in this region (chassis members, compressors and various bolts and other extrusions) that reduced the ground clearance on particular buses. The fact that some buses had nothing in particular fitted underneath the bus floor in this area indicates that these features could be removed or placed elsewhere where the clearance is not so critical.

Differences in performance of the suspension meant that the kneeling mechanism had different effects. In addition, different kneeling systems were in evidence: we experienced buses where the kneeling mechanism worked on all wheels, both axles nearside only, front axle only and front nearside only. The amount by which the bus lowered varied from 70 mm to 100 mm. There is also a wide variation in the lateral overhang: at the front axle, this varied between 35 mm and 95 mm; at the rear axle we encountered a range from 25 mm to 70 mm. The rear axle was placed at different places along the bus length, and the rear overhang varied from 2.2 m to 3.3 m. The front axle was also quite variable, with the front overhang ranging from 2.175 m to 2.67 m (all the buses we examined had the front door in front of the front axle). Given the degree of accuracy required by the passengers' needs it is clear that the drivers are given a very difficult job to do by the manufacturers (Box 5.5).

Box 5.5   Adjustment of driving height in the vehicle suspension system

> The importance of the differences have only come to light as a result of this work and could be made easier without too much difficulty. To take just one example, the differences between different vehicles in ride height and kneeling height could be solved quite easily. Air suspension systems have a height regulator valve which is placed underneath the vehicle. Normally this is adjusted every few (maybe six) months as part of the regular maintenance of the vehicle. The requirements of accessible bus driving mean that the heights are critical, and therefore this valve needs much more frequent attention. Placing the control mechanism in the driver's cabin, with an indicator to show the height at which the bus is riding, would mean that the driver could, as part of the checking routine, check that the bus is operating at a satisfactory height before starting each journey. Retrofitting such a device would be costly, but incorporating it into the initial manufacture would not affect the price as much.

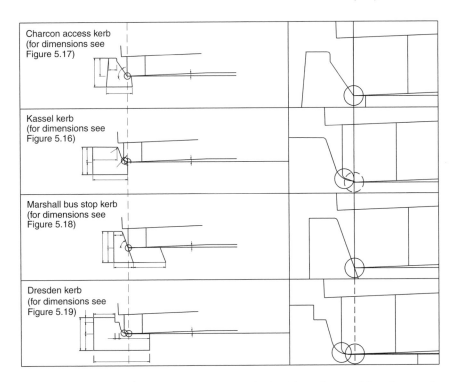

Fig. 5.21 The vertical and horizontal gaps obtained by a bus positioned correctly against different special kerbs

When parked with the wheel against the kerb, as the special bus stop kerbs are designed to work, the horizontal gap then depends on the relationship between the wheel and the bodywork. Figure 5.21 shows the theoretical effect of different kerb profiles with respect to both vertical and horizontal gaps. Figure 5.21 shows the ideal position of the bus against the kerb. In general, a Kassel kerb will deliver a smaller horizontal gap than either of the other kerbs, for two reasons. First, its profile allows for a steeper face than the other kerbs (75° to the horizontal rather than 55° or 70°) so the top edge of the kerb is nearer to the vehicle when the wheel is positioned properly against the bottom of the kerb. Secondly, the round profile at the contact point between the tyre and the kerb supports the profile of the tyre and thus makes it easier for the tyre to remain in the correct position as it moves along the kerb. However, the 180 mm height will deliver a larger vertical gap than the 200 mm or 220 mm of the other kerbs. Figure 5.21 shows that, in principle, a vertical gap of 80 mm can be obtained with a Kassel kerb, with a slight overhang which gives no horizontal gap. The access kerb has a horizontal gap of some 37 mm, but the vertical gap would be 40 mm. The Marshall kerb brings the bus close to the kerb, with an overhang, and thus the vertical gap would be the same as the floor depth (around 80 mm, i.e. about the same as for a Kassel kerb). Dimensions can vary a lot depending on the type of vehicle using the bus stop and the effect of the road camber at the bus stop. However, the way in which these kerbs perform in practice is rather different, as we shall discuss below.

Dresden kerbs (see Figure 5.19) work in a similar way to Kassel kerbs, but present a higher platform to help reduce the vertical gap. They also extend the footing to accommodate the whole tyre.

The difference in lateral gaps is also a matter for the manufacturers. There are two reasons why wheels are set so far inside the bodywork. First, the body has been widened (most recently from 2.50 m to 2.55 m), but the chassis is still the same size. Secondly, the wheel nuts are exposed and the risk of injury and damage caused by these if the wheel is too close to the outside of the vehicle is considered to be too high. There is a case for local authorities, as 'providers' of the bus stop infrastructure, to discuss suitable vehicle dimensions with bus operators. The dimensions of interest for accessible bus stops are not normally of much concern to an operator when specifying a vehicle, as they affect neither operating costs nor passenger capacity. However, they can make a lot of difference to the ease with which accessibility can be delivered at bus stops. More compatibility between bus and bus stop design could also reduce damage to both infrastructure and vehicles. Recent discussions with one bus manufacturer revealed a blank refusal to redesign the chassis to reduce the lateral gap problem on the basis of the investment cost that would be incurred. A manufacturer with this sort of view will only be persuaded to change by pressure from potential purchasers. This will only be forthcoming if bus operators and infrastructure providers combine forces to produce a consistent requirement for such elements to be included in vehicle specifications. The design of the lateral gap is considered in Box 5.6.

The rear overhang of the bus is also important. If the bus turns too sharply on leaving the stop, the rear of the bus will overhang the kerb. We found examples of buses with a rear overhang of over 3 m (measured from the rear axle). In order to help ensure the safety of passengers on the platform (who will, by and large, not be visible to the driver as the bus leaves the stop) the exit angle needs to be reduced. Improved arrangements for rear and side view mirrors would make the driver's job a lot easier. We have seen in Figure 5.6 the nearside mirror cluster used on buses in Kassel, Germany.

Quality contracts and partnerships would seem to be a good opportunity to improve the buses and provide the corresponding accessible infrastructure. It would certainly be interesting to see the horizontal and vertical gaps obtained in operation being measured as one of the performance measures in such a partnership.

Box 5.6   The design of the lateral gap

In principle, there is no reason why the axles could not be lengthened: there would be some design work to do on steering equipment and suspension, but this was not considered to be too difficult. We asked if the wheels could be redesigned. Again, it was a question of rethinking the principles. The nuts are prominent in order to make them easier to remove using a wheel brace. However, nobody uses a wheel brace to remove nuts from bus wheels: the usual method is a powered socket spanner. Therefore, there is no reason why, in principle, adjustments could not be made to the wheel design to enable the wheel to be less threatening to people if it were nearer the outside of the bus. It is possible to cover the wheels in order to resolve the wheel nut problem, as has been done with the CIVIS bus used in Clermont Ferrand, France.

Balancing Crossfalls at the Bus Stop Platform and Footway

The choice of kerb also affects the crossfall at the bus stop platform and the footway. It is usually impossible to increase the height of the platform without having to adjust the drainage in some way. IHT (1991) states that the maximum acceptable crossfall should be 2%, other literature about disabled users' needs asks for 1%. In the EXCALIBUR experiments, we found that people in wheelchairs and, more particularly, people who need mobility aids such as sticks to walk, began to detect a difficulty with crossfalls approaching 4%. We advocate a 2% crossfall as a best compromise, but realise the difficulties in achieving this in many cases. A crossfall as steep as 4% is acceptable only if this means that otherwise there would be no accessibility at all at the bus stop. Given the practicalities of constructing crossfalls with small gradients, it is likely to be difficult to achieve crossfalls less than 2%. We give here a practical guide on how to set about dealing with the problem of footway and platform crossfalls.

It is essential for the design process that we set a horizontal datum and this is helpful in the discussion of the effects of relative kerb and platform heights:

(1) Set a datum coincident with the road surface level at its boundary with the kerb.
(2) Check the width of the footway from the non-road edge to the edge of the road at various points along the proposed bus stop environment (also note the ownership of the curtilage). The aim is to have a minimum of 2.00 m for the footway and a minimum of 2.30 m for the platform, if a one-sided shelter is to be adopted. So the

total width equals 4.3 m. If less than 4.3 m is available, an alternative bus stop layout should be considered. The most common case of this sort is where a kerbside layout needs to be changed to a half or a full boarder. It is important to note that if a bus shelter with an end panel is required, this will increase the necessary width of the platform because of the need to maintain access to the platform for people with pushchairs or in wheelchairs. This is discussed further below.

(3) Check the heights of the existing kerb in the whole area of the proposed bus stop environment.

(4) Check the current crossfalls. This will enable you to calculate the heights of the footway from the datum line at the non-road edge.

(5) Calculate the crossfalls for both the footway and the platform as a result of using a raised kerb at the edge of the proposed platform (common heights: 160 mm, 180 mm and 220 mm).

(6) Then:

(a) If the proposed crossfall is positive (i.e. sloping towards the kerb edge) and less than 2%, the proposal can go ahead and there should be no need to install a new drainage system for the footway.

(b) If the proposed crossfall is positive and greater than 2%:
- check if the non-road edge could be adjusted so that the crossfall is reduced to 2% or less
- consider if a step (with the necessary safety measures) could be placed between the footway and the platform, thus improving both crossfalls in order to achieve 2% or less.

(c) If the proposed arrangement is to arrange drainage along the footway–platform interface:
- Check that both positive and negative crossfalls will be satisfactory.
- Check that drainage into and from the gully can be accommodated without causing ponding or other problems.
- In some cases it will be impossible to provide satisfactory crossfalls without a step between the footway and the platform. In this case, check pedestrian and passenger flows and movements and, if appropriate, install a step. This will have to be protected by a handrail in order to avoid becoming a trip hazard. Check that the transfer from the platform to the footway is smooth and safe at each end of the platform.

(d) If the proposed crossfall is negative the non-road edge must be examined:
- If the non-road edge is a wall (rather than a building) or vegetation and the proposed crossfall is less than 2%, check if it is possible to leave the crossfall as it is.

- If the non-road edge is a wall (rather than a building) or vegetation, check if it is possible to make the crossfall positive by increasing the height of the footway at the non-road edge.
- If there are buildings with frontages at the non-road edge, then it is better to leave the non-road edge as it is and concentrate on the platform side:
  - A solution with a step between platform and footway might be necessary (see above) along with the alterations to the drainage system.
  - Check if the construction of a boarder might help (it would give a greater width in which to deal with the crossfall problem, but could make it more difficult if the road camber is steep).
  - Consider reducing the height of the new kerb, even though this will reduce accessibility to the buses. Consider who would be excluded from the bus service as a result.
  - If other road works are being undertaken at this point, consider lowering the road level (this was done in one case where a major rebuild was in progress, but normally this would be far too costly).

Balancing the crossfalls is not an easy engineering task but it is an extremely important part of building an accessible bus stop. Kerbside bus stops generally attempt to fit an accessible bus stop into an existing space. A full or half boarder bus stop adds to the width available for the footway and platform at the expense of space within the roadway. At one level, the decision about which of these solutions to adopt is a matter of policy (e.g. the preference for public rather than private transport). However, as we have seen, the problem could be a physical issue: it might be impossible to construct an accessible bus stop within the existing space and thus additional space must be created or the bus stop moved to a more accessible location. The latter possibility needs to be considered in the light of overall effects on the accessibility of the network as a whole (as discussed in Chapter 3). The issue of 'compatible' bus stops is considered in Box 5.7.

Setting the Design for Surfaces in the Passenger Area

As mentioned before, bus stops need to have sufficient space for people to arrive and leave them, whether they are intending to board a bus or have just left one. Here we are going to discuss practical issues such as:

- locating the entrance door of the bus along the platform
- adopting safety measures (the need for a warning line or railings)
- establishing the position and shape of the shelter.

Locating the entrance door

A common complaint from users was that they did not know where the bus door would be. It is only possible to advise where the entrance door of the bus will be if the bus stop has been designed to enable bus drivers to stop consistently along the platform. The issue for the drivers is discussed below. As far as the passengers are concerned, a number of cities have attempted to provide such an indication. This is usually done by using paving with a contrasting colour, a painted symbol or a painted line on the platform surface, which can be used by both drivers and passengers as an indication of where the door(s) will be. Figure 5.22 shows the solution being adopted in Grenoble. One line of pavers in a colour that contrasts with the platform surface marks the front door and two lines mark the centre door (where wheelchair users are expected to board and alight). In Rouen, the location of the door intended for use by people in wheelchairs is indicated on the platform by the international symbol for disabled people (Figure 5.23). Stopping positions are considered further in Box 5.8.

For these indicators to work credibly, drivers must have some indication so that they know how to deliver the doors to the correct points

Box 5.7   'Compatible' bus stops

In some cases it may prove impossible to obtain the correct crossfalls and it may be necessary to concede temporary defeat and have a bus stop which is less accessible than is acceptable. In such cases the nearest accessible bus stop must be as close as possible to the inaccessible one. Its location and the accessible routes to reach it must be made absolutely clear and a time-scale published to indicate when it will be made accessible.

In Grenoble, a programme is in place for making all bus stops accessible, but for some stops a two-stage process is being adopted. Minor amendments to the infrastructure are made in order to make the bus stop 'compatible' with accessibility objectives while not being fully accessible. The bus stop contains information for both bus drivers and passengers to indicate exactly what is and is not accessible about the stop. This includes whether the bus can or cannot be lowered at the stop and whether or not it is accessible to, for example, wheelchairs. The programme indicates that at a defined point in the future the compatible stop will be made accessible. This approach at least has the advantage that people will know that the inadequacy of the initial design is (a) not intended to be the final version for the stop and (b) that it will be made accessible within a defined and programmed time-scale.

Fig. 5.22   A Kassel bus stop in Grenoble, showing the door markings

Fig. 5.23   A platform in Rouen, with marking to indicate the boarding position for people in wheelchairs

along the platform. We explored the needs of bus drivers with respect to controlling the stopping position of the bus in the course of our EXCALIBUR experiments. We found that the bus drivers could stop their buses within ±200 mm of a given stopping point, whatever means of indicating the position was adopted (e.g. a conventional pole, line on the roadway, line or other markings on the footway).

We also realised that we should indicate the door positions to people other than users of wheelchairs, so we were interested to find ways of communicating this information to others (e.g. blind or partially sighted people). We therefore adopted the tactile *information surface* (DETR, 2000) to indicate the location of the front door to passengers. The surface in question is made of the rubberised material used in children's playgrounds as a safety surface because of its slightly soft feel. Blind people can detect this change of surface so it indicates to them where the doorway will be. The surface is a highly visible orange colour in order to help partially sighted people and to help the driver position the bus correctly. Taking into account the ability of drivers to stop within ±200 mm, we arranged for the surface to be 400 mm wider than the doorway to allow for this variation. Using the tactile surface in this way helps everyone, but it is of special interest to blind and partially sighted people. It enables us to designate this part of the bus stop as the place where tactile and audible information is available. Drivers use this surface as the marker for their stopping position. The EXCALIBUR surface for locating the bus doorway is shown in Figure 5.24.

Where buses have a second door, we mark the platform surface around the expected location of the second door with buff pavers so that people can leave it clear for alighting passengers. Transport for London requires wheelchair users to use the centre door for boarding and alighting, so the area in front of the centre door also serves the wheelchair users. As the contrasting colour surface indicates the likely location of the centre door it also serves to indicate to people in wheelchairs where to wait in order to be conveniently positioned to board the bus when it arrives. This is also a good place to put information at a convenient height for someone sitting in a wheelchair. We have also tried to ensure that the shelter reaches to this point so that wheelchair users can wait near the doorway with the benefit of the shelter. This has proved problematical in practice, as it is felt by local businesses in particular that the resulting shelter is too long and by the advertising company to be too expensive.

Box 5.8   Stopping positions

In neither Grenoble nor Rouen has much attention been paid to the actual stopping position of the buses. The 'indication surface' in Grenoble is exactly the width of the door and located where it is intended that the door should be. In Rouen, the symbol gives no indication of the door width. The advantage of the Greonble system over the one in Rouen is that the marking at the front door position makes it a lot easier for the drivers to see where to stop the bus. In Rouen, the driver has to stop the bus with less help from these markings in order to ensure that the correct door is delivered to the correct position along the platform.

Orange tactile
surface

Fig. 5.24   The EXCALIBUR doorway location surface

The position of the area corresponding to the centre door will vary according to the type of bus using the stop. As a result, the area to be identified needs to accommodate buses with the centre door nearest to the front as well as those with the centre door placed nearest to the back of the bus. We also need to allow for the ±200 mm variation in the stopping position. In the EXCALIBUR project we made this area 2.4 m long in order to accommodate the range of buses using the bus stop at the time.

The rest of the platform surface area should be in natural (e.g. grey) pavers. Tactile paving is not appropriate at bus stops because the limited information that it provides already indicates very specific situations within the street environment (e.g. pedestrian crossings, stairs, guidance paths). It is felt by organisations such as the Royal National Institute for the Blind that the difference in kerb height at a raised bus stop platform is not a hazard that warrants another specific tactile surface. However, there is a lot of sense (and no objection from the Department of the Environment, Transport and the Regions) in using non-slip paving on the lateral ramps between the footway and the (higher) platform surface. Further information on detecting bus stops is given in Box 5.9 and Figures 5.25 and 5.26.

Adopting safety measures
The experiments we carried out in the EXCALIBUR project showed that, in the worst situation, when the entry side of the bus stop area is full

of parked cars, the approach manoeuvre of the bus will result in its overhanging the kerb at some point. As a result of this overhang, the clearance between the underside of this part of the bus and the ground needs to be sufficient to be sure that the bus will not come into contact with the top of the kerb. Figure 5.27 shows the region of the bus that needs to be considered in this respect.

For safety reasons, we decided to indicate a line, along the platform, behind which people should stand while they waited for their bus. This is

Box 5.9   Detecting bus stops

This problem has also been approached in Leipzig, where the boundaries of a bus stop are indicated using a 400-mm wide ribbed surface. This is also used to indicate the intended position of the bus doorway and acts as a line behind which people should stand while waiting for a bus (Figures 5.25 and 5.26). The ribbed surface is effective in being detected by a long cane and the white colour contrasts strongly with the background colour of the platform surface. However, it might be questioned whether the surface is being used to indicate too many different things (it is also used elsewhere as a guidance path). This means that there is a risk that people might misinterpret its meaning in any context. Care needs to be taken so that any confusion does not result in an unacceptable safety hazard.

Fig. 5.25   A ribbed tactile surface is used to indicate the boundaries of a bus stop platform in Leipzig

Fig. 5.26   *A ribbed surface is used to indicate the location of the entrance door of buses at a bus stop in Leipzig*

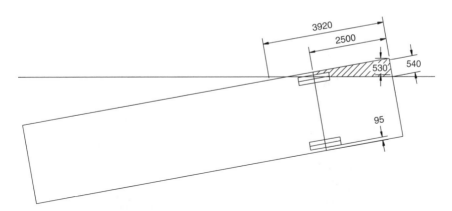

Fig. 5.27   *The overhang region for a bus as it approaches a kerb (dimensions in mm)*

not easy because the way in which a person using a long cane sweeps with their cane could easily miss the warning, especially if they are walking parallel to the line. We looked at an attempt to do this in France, which involved a block paver with a groove cut along it. The problem with this was how to make it large enough to distinguish it from, for example, the gap between lines of pavers, yet not so large that it could constitute a trip hazard in its own right. We were not convinced that the blocks we saw were really able to achieve this. Nevertheless, the idea is interesting

(Figures 5.28 and 5.29). We added a line to encourage passengers to stand back from the platform edge. We set this line in 100 mm wide yellow blocks on the platform, 500 mm from the kerb edge. This seems to work well. However, the line must also be able to warn people who cannot see it. We therefore needed something which could be sensed by blind people but that would not confuse them about its meaning.

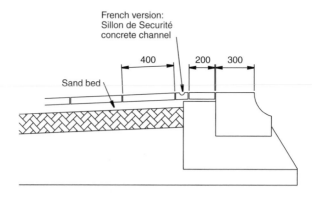

Fig. 5.28   Cross-section of the tactile line indication used in France (dimensions in mm)

Fig. 5.29   The Sillon de Securité tactile line indication used in France

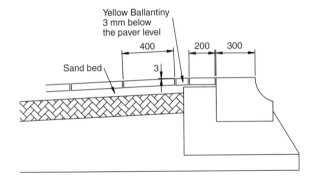

Fig. 5.30   Cross-section of the EXCALIBUR warning line (dimensions in mm)

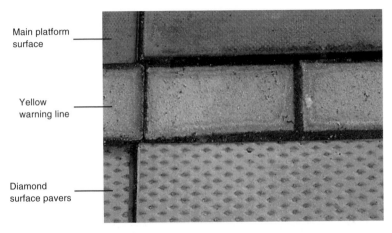

Fig. 5.31   The warning line and contrasting surfaces at an EXCALIBUR stop

The upper surface of a Kassel kerb is characterised by a non-slip surface with a diamond pattern. This is not a tactile surface, but it does present a definite, regular and rougher surface than a standard concrete paver. By adding a diamond-surface paver behind the Kassel kerb we could continue the diamond surface for 500 mm behind the kerb edge. We then placed the yellow warning line behind the paver and started the main platform surface behind the line. The warning line is therefore distinguishable as being the boundary between a rough and a smooth surface. This arrangement is shown in Figures 5.30 and 5.31. A similar arrangement can be provided for the other special kerbs – as their horizontal surface is smaller than the Kassel kerb, this will require two 200-mm pavers rather than one, and the kerb itself will not have the diamond surface. The

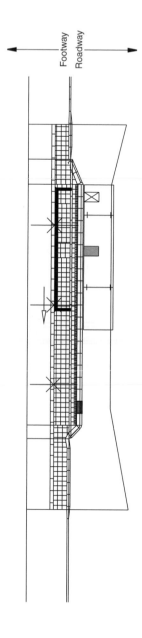

Footway

Roadway

Fig. 5.32   The general arrangement of the platform at an EXCALIBUR bus stop (half boarder)

result will still leave enough diamond surface to provide a detectable contrasting surface. The warning line has another purpose. It provides visual feedback to the bus drivers so that they can judge where the vehicle is positioned relative to the kerb during its final approach to the stopping point.

Figure 5.32 shows the general arrangement of the bus stop platform at an EXCALIBUR bus stop, including the various surfaces. This is shown for a half boarder arrangement, but the platform surface is identical for all bus stops, giving a consistency to the bus stop area that is helpful to passengers and drivers.

Railings near bus stops are quite common, but are often obstructions to smooth operation at the bus stop. Careful consideration should be given to removing them. If they cannot be avoided, they should be set so that the requisite number of buses can use the stop without the passengers being impeded by the railings. At the very least they should enable both doors of the number of buses expected to be at the stop at the same time to be used without any of the buses having to move. In the example shown in Figure 5.33, the gap between the end of the bus and the start of the railings is about 3 m: it would be just enough for passengers wishing to board a second bus (although it would be easier if the rubbish bin were moved) if the first bus stopped in exactly the right place. However, passengers would not be able to leave the second bus as the centre door, which would be obstructed by the railings. Buses often have to stop twice at this bus stop as a result. This causes needless problems at peak times when more than one bus arrives at the stop at a time – especially important in this case as it is an interchange where passengers from a number of bus lines alight to enter a commuting railway station.

The points made above apply with respect to different buses using the same stop. The main point is to design the stopping points in such a way that the driver of each bus knows where to stop in order to deliver the entrance and exit doors to the correct places along the platform. To have any realistic chance of achieving this, it is essential that drivers can, and do, treat every stop in the same way. The idea is not workable if drivers have to remember that different stops have to be approached differently or that if there is a wheelchair user at the stop they should make a different approach. Just as drivers have to start preparing their approach to the stop several metres upstream, so the designers must prepare the stop to accept the bus in a way that presents a consistent approach for the driver. We discuss this later in this chapter.

Establishing the position and shape of the shelter
One of the key elements to improve the area of bus stop is the shelter. A bus shelter is multifunctional. It is considered to be the place to:

Fig. 5.33   Railings can cause limitations to the accessibility of a bus stop (and to its capacity)

- Protect: consideration needs to be given to the prevailing wind, rain, sunlight and heat.
- Inform: the shelter is also the location for information about the bus services and the local area. It is the point where people have continuous access to information to proceed on their journey, whether they are waiting for a bus or have just left one.
- Provide comfort: all bus stops should have seats, preferably located within the shelter. Space for wheelchairs, pushchairs, shopping and luggage must also be included.
- Promote safety: shelters must enable people to feel secure and safe while they wait for a bus.

These needs should be met for all users of the bus system, so a shelter must be able to accommodate people with wheelchairs, pushchairs, shopping and young children, as well as elderly people. The shelter should enable people to wait for the bus and to enter the vehicle in comfort.

There are two basic types of shelter: one which consists of a longitudinal panel with a cantilever roof (sometimes called an *L-type shelter*) (Figure 5.34) and one which has two or more sides and a roof (sometimes called an *enclosed-type shelter*) (Figure 5.35). In urban areas, enclosed shelters

Fig. 5.34   An L-type shelter

Fig. 5.35   An enclosed-type shelter

typically consist of an L-type shelter with one or two end panels (often used for advertising) and thus can have two or three sides. In rural areas, there may be a need for a four-sided shelter because of the more isolated location of many rural bus stops. This requires thought about space both inside and outside the shelter, and we discuss this below. The type of shelter considered will affect the width of the platform. The shelter should be located so that it does not obstruct the minimum footway width (2.0 m) or the minimum space required for a wheelchair to pass along the platform between the kerb edge and an obstacle (1.2 m).

The dimensions for positioning a one-sided shelter are shown in Figure 5.36. Note that it is necessary to ensure that there is enough space for a wheelchair or buggy to pass between the bus stop pole and the edge of the shelter and that the shelter needs to be long enough to ensure that there is covered waiting space for the centre door if buses are so equipped.

When considering two and three-sided shelters, a bus stop pole (if it is to be installed) has to be installed about 0.6 m back from the kerb in order to avoid obstructing the wing mirrors and overhangs of arriving buses. This means that if the end of the shelter and the pole are aligned, the shelter needs to be set back so that the widest lateral panel is at least 1.2 m from the bus stop pole (i.e. 1.8 m from the kerb edge). This could be reduced if an access path of 1.2 m were provided at an angle. These two layouts are shown in Figure 5.37.

The measurements shown in Figure 5.37 assume an empty shelter: turning movements will be difficult for wheelchair users if there are many passengers waiting to board the bus, so it is important that enough space is

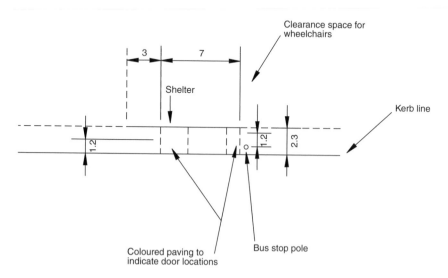

Fig. 5.36 *The dimensions (in m) of an L-type shelter*

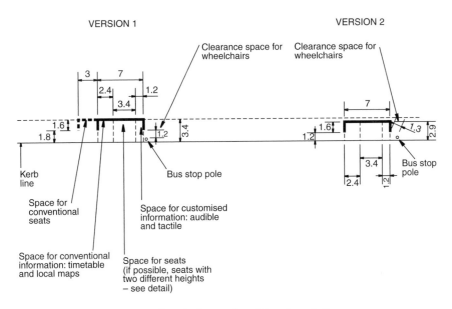

Fig. 5.37   The dimensions (in m) of an enclosed-type bus shelter

Box 5.10   Bus shelter length

In London, the usual length for a bus shelter is three or four panels. Each panel is 1.3 m long, thus giving a shelter length of 3.9 m or 5.2 m. As noted above, the use of centre doors for boarding for some people means that the shelter should really extend to the rear of the centre door. Depending on the position of the centre door on the buses using the stop, this could require a minimum shelter length of 8.725 m (seven panels), as in some cases this is the minimum length from the front of the bus to the back of the rear door. The reason for this determining the length of the shelter is that wheelchair users can wait comfortably in the shelter near to the door at which it is intended that they should board the bus. This avoids the stark choice between (a) having to move along the platform to find their entrance door after the bus has arrived and (b) waiting in the rain.

allowed for both the manoeuvres and the expected number of waiting passengers (Box 5.10). Bus shelters should be large enough that they are able to accommodate the number of passengers expected to be waiting for the bus services at the stop. As noted in Chapter 4, PASSION can provide an estimate of the number of passengers to be accommodated for conditions of bus and passenger arrivals. We worked with some wheelchair users to examine the space and conditions required to accommodate people in wheelchairs. This helped to focus attention on the space needed for manoeuvring the wheelchair and, in addition, we could explore with the wheelchair users their perception of space and security.

As we were examining a four-sided shelter, we felt that our experiments should reflect the overall space requirements appropriate to a rural community. This was also helpful as it provided advice to the Cumbria Plusbus project (described in more detail in Chapter 8). For the purpose of this study it was assumed that there was a need to accommodate up to eight people, including facilities for six seats, one wheelchair, one pushchair and some luggage. Where available, the dimensions and shapes of the various features were obtained from existing publications (IHT, 1991; DOE/DTp, 1992; DETR, 1999). Recommended dimensions are included in the list given below:

(a) space for six seats, each 0.5 m wide by 0.5 m long plus 0.5 m legroom
(b) space for one wheelchair, 1.2 m wide by 1.2 m long
(c) space to manoeuvre the wheelchair into a forward-looking position within the shelter, 1.2 m wide
(d) space for one pushchair, 1.0 m wide by 1.2 m long (IHT, 1991)
(e) space for shopping and luggage, 0.5 m by 0.5 m
(f) cost-effective use of overall space in relation to visibility, lack of obstruction and ease of access into and within the shelter
(g) modular construction to facilitate manufacture, re-use and interchangeability (0.8 m to suit Cumbria County Council in this case; this was subsequently increased to 1.2 m).

Other design considerations, which are not treated here relate to:

- Cost: optimise value for money with the needs of the community.
- Weather: protect users from rain, snow and wind; optimise the orientation of shelter and/or entry point.
- Security: maximise two-way visibility; provide easy exit.
- Vandalism: choose materials to minimise damage caused by fire, impact and graffiti.
- Aesthetics: optimise the cost and appearance to take into account the views of the local community wherever possible.

As we shall see in Chapter 8, in the Cumbria Plusbus project the bus had an all-round lowering suspension which could reduce the height of the step onto the bus to about 250 mm above carriageway level. Recognising that in many cases a four-sided shelter will require a free-standing platform, we also considered the dimensions of such a platform. Recommended space and other requirements are as follows (DETR, 1999):

(h) sufficient footway width on the platform in front of the bus shelter (suggested 1.2 m wide minimum) to manoeuvre a wheelchair easily into and out of the bus

Box 5.11   Wheelchair types used in manoeuvre tests

Type A: large rear wheel, manually driven, lightweight construction, small wheels at the front, adjustable wheelbase, no footrests

Type B: attendant propelled, small wheels at the rear (e.g. NHS model 9L)

Type C: electrically driven, four medium sized wheels, footrests, battery powered, controlled by means of a joystick or similar device

---

(i) sufficient footway width on the platform in front of side entry bus shelter (suggested 1.2 m wide minimum) to manoeuvre a wheelchair easily into and out of the bus.

Other factors, not considered here, deal with:

* The kerb, platform and the bus shelter floor. This should be constructed of durable material, which can act as the foundation raft for the shelter superstructure and should be at 0.25 m approximately above the level of the carriageway, laid to fall towards the kerb.
* In the absence of a footway, a ramp 1.2 m wide minimum, with handrails where appropriate, at a maximum gradient of 8% should connect the platform to the carriageway.

We considered three types of wheelchair in this study. These are described in Box 5.11. In order to check the practicability of various shelters and platforms, several shapes and sizes were considered, the object being to satisfy as many of the requirements as possible. Several bus shelter layouts (Figure 5.38) were evaluated using the three types of wheelchair described in Box 5.11. Other layouts were considered but were not evaluated due to lack of time and duplication of effort.

The shelter and platform layouts were set out full size, using coloured adhesive tapes, on an untrafficked area of carriageway. Each wheelchair user was then invited to 'enter' the shelter from the platform area without 'falling off' the platform or 'colliding' with the shelter. Records of the manoeuvres of each wheelchair were made on video camera for type A wheelchairs and on still photographs for type B and C wheelchairs. The results of the investigation, including wheelchairs users' comments, are given in Table 5.2. The space requirements for pushchairs were not tested.

Shelter layout 1 was more than adequate to accommodate six able-bodied travellers and any luggage. This shelter was checked by users of type A wheelchairs and was found to be satisfactory, although they considered that marked spaces for wheelchairs would avoid the need to ask others to move. It was assumed that the layout would be adequate for users of wheelchair types B and C and also that there would be enough space for a pushchair. There were no adverse comments in relation to visibility,

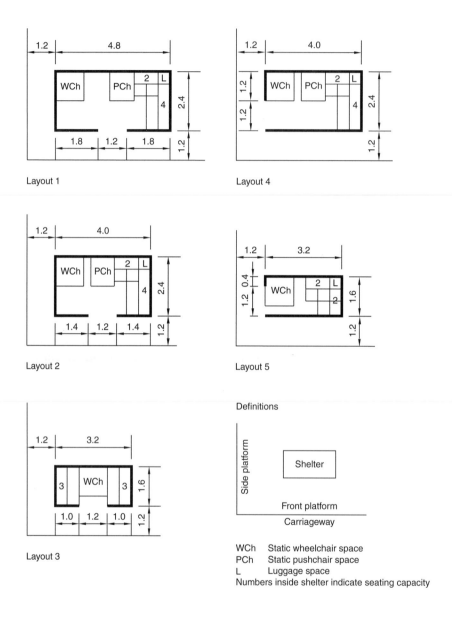

Fig. 5.38   Layouts for four-sided bus shelters (dimensions in m) tested in experiments (the outcomes of the experiments are given in Table 5.2)

access into the shelter or the width of platform in front of the shelter. However, overall it was considered that this shelter layout was larger than necessary.

Shelter layout 2 was able to accommodate six able-bodied travellers and their luggage. The layout was evaluated by users of type B and C wheelchairs only. It was found to be satisfactory. By inspection it would be suitable for type A wheelchairs and for a pushchair. As for layout 1 there were no adverse comments on visibility, access into the shelter or the width of platform width in front of the shelter. Overall, all users considered that the size of this shelter layout would be adequate.

Shelter layout 3 could accommodate six able-bodied travellers only if they had no luggage. The layout was checked by users of the three types of wheelchair. All users were unhappy about the proximity of fellow travellers. In addition, users of wheelchair types B and C were unable to turn within the shelter, so they could not look forward unless they had entered the shelter in reverse. There was no space for a pushchair. Overall, wheelchair users considered that this shelter layout was too small, lacked proper access and suffered from inadequate personal security.

Shelter layout 4 could accommodate six able-bodied travellers and their luggage. The layout was tested successfully using the three types of wheelchair. In addition, it was considered that there would be sufficient space for a pushchair. However, several users perceived a security problem and felt that it would be essential to have good visibility at both ends of the shelter. All users thought that the platform at the side of the shelter was too narrow for manoeuvring wheelchairs. They would be content if it were 1.5 m wide. They also preferred the bus to stop so that its entry point would be opposite the side platform. If the entry point were to be in front of the shelter, the front platform would also need to be wider than 1.2 m. The preferred width was 1.5 m, to allow for turning and overcoming any difference in level between the platform and the bus entry point. Overall, it was considered that the size and shape of this shelter layout was adequate, but the access to it would involve a larger platform than had been provided.

Shelter layout 5 could accommodate only four able-bodied travellers and their luggage. Although checked by users of all three types of wheelchair, users of wheelchair types B and C considered that there was not sufficient space to manoeuvre if others were already in the shelter. Also, there was not enough space for others to pass the wheelchair when carrying shopping bags. There was no space for a pushchair. For comments on security and platform width, see the discussion of layout 4 above. Overall, this shelter layout did not meet the objectives.

We therefore concluded that shelter layouts 3 and 5 would be unacceptable, layout 4 would be adequate if the platform were larger (but could present manoeuvring difficulties for a reference wheelchair) and

Table 5.2 Results of the shelter and platform tests

Layout No.	Wheelchair users Chair type	No.	a	b	c	d	e	f	g	h	i	Wheelchair users' comments
1	A	3	✓	✓	✓		✓		✓	✓	NA	Users suggested that wheelchair spaces should be marked on the floor and be placed opposite or next to the exit Wheelchair types B and C were not available
2	B	2	✓	✓	✓		✓	✓	✓	✓	NA	Wheelchair type A not available
	C	2	✓	✓	✓		✓	✓	✓	✓	NA	
3	A	3	✓	✓	✓		✗	✗	✓	✓	NA	All users felt confined in an unfriendly situation, their personal space invaded and generally claustrophobic
	B	2	✓	✓	✗		✗	✗	✓	✓	NA	
	C	2	✓	✓	✗		✗	✗	✓	✓	NA	
4	A	3	✓	✓	✓		✓	✗	✓	✗	✗	Users of type A wheelchairs considered that the layout was inadequate for more than one wheelchair facing forward
	B	2	✓	✓	✓		✓	✗	✓	✗	✗	
	C	2	✓	✓	✓		✓	✗	✓	✗	✗	

Users of wheelchair types B and C felt they needed windows at both ends for security and good visibility

All users considered that the front and side platforms were not wide enough for manoeuvres; suggested that 1.5 m would be sufficient

All users wanted the bus to stop with its door opposite the side platform

Users of wheelchair types B and C considered that there would be insufficient space to manoeuvre or for others to pass the wheelchair, particularly with shopping bags

See also the last three comments for shelter layout 4, above

5										
	A	3	✗	✓	✗	✗	✓	✗	✗	✓	✗
	B	2	✗	✓	✓	✗	✓	✓	✗	✓	✗
	C	2	✗	✓	✗	✗	✓	✗	✗	✓	✗

NA, not applicable

*Criteria (a)–(i) on pages 192 and 193

that layout 2 was acceptable. Layout 1 was considered adequate, but was likely to be larger than would be feasible in most applications. A summary of the minimum shelter and platform dimensions deemed acceptable to the wheelchair users resulting from these tests is given in Tables 5.3 and 5.4.

Figure 5.39 shows an example of a shelter where the edge of the panel is just 750 mm from the kerb edge, meaning that it would be hazardous for a wheelchair user to attempt to pass through this gap. Some shelter designs are not able to accommodate wheelchair users because their entrances are too narrow. The entrance to the shelter shown in Figure 5.39 is shown in Figure 5.40. In this case, the entrance is 600 mm wide, which is far too narrow for a wheelchair to pass through. A person in a wheelchair, or someone with a baby buggy, can only enter the shelter from the upstream end. A shelter with two or more sides and a bus stop pole (or some other similar obstacle) aligned at one end needs 3.5 m of platform width in order to ensure that the shelter is accessible to people in wheelchairs (see Figure 5.37). If a ramp is expected to be deployed the width required would be 3.5 m plus the appropriate ramp length.

A brief discussion of the advertising space on shelters and access issues is given in Box 5.12. An example where the decision to include an advertising panel has a serious effect on the availability of the bus stop to people is shown in Figure 5.41. In this case the platform width is 2 m and

Table 5.3   Acceptable minimum internal dimensions of four-sided shelters and associated space requirements

Description of the space inside the shelter	Minimum dimensions	
	Length (m)	Width (m)
Internal shape of shelter	4.0	2.4
Entry to shelter	–	1.2
Manoeuvring space for a wheelchair	–	1.2
Seating area per person	0.5	0.5
Legroom per person	0.5	0.5
Area for luggage	0.5	0.5
Space for pushchair	1.2	1.0
Space for wheelchair (marked on ground)	1.2	1.2
Essential: all-round visibility for wheelchair users; minimum zone of visibility 0.9–1.2 m above finished floor level	Full length of shelter; full width of shelter at both ends	

Table 5.4   Acceptable minimum dimensions of footways on free-standing platforms for four-sided bus shelters

Type of shelter	Footway	Minimum dimensions	
		Length (m)	Width (m)
Front entry	Front (including ramps and/or stairs)	Equal to length of shelter plus either two ramps ≤ 8% incline, or one ramp and one flight of steps	1.5
	Side	No footway required	–
Side entry	Front (including ramps and/or stairs)	Equal to length of shelter plus 1.5 m, plus either two ramps ≤ 8% incline, or one ramp and one flight of steps	1.5
	Side	Equal to width (front to rear) of shelter	1.5

the width of the footway is 2.3 m. The shelter panel is 1.3 m and has been placed across the platform so that people wishing to leave the bus stop area at the downstream end often find that they have to step into the road in order to avoid the shelter. This is not acceptable. Apart from the safety aspects of such a manoeuvre, the end panel of the shelter renders the bus stop inaccessible from that end to people who require more than a gap of 700 mm between the panel edge and the kerb edge to pass through.

Modern shelters make a lot of use of glazed areas, which is good from the point of view of increasing ambient light in them, but can make them a hazard for people with impaired vision. Where glazing is used, a bold brightly coloured band 140–160 mm wide should be placed on the glazing about 1500 mm from the ground.

All shelters should be set with their solid side(s) away from the road edge. This provides much more space for passengers to board and alight from the buses and helps to separate the bus stop area from the footway space. It also avoids the problem for bus drivers in bringing the bus close to the kerb – a shelter positioned close to the kerb edge will tend to 'push' the driver away from the kerb and thus increase the horizontal gap. It is also a lot harder to see on-coming buses from seats with their back towards the roadway (Figure 5.42). It is necessary to turn about 120° to see an arriving bus from this position. A shelter position with the back away from

Fig. 5.39   A shelter end panel that is very close to the kerb

Fig. 5.40   The entrance to the bus shelter shown in Figure 5.39

Box 5.12   Bus shelters and advertising

There is a problem with shelters because of the way in which they are currently funded as advertising panels – an activity that does not always fit neatly with an accessible bus stop. A problem that has become increasingly difficult with the advent of the need for accessible bus stops is that the needs for accessibility are often seen by the advertising companies as counter to their needs. The problem arises in the following way. The advertising company provides a number of bus shelters for the local area on the basis that the cost will be recouped through the sale of advertising. The value of the advertising sales depends on the position of the advertising panel. To maximise revenue from a panel, the panel needs to be near the roadside and visible for the maximum amount of time to the intended audience (i.e. car drivers). We have shown that, in order to be accessible, a shelter should be set away from the road edge, so one conflict is the actual positioning of the shelter on or near to the platform. Secondly, the advertising panel is worth less if it is likely to be obstructed by waiting passengers, so a busy bus stop could well be unattractive to the advertising company. It is therefore essential that a local authority intent in making its bus stops accessible exercises a strong control over the type, positioning and general layout of the bus shelters provided in this way by advertising companies. Many local authorities have met problems in this area as a result of other pressures (e.g. conservation areas in which advertising is not welcome). However, an inaccessible shelter can render the bus stop inaccessible even if all the other accessibility features are included in its construction.

The site illustrated in Figure 5.41 was constructed under EXCALIBUR recommended standards. Many aspects were studied in detail to guarantee a good level of accessibility – special efforts were made to achieve a good crossfall, including the solution with a step and a formal division between pedestrian and passenger flow. Everything was at a good standard until the installation of the shelter. The choice of shelter design and its position were both fixed arbitrarily by the advertising company. This often compromises the level of accessibility at bus stops. This sort of activity has to be changed and there is an urgent need to revise the relationship between local authorities and the companies that provide bus shelters and other facilities at bus stops so that such decisions do not obstruct accessibility objectives. The lack of discussion between advertising companies and local authorities is a problem found not only in the UK. Unfortunately, similar inappropriate behaviour has been observed in France and Germany.

the kerb means that buses can be seen by turning about 30°. The difference is considerable, and is important for people with back or neck problems.

In some cases it is necessary to provide protection against a prevailing wind which comes from the direction of the roadway. In this case, the shelter should be four-sided. This causes other problems for shelter design, as discussed above, which need to be resolved so that accessibility is assured. A further aspect regarding the orientation of shelters is described in Box 5.13.

There are lots of different types of seating, some being more suitable than others for people with different kinds of needs. *Conventional seating* should be 480–500 mm high to the seat surface with a back angled between 95° and 100° to the (horizontal) seat surface. The seat surface should be 420 mm deep. Seats should be provided even where it is not possible to install a shelter, and only in exceptional circumstances should a bus stop not have seats. Whether in a shelter or not, seats should be available in two or more different heights to cater for children and older people.

Conventional seating should be complemented by *lower seats*. These should be 300 mm high and with the seat surface 300 mm deep. The angle

Fig. 5.41   An example of an advertising panel that inhibits accessibility

Fig. 5.42   Viewing angles from different seat positions: (a) from a back-to-kerb shelter; (b) from an open shelter

Box 5.13   Orientation of bus shelters

One common reason for placing the shelter with the back along the kerb edge is that it reduces splashes from passing traffic. This is a drainage problem and should be treated as such – it is not an excuse for making the shelter and its seating arrangements less accessible.

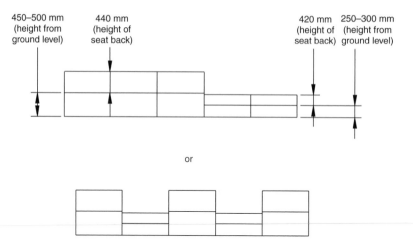

Fig. 5.43   Seat details

of the back should be angled between 95° and 100° to the (horizontal) seat surface. The choice of seat height is to accommodate people who have difficulty in sitting, getting up or down to high or low seats. Armrests should be provided at least to pairs of seats so that people have some support when leaving the seat. These also serve to discourage people from sleeping on the seats. Some alternative arrangements for dual-height seating are shown in Figure 5.43. Armrests should be approximately 200 mm above the seat surface.

Perch-type seats are designed for a passenger to lean or 'half sit' for a short period of time. They take up very little space and are attractive to some passengers with arthritis, stiff joints or back problems who find it difficult to get up from a low seat. However, for perch seats to be effective for people with back problems or who find it difficult to use lower seats, it is necessary to construct them at a higher level. The sciatica seat (see Figures 5.12 and 5.13) and the other 'leaning' seats (see Figures 5.14 and 5.15) are examples of this type of seat. In the case of the sciatica seat, the height of the perch is some 780 mm from the ground (this dimension might need to be adjusted if the seat is used in the UK). An important dimension of the sciatica seat is the diameter of the rails – this is quite large (about 40 mm) compared with many perch seats and helps make the seat more comfortable. Perch seats should be provided in conjunction with other seating.

Tip-up seats in shelters are typically too small and are difficult for elderly people to use. The *bench seat*, with end armrests, should be set about 480–500 mm from the ground for sitting. As such, this is generally felt to be comfortable by those people who can use seats at this height. Bench seats are often found in a plastic variant with a slippery surface and without armrests. In this form they are almost uniformly unpopular with passengers. A new version is now available that is made from two or three 'banana-shaped' pieces, set to form a seat. However, these seats still lack armrests, which provide the means for getting up for many people, and the dimensions are odd (e.g. the back is too low to provide support).

A brightly coloured coating which contrasts strongly with the background helps visually impaired passengers both to find the seat and to avoid it when they are not looking for it. Seat surfaces should be covered so that they are not cold or slippery.

Seats should be arranged so that a passenger can see oncoming buses without the need for excessive movement. It is usually impractical in this respect to set the seats so that they actually face oncoming buses, but they should be set so that their occupants face the roadway. This has been discussed above in terms of the positioning of the back of the shelter and is an important accessibility issue, especially for elderly people and people encumbered with luggage and shopping. This is because such people need early notice of the bus arrival so that they have time to prepare themselves to board the bus. Dimensions of various seats and an indication of how different heights can be combined are shown in Figure 5.43.

Helping the Driver with a Guidance System

Accessible bus operation relies very heavily on the skills and performance of the drivers.

- The driver needs to be able to bring the bus close to the kerb at a consistent position with respect to the bus stop: consideration needs to be made of the physical limitations of moving a rigid vehicle within the appropriate limits.
- The driver needs to see the kerb edge: some sort of feedback on the position of the bus relative to the kerb is required.
- The driver needs to see that he will be able to manoeuvre the bus into the bus stop from the 'driving' position and to re-enter the traffic stream when leaving the bus stop: bus stops need to be cleared of parked vehicles for a suitable distance before and after the stop.
- Drivers are sensitive to the dangers of approaching a platform with obstacles (including people) near to the kerb edge: the platform should be maintained free of obstructions near to the kerb edge.

We therefore need to do what we can to help drivers perform as consistently as possible. The issues to be tackled in the design are:

- How does the bus react to the 'stimuli' from the infrastructure?

- What is the best approach path that will enable the bus to use the infrastructure correctly?
- How can we ensure that this approach path is attained accurately and consistently?

During the experiment phase of the EXCALIBUR project we found that, in order to make use of the kerbs to bring the bus close to the kerb, the vehicle had to approach the kerb within a very narrow range – between about 9° and 12°. It is highly unlikely that a driver would be able to approach every bus stop within this range without some form of assistance, given the traffic and other conditions that they have to deal with. We therefore tried a guidance line on the roadway, running from the offside position of the bus at its driving line a little upstream of the stop and directing it towards the kerb at an angle of 10°. We set the starting point for this line so that it allowed 2.3 m for a parked car and 2.8 m to the offside position of the bus. The starting point was therefore set at 5.1 m from the kerb, 13 m upstream of the point at which we expect the front wheel to strike the platform. The actual path of the bus as it approaches the kerb is actually an 'S' bend, with a steep approach to the kerb which is steered out as the bus approaches the kerb so that the angle of the vehicle when the wheel contacts the kerb is correct. The performance of the drivers in this respect was that they tended to start steering earlier than they did without the guidance line and at a less sharp angle to the kerb. The whole process was therefore smoother and more comfortable.

Drivers asked for a target kerb to be provided in a contrasting colour to help them steer the bus correctly, and this is positioned at a particular point along the platform. We tested the positions for the target kerb and located it on the basis of drivers' performance. Once the drivers had become acquainted with the idea of letting the kerb steer the bus, they found it relatively easy to come to a stop with a horizontal gap of 0–70 mm.

Another problem for bus drivers is that they will not drive close to the kerb if they cannot see a clear exit from the stop. We therefore had to determine a clear exit path for them. When asked, all bus drivers said that they could turn the bus to leave a stop to avoid a parked vehicle within about 2 m of their stationary position. Some drivers remarked that this could leave a problem at the back of the bus and this is undoubtedly true. Some of the buses we tested had a rear overhang of some 3 m. This poses a safety hazard, especially under acceleration as the bus leaves the stop. We therefore introduced a guidance line at the exit end of the stop. This was set at 14° to the line of the platform, which was steep enough to reduce the kerb-take of the stop, but not so sharp as to cause a problem for people standing on the platform. The exit taper is designed to indicate the point downstream of a bus stop up to which a car can park without affecting the performance of the stop.

A set of guidance facilities was tested and converted into a form that could be used on-street. The guidance system incorporates three major parts, which are then divided into seven elements:

- *Entry taper*: this varies according to the chosen layout and is the distance necessary to pass a parked car before the bus has to turn towards the kerb.
  (1) The guidance line is painted in the roadway at 10° to the line of the kerb, starting upstream at the nearest point that a parked car could be to the bus stop (the actual distance depends on the type of bus stop layout and the width of the parked vehicle being considered) and 5.1 m from the kerb edge at that point. The entry taper must be kept clear of parking. This will require a rigid and effective enforcement system. The distance from the beginning of the entry taper to the end of the exit taper defines the extent of the bus stop environment.
- *Platform*: in addition to providing the space for passengers, the platform is an essential part of the guidance system as it provides the basis for steering the bus towards the correct stopping position, close and parallel to the kerb.
  (2) The platform length is a function of the vehicle dimensions (front overhang, wheelbase, total length, distance between the wheel and the side of the bus).
  (3) One kerb unit is coloured and is positioned precisely to act as a target kerb on the nearside.
  (4) The bus stop cage width is reduced to 2.5 m along the platform between the entry and exit tapers.
  (5) The guidance line along the platform is 500 mm behind the kerb edge.
  (6) There is an indication of the stopping position.
- *Exit taper*: like the entry taper, this varies according to the layout and is the distance necessary to pass a parked car.
  (7) The guidance line on the offside from the stopping point is at 14° to the line of the kerb to the nearest point that a parked car could be to the bus stop without affecting its operation (the actual distance depends on the type of bus stop layout and the width of the parked vehicle being considered) and 5.1 m from the kerb edge at that point.

The length of the bus stop environment is the sum of these three parts. It is important to note that the guidance system is a complete set. Each of the seven elements noted above is required because each contributes to the driver's ability to perform adequately at the stop. Removing one of these detracts from the performance. The only exception to this general statement is for full boarder bus stops, where the exit taper is not really necessary. The special nature of the bus stop within the road space could be indicated by a special surface colour or other road marking. The more controlled approach path of the buses means that the entry taper is effectively a track over which all buses will pass. The special colour emphasises this to other road users as well as to bus drivers.

The dimensions shown in Table 5.5 are the physical lengths required for the physical manoeuvre of the bus from its driving line in the road to a position close to the kerb at the bus stop. Table 5.5 also indicates the position of the target kerb. The next issue is how to help the driver manoeuvre the bus with this level of precision so that the desired accessibility can be delivered at the bus stop. Performance at the on-street EXCALIBUR stops has shown that a skilled driver can bring an otherwise incompatible older bus to a stop at the correct stopping position without causing damage to the bus or platform (Figure 5.44). For the EXCALIBUR stops, the driver positions the bus in line with the guidance line and steers towards the kerb to achieve the correct angle at the strike point. They then allow the kerb to steer the bus along the platform. The bus will be aligned correctly as the bus reaches the correct stopping point (indicated by the orange tactile surface). The driver then kneels the bus in order to reduce the vertical gap. When this is achieved, there is often no need for the ramp to be deployed for a wheelchair user as the vertical and horizontal gaps are small enough for many wheelchair users to cross.

Table 5.5   Summary of dimensions for EXCALIBUR stops

Layout type	Strike point (exp.)	Platform (total)	Entry taper	Exit taper	Bus stop (total)	LT
Kerbside	3	21.5	13	9	43.5	37
Bus bay	–	20.5	24	20	64.5	53
Half boarder	2	20.5	7	5	32.5	27
Full boarder	5	23.5	2	–	25.5	9–17
Multiple bus stop, second build-out 0.5 m	2	20.5	15	10	45.5	41
Multiple bus stop, second build-out 1.0 m	–	21.5	15	8	44.5	–

Exp., experimental; LT, total length for a bus stop given in London Transport (1997)

Fig. 5.44   A small horizontal gap can be achieved by an old high floor bus with low entry step at an EXCALIBUR stop

The guidance system was explained to drivers and illustrated in two forms. The first was as a diagram showing where the bus should be at various points during the approach, docking and exit manoeuvres. The other was a set of photographs showing buses carrying out the manoeuvres as described. These were part of a set of posters which were left for drivers to look at and comment upon as part of the training exercise (Figures 5.45 and 5.46).

We now turn to the basdic designs for the EXCALIBUR bus stops that resulted from our research. The overall dimensions of each of the four basic bus stop layouts (kerbside, full boarder, half boarder, bay), together with a sketch drawing for each case, are given in the following sections, for both for single-berth and multiple-berth bus stops.

EXCALIBUR Bus Stop Layouts

Kerbside Bus Stops

The guidance system for a kerbside layout at London Docklands is illustrated in Figure 5.47. It can be seen that we can conclude that a kerbside bus stop with a platform length of 22 m would satisfy the needs of all the bus types. The total length of a single-berth kerbside stop (i.e. including entry and exit tapers) would therefore be 44 m.

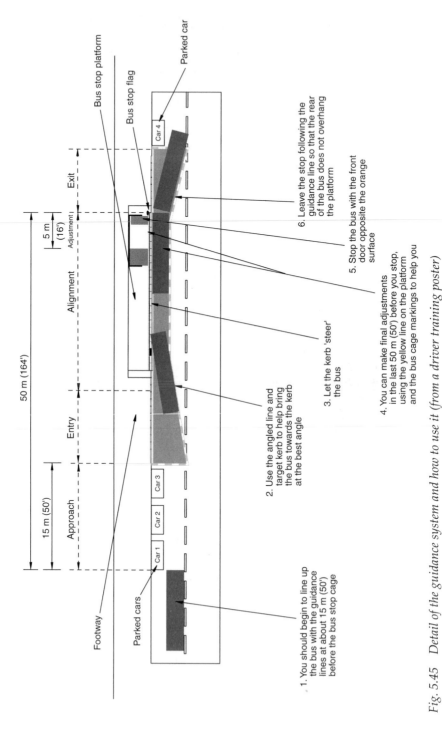

Fig. 5.45 Detail of the guidance system and how to use it (from a driver training poster)

Fig. 5.46   *Photographs from the driver training poster, showing the positions described in the guidance diagram (figure continued overleaf)*

Fig. 5.46   (Contd)

Half Boarder Bus Stops

The half boarder guidance system follows the same principle of the kerbside system. The main difference is the reduction on the entry and the exit taper as the lateral movement is reduced to 1.3 m, because of the presence of the boarder. The guidance system for a half boarder layout set at London Docklands is illustrated in Figure 5.48.

For half boarder single-berth bus stops, the total bus stop length is 32 m. The difference, compared with the kerbside layout arises because less distance is required for the entry and exit tapers as a result of the reduced lateral manoeuvre required by the bus to reach the platform. The driver

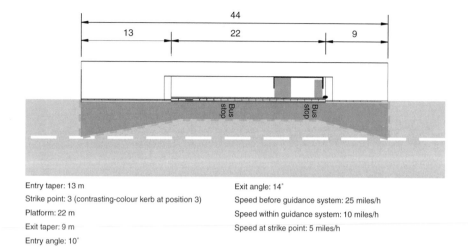

Entry taper: 13 m

Strike point: 3 (contrasting-colour kerb at position 3)

Platform: 22 m

Exit taper: 9 m

Entry angle: 10°

Exit angle: 14°

Speed before guidance system: 25 miles/h

Speed within guidance system: 10 miles/h

Speed at strike point: 5 miles/h

Fig. 5.47   Generic design for a kerbside bus stop (dimensions in m)

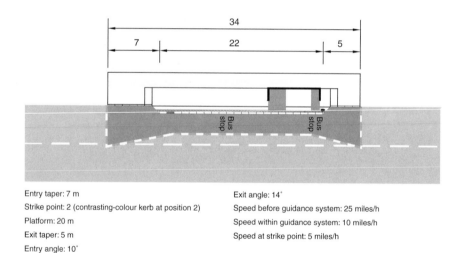

Entry taper: 7 m

Strike point: 2 (contrasting-colour kerb at position 2)

Platform: 20 m

Exit taper: 5 m

Entry angle: 10°

Exit angle: 14°

Speed before guidance system: 25 miles/h

Speed within guidance system: 10 miles/h

Speed at strike point: 5 miles/h

Fig. 5.48   Generic guidance system for a half boarder bus stop (dimensions in m)

has less space to manoeuvre and so tends to approach the platform at a sharper angle, but he has less lateral distance in which to correct himself using the guidance system. This is the reason for the change in the position of the target kerb – it allows for inaccuracies in touching the kerb at the strike point.

214

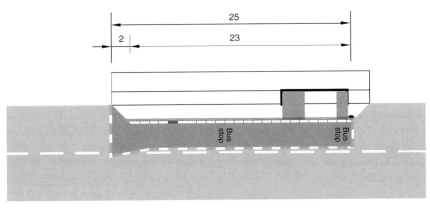

Entry taper: 2 m

Strike point: 5 (contrasting-colour kerb at position 5)

Platform: 23 m

Exit taper: none

Entry angle: 10°

Exit angle: 14°

Speed before guidance system: 25 miles/h

Speed within guidance system: 10 miles/h

Speed at strike point: 5 miles/h

Fig. 5.49   Generic guidance system for a full boarder bus stop (dimensions in m)

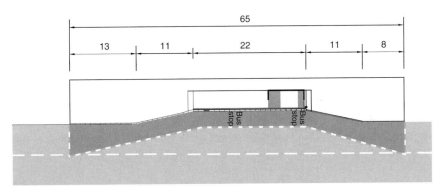

Entry taper: 24 m

Strike point: 3 (contrasting-colour kerb at position 3)

Platform: 24 m

Exit taper: 19 m

Entry angle: 10°

Exit angle: 14°

Speed before guidance system: 25 miles/h

Speed within guidance system: 10 miles/h

Speed at strike point: 5 miles/h

Fig. 5.50   Generic guidance system for a bus bay bus stop (dimensions in m)

Full Boarder Bus Stops

The lateral movement considered for a full boarder is small (about 500 mm in practice). However, although it might appear that the driver would approach the stop in a straight path and just park the bus in front of the bus stop pole, this will not provide the required horizontal gap. The guidance is therefore designed for the worst situation – a car parked irregularly before the boarder. In this case the distance allowed for steering from the driving position to the platform is short, with the result that it is very difficult for drivers to strike the kerb at the correct angle. Therefore the platform has to be slightly longer in order to allow the vehicle to straighten before it comes to a stop at the correct position. The guidance system for a full boarder layout set at London Docklands is illustrated in Figure 5.49. It can be seen that the platform length is rather longer than that for a kerbside or half boarder stop. However, as the entry and exit tapers are very small, the total distance required for the bus stop is considerably shorter than that required for the other designs. The total distance required for a bus stop with a full boarder is 25 m.

Bay Bus Stops

The guidance system for a bus bay layout set at London Docklands is illustrated in Figure 5.50. The bus bay requires a very large distance to be reserved to guarantee access to the stop. In this case the buses require about 65 m for the stop. This is because the guidance must bring the driver in from the driving position (i.e. outside parked cars) into the bay. The consequences of bus bays are severe in terms of parking constraints and should therefore be avoided.

Multiple-berth Bus Stops

As we discussed in Chapter 4, bus stops must be designed with sufficient capacity: an oversaturated bus stop will not be able to deliver the accessibility we require because the buses will not be able to reach the kerb. One of the ways of increasing the capacity of a bus stop is to increase the number of berths. The modelling approaches discussed in Chapter 4 indicate the number of berths required for a given level of operation. We consider here the infrastructure requirements of constructing a bus stop with multiple berths. We will consider the two base cases:

- *Two adjacent berths*: (1) a bus cannot enter the front berth unless the rear berth is empty; (2) a bus cannot leave the rear berth unless the front berth is empty (see Figure 5.51).
- *Two independent berths*: (1) a bus can enter the front berth even if the rear berth is occupied; (2) a bus can leave the rear berth even if the front berth is occupied (see Figure 5.52).

Although bus stops can be much more complex than these simple cases, the complexity will always be a variant of one or other of these or a combination of both.

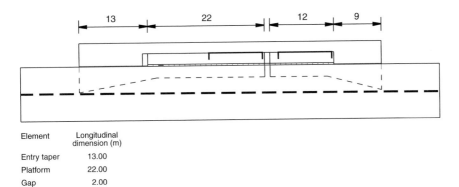

Element	Longitudinal dimension (m)
Entry taper	13.00
Platform	22.00
Gap	2.00
Platform	12.00
Exit	9.22
Total	58.22

Fig. 5.51   A bus stop with two adjacent berths (dimensions in m)

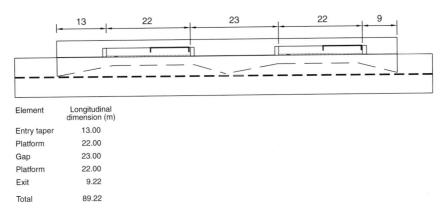

Element	Longitudinal dimension (m)
Entry taper	13.00
Platform	22.00
Gap	23.00
Platform	22.00
Exit	9.22
Total	89.22

Fig. 5.52   A bus stop with two independent berths (dimensions in m)

Adjacent berths

The arrangement in this case requires that the platform is long enough for two bus lengths and a sensible gap between them, plus the length of platform required to straighten the bus for the rear berth. This will ensure that the bus occupying the second berth will be able to stop close and parallel to the kerb. It might be tempting to think that the rear berth could be squeezed in by adding the length equivalent to the distance between the front of the bus and the rear of the front doorway, plus 1 m for the gap between two stopped buses. However, neither bus would be parallel to the platform in these circumstances and the rear bus would find it very difficult to obtain the appropriate horizontal gap. A two-door bus requires the full length platform in order to ensure that the rear doorway is parallel to the kerb, so that a ramp fitted to the second door can be deployed safely. The platform surface markings (tactile surface and any markings for a second door) must be repeated for the second bus in the appropriate positions. The yellow line is required along the whole platform.

The entry taper should be provided to guide the bus driver towards the rear berth. The driver approaching the front berth will have enough space to make the lateral manoeuvre without an additional guidance line. A second target kerb placed 20 m upstream of the stopping point for the front berth will help the driver make the correct approach at the right place. The exit taper leads from the front berth in the same way as for a single-berth stop. This is shown with respect to a kerbside stop in Figures 5.51 and 5.52. A two-berth bus stop with two adjacent berths is, therefore, some 58 m long.

Independent berths

The situation is slightly more complicated if the required capacity means that berths have to be independent of each other. In this case we must allow for the buses to manoeuvre around each other in such a way that the presence of one bus does not affect the other. The key point is the gap between the two berths. This is calculated on the basis of the entry taper for the front berth. This is not quite the same as for the entry taper for the rear berth, which is the same as that for a single-berth stop. The reason for the difference is that the bus arriving at the front berth must be able to pass around a bus stopped in the rear berth: the entry tapers described above are calculated on the basis of a parked car and so we have to calculate using a wider vehicle. This allows for the bus to be close to the kerb plus two rear-view mirrors plus a gap between them. This is 2.55 + 0.5 (offside wing mirror of front bus) + 0.5 (gap) + 0.5 (nearside wing mirror of rear bus) = 4.05 m. The entry taper required to allow the bus to reach the kerb from this distance is 23 m. This is the length of the gap required between the stopping point of the rear berth and the target kerb of the front berth in order to maintain independent and accessible operation of both berths. A multiple-berth stop with single independent berths can, therefore, be designed as a single-berth bus stop with an additional platform length and gap for each additional berth.

The lengths of each element of the bus stop are shown in Figure 5.52. A two-berth bus stop with independent berths is therefore some 89 m long. A four-berth bus stop, laid out in two pairs of adjacent berths, would require 115 m of sterilised kerb, the difference between this and the dimensions shown in Figure 5.52 being the length of the two additional berths.

We used this approach when we produced the bus stop part of the award-winning design for an intermodal interchange in Buenos Aires, where we needed to ensure that buses could not enter the bus stop at the rear berth and just travel along the whole of the platform. Drivers

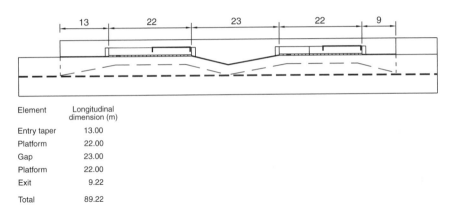

Element	Longitudinal dimension (m)
Entry taper	13.00
Platform	22.00
Gap	23.00
Platform	22.00
Exit	9.22
Total	89.22

Fig. 5.53   Four-berth (two independent pairs of adjacent berths) bus stop, showing the inclusion of an angled build-out between the two pairs of berths (dimensions in m)

were tempted to do this because of the possibility of collecting 'extra' passengers on the way. We therefore filled the gap between the berths with a platform, angled at 14° on the exit side of the rear berth and 10° on the approach side of the front berth. This profile matches the exit angle from the rear berth and the approach angle to the front berth. This can be seen with respect to a four-berth bus stop, with two independent pairs of adjacent berths, in Figure 5.53. Note that we had to allow for slightly narrower buses than in the UK, but we also had to consider a greater variability between different drivers in the precision of their approach to the stop. This is largely reflected in the provision of a wider cage.

One possibility is to park the rear bus at an angle to the kerb in order to reduce the width from the kerb line that is necessary to avoid on entry to the stop. We were not able to test this in practice, but Figure 5.54 shows what would happen if the principles explained above were to be followed in the design of an angled bus stop (correct approach, correct alignment distance along the platform and safe exit). The idea behind an angled bus stop is to try to make it easier for a bus arriving at the front berth (although it will still have to negotiate around the rear offside corner of the stationary bus in the rear berth) and to reduce the amount of kerb space required. The bus will still need enough platform to allow the bus to come close to the kerb, so the platform length required for these berths is the same as would be required for single berths (i.e. about 22 m).

The first question to resolve is the correct angle to use for the angled berths. If the angle is large, the total longitudinal length of the stop would be reduced, but it could be harder for buses to reach and (more particularly) leave the kerb. If the angle is too small, the length of the stop would be increased and the buses would find it harder to avoid other buses on arrival or departure. To demonstrate the principles we use an angle of 8°, which allows the front of the bus to be contained within the bay area at the front of a 22-m platform and the back of the bus to protrude only about 1 m into the roadway. The entry taper is set at 10° to the line of the angled kerb (i.e. 18° to the driving line) and starts 7.1 m before the first of the angled kerbs. As mentioned above, the platform length is 22 m. The target kerb is the third unit (i.e. 2–3 m after the start of the angled kerbs). If the angle is 8°, the kerb line at the front of the berth will be 3.05 m from the original kerb line. The exit from the platform has to be 14° to the line of the platform (remember that this is set because of safety and damage problems with the rear overhang). The platform should continue for 5 m to permit the bus to start the turn and then the kerb line needs to be designed so that it remains clear of the bus as it manoeuvres.

Our desktop study suggests that about 16 m is required from the end of the rear bus stop to the beginning of the front platform at the original kerb line. The dimensions and angles for the front berth and exit are the same as those for the first berth. An exit taper required to avoid the nearest parked car needs to be added downstream of the stop. The overall length of the bus stop in this analysis is about 89 m. The lengths of each element of the bus stop are shown in Figure 5.54.

Perhaps the most surprising element of the angled bus stop is the distance required between the two berths. This is because the exit angle has to be calculated with respect to the platform and not with respect to the roadway. The gap between two berths at a multiple-berth stop is determined by the manoeuvre that requires the most space: exit or entry.

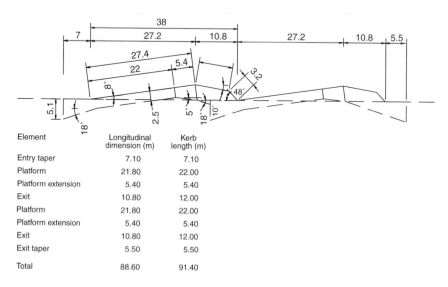

Element	Longitudinal dimension (m)	Kerb length (m)
Entry taper	7.10	7.10
Platform	21.80	22.00
Platform extension	5.40	5.40
Exit	10.80	12.00
Platform	21.80	22.00
Platform extension	5.40	5.40
Exit	10.80	12.00
Exit taper	5.50	5.50
Total	88.60	91.40

Fig. 5.54   Angled bus stop (dimensions in m)

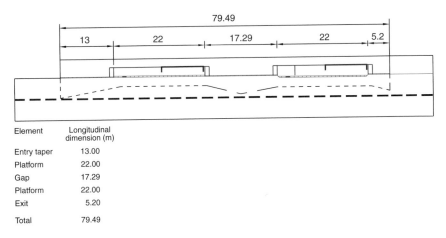

Element	Longitudinal dimension (m)
Entry taper	13.00
Platform	22.00
Gap	17.29
Platform	22.00
Exit	5.20
Total	79.49

Fig. 5.55   Multiple berth with platform build-out (dimensions in m)

At a bus stop where the two berths are in line (e.g. as shown in Figure 5.52), the entry manoeuvre determines the length of the gap because it occurs at a greater speed and smaller angle than the exit. In the case of the angled stop, the exit manoeuvre defines the gap because the bus has to turn through a greater angle in order to leave the stop, thus requiring more space to regain the traffic lane.

In the example shown in Figure 5.54, the additional space required for exit at the angled stop is more or less compensated for by the reduced space needed for entry so the bus stop requires about the same kerb length as the straight kerbside version shown in Figure 5.52. Increasing the angle of the platform relative to the kerb line might be tempting on the grounds that it would reduce the amount of kerb space required for the bus stop. However, as the angle increases, the entry manoeuvre becomes more difficult because it necessitates a sharper turn from the driving line. If the platform angle is reduced, the entry and exit become easier, but the effect on the kerb space is less. Placing the bus stop at an angle in this way does little for saving kerb space and it has implications for the safety of the buses at and around the bus stop.

The bus driver has to look in the rear-view mirror when he is about to leave the stop. However, the view from the mirror is worse at an angled stop than at a 'straight' stop because the bus is stopped at an angle to the traffic and the mirror cannot show the traffic conditions upstream of the bus stop. The bus driver cannot really see approaching traffic until he has moved away from the stop and straightened the bus up (when the mirror would be better aligned to show the oncoming traffic).

Another option is to extend the platform into the front berth by 1 m. This reduces the lateral movement required to reach the front berth, which in

Table 5.6 *Principal elements to consider at a bus stop environment*

Element	Measure	Comments
Layout	Generic types: kerbside, half boarder, full boarder, bus bay	Any layout option should respect the free space for pulling in and out without any kind of obstruction. Bus bays are therefore not a good idea in most cases
Footway width	2000 mm	Minimum 1800 mm
Footway crossfall	Aim for 0.57° (1%) 1°30′ –2° (2.5–3.5%) is possible, but the compromise would exclude some people 2°–2.3° (3.5–4%) will exclude more people and an alternative solution should be sought 2.3°–3.5° (4–6%) should only be attempted in extraordinary situations >3.5° (6%) is impossible and an alternative must be sought	It may be impossible to achieve a satisfactory crossfall. If this is so, accessibility can only be maintained if suitable support is provided along the footway Difficulties with crossfalls may be a reason for considering a boarder
Platform width	2300 mm with an L-type shelter 3400 mm with an enclosed-type shelter	Any reduction in this measure will affect a wheelchair user's ability to manoeuvre to and within the bus stop environment Insufficient platform space may be a reason for considering a boarder
Platform crossfall	Aim for 0.57° (1%) 1°30′ –2° (2.5–3.5%) is possible, but the compromise would exclude some people	It may be impossible to achieve a satisfactory crossfall. If this is so, accessibility can only be maintained if suitable support is provided along the platform

	2°–2.3° (3.5–4%) will exclude more people and an alternative solution should be sought 2.3°–3.5° (4–6%) should only be attempted in extraordinary situations >3.5° (6%) is impossible and an alternative must be sought	Difficulties with crossfalls may be a reason for considering increasing the width of the platform
Kerb height at platform	160–220 mm	Kassel, Charcon and Marshalls kerbs for bus stops are available in the UK. These are designed to permit buses to stop close to the kerb without damaging the vehicle
Transition kerb	–	Should be provided with a non-slip surface
Main surface	Pavers	Natural grey, small (400 mm × 400 mm) pavers are preferred. Asphalt is not a good surface for a bus stop platform
Warning line	A strip of contrasting-colour surface blocks must be set 500 mm back from the kerb edge to warn about the possible bus overhang along the platform	Blocks provide better durability than a painted line. Reflective blocks work well in this case. Yellow is a preferred colour
Tactile surface	Coloured tactile surface to indicate where the bus door will be	The only tactile surface to be used at a bus stop is the 'information surface'. This should be laid, in accordance with DETR guidance, from the warning line to a point 400 mm before the back of the shelter
Other surface	Coloured pavers to indicate where the rear bus door will be (if buses are fitted with more than one door)	Buff pavers are suitable for this purpose. The exact location of the pavers depends on the design of the buses using the stop. The 'worst' case should be incorporated in the design

Table 5.6 (Contd)

Element	Measure	Comments
Shelter	This should be designed in accordance with the bus stop characteristics. It should be large enough to accommodate the expected number of waiting passengers. Space should be provided for wheelchair users and people with shopping or other encumbrances. Information for people with vision and hearing impairments should be provided at a consistent location within the bus stop environment. An adequate, accessible information system is necessary for all users. Different heights and types of seat should be incorporated	The dimensions and type of shelter will depend on demand (number of passengers waiting at the bus stop), available space and climate. However, accessibility for wheelchair users to enter and leave in a forward direction is probably the major design constraint (this consideration will generally include other encumbrances, such as baby buggies)
Guidance system	Guidance line before bus stop	Starts upstream of the bus stop to help the driver position the bus correctly to carry out the stopping manoeuvre
	Target kerb	Located at the correct point along the platform
	Guideline on platform	500 mm from the platform edge, along the whole platform
	Reduced width of bus stop cage	2.5 m from the kerb edge, along the platform length
	Stopping position	Must be consistent in design and position for all stops. Can be indicated adequately by the coloured tactile surface
	Guidance line after bus stop	Encourages driver to pull out without the rear of the bus sweeping over the platform

turn reduces the length of the gap between the two berths. With this arrangement the lateral manoeuvre would be 3.05 m instead of 4.05 m and the entry taper would become 17.3 m instead of 23 m. However, the rear bus would have to clear $1 + 2.55 + 0.5 + 0.5 = 4.55$ m on exit and this would require an exit taper of 18.25 m. However, the bus stopped at the front berth would be sufficiently far forward that it would not interfere with the exit from the rear berth. This arrangement and the dimensions of each element are shown in Figure 5.55. A two-berth bus stop with independent berths and a platform build-out for the front berth is therefore some 80 m long.

All other things being considered, if a bus stop with two independent berths is required, the design requiring the least amount of kerb length has the platform build-out for the front berth. The worst design with respect to 'kerb-take' is the angled bus stop. A bus stop with two adjacent berths requires about 58 m of kerb, but will have significantly lower capacity than the bus stops with independent berths.

As with the designs for single-berth bus stops, any reduction from the dimensions discussed here will inevitably result in a reduction in accessibility at the bus stop. Undoubtedly, compromises will have to be made in many cases which will result in such a loss. Each compromise must be considered with the people who will be excluded from using the bus stop as a result and a suitable alternative provided.

Comments

It is worth noting that the guidance line is set at 10°, but the buses tend to arrive at a much sharper angle. This is because of the way in which bus drivers manoeuvre the vehicle: first quite a sharp turn (towards the target kerb) which is then adjusted in response to the guidance system to obtain the correct approach. The distance allowed for the kerbside and bus bay arrangements allows this correction to be made within the entry taper. However, the much shorter entry taper for the boarders does not provide enough space for this. The result is the additional length of platform needed to straighten the bus. We know from the initial experiments that without the 10° line the approach starts much later and is much steeper. We therefore recommend that the line be kept to 10°. If the driver approaches the platform at a much smaller angle, the straightening-up process is less severe than for a sharper approach. However, it is much harder to strike the target kerb correctly, and so an additional platform length is required to allow for undershooting the platform. The outcomes from the experiments were the definition of four designs for bus stop guidance for drivers.

There are some standards to be adopted in the platform design process. These standards (Table 5.6) reflect a commitment between users' requirements and technical engineering restrictions. In a survey phase

Table 5.7   East Ham Station and Manor Park Station bus stops before and after the EXCALIBUR project

	Before	After
East Ham Station		
Layout	Half boarder, 0.7 m wide, 10 m long	Half boarder, 1 m wide, 20 m long
Special kerbs	None	180 mm Kassel kerbs along the boarder, and one target point (contrast-coloured kerb)
Crossfalls	1.5–8.7%	3.5% along whole platform
Waiting area	Bus stop pole on boarder	Physical definition of the areas for boarding and alighting
	Boarder obstructed by telephone box	Implementation of a safety line along the platform
	Confusing clutter, resulting in being difficult to determine where the bus stop actually was	Sufficient assured space for wheelchair users' manoeuvres
		Uninterrupted space on platform
Shelter	Downstream of boarder	New shelter alongside boarding area
Guidance system	None	Red cage painted on the roadway

Manor Park Station		
Layout	'Standard' kerbside layout	20 m raised platform
Special kerbs	None	160 mm Charcon kerbs along the platform, and one target point (contrast-coloured kerb)
Crossfalls	3.5–10.5%	5% along the whole platform
Waiting area	No defined area	Physical definition of the areas for boarding and alighting
		Implementation of a warning line along the platform
		Sufficient assured space for wheelchair users' manoeuvres
Shelter	None	Installation of a shelter
Guidance system	None	Red cage painted on the roadway

they might indicate what to look at in and how to look at a bus stop environment in order to improve the area.

EXCALIBUR Bus Stops in Service

Construction Phase

The results of these experiments were applied to two pilot demonstration bus stops in Newham, East London. We are currently monitoring

Fig. 5.56   East Ham Station site before (a) and after (b) reconstruction

Fig. 5.57   Manor Park Station site before (a) and after (b) reconstruction

these stops to see whether they provide a more consistent and accessible environment for all people to board or alight buses.

The reconstruction of the two EXCALIBUR bus stops was done considering the objectives noted above. The first stop is located at High Street North in Newham, upstream of East Ham Underground Station, and is a half boarder layout. The second stop is located at Station Road, upstream of Manor Park Rail Station, and is a kerbside stop. A summary of the changes made to these bus stops is given in Table 5.7 and Figures 5.56 and 5.57 illustrate both sites before and after reconstruction.

Some differences between the design and the implementation of the EXCALIBUR stops arose, for various reasons:

- There was a lack of flexibility in adapting elements that were already established and in use (e.g. shelters, benches, information system).
- There was a tendency to do things during the construction phase at the site without thinking about the accessibility standards agreed at the design stage.
- There were difficulties in convincing the engineering/groundwork side of the group of the importance and functionality of each element (e.g. position of shelter, position of bus stop pole).
- At Manor Park, the local authority refused to countenance a step between the footway and the platform (as can be seen in Fig. 5.41), resulting in an unacceptably steep crossfall.
- It proved impossible to install shelters long enough to provide cover for people waiting to board at the rear door.
- The public consultation process involving the local authority, traders, users and technicians was less comprehensive than it should have been.
- There was a lack of co-ordination and co-operation between local authority departments.

The most worrying feature of this was that, in some cases, the changes were made without consulting the designers, resulting in errors of detail that could affect the accessibility of the stop. This is just an immediate consequence of the much bigger problem mentioned above: a general lack of co-ordination and co-operation between local authority departments. This highlights the need for attention to the detail of the design to ensure that accessibility is obtained and the change in culture that is required of engineers, planners and construction workers in order to ensure that the infrastructure is constructed properly. Examples include the crossfalls at Manor Park (which are too steep), the position of the wide yellow line on the carriageway at East Ham (which encourages drivers to stay away from the platform), incorrect installation of the information surface at Manor Park (too close to the back of the shelter) and the type of shelter installed at both sites.

Costs

The implementation cost was substantial, but mostly because of the need to ensure that the footway around the bus stop area was of sufficient quality to be able to join onto the new platform area without causing trip hazards and the need to lay the entire platform area at the bus stop because of the insufficient quality of the existing footway. The additional cost of the accessibility features at the bus stops (special kerbs, information surface, yellow line, diamond-surfaced pavers, guidance lines) was actually quite small. The additional cost of making a bus stop accessible should, therefore, be seen in the context of the cost of making sure that the surrounding footway is of an appropriate standard. This is important in the context of Part III of the Disability Discrimination Act 1995.

Monitoring Phase

The monitoring phase of the EXCALIBUR project is analysing the two accessible bus stops mentioned above, after their reconstruction according to a three-phase methodology: pre-training, training and post-training phases of monitoring and evaluation.

The pre-training phase took place 2 months after construction was completed. Each site was recorded over different time periods: peak time, 7:30 a.m. to 9:30 a.m.; midday, 10:00 a.m. to 12:00 noon; and evening, 5:30 p.m. to 7:30 p.m. The bus stops were video recorded using two cameras.

Prior to this phase of the monitoring no training was delivered, either to bus drivers or to the disabled community, in relation to how to use EXCALIBUR bus stops. The monitoring was done this way for two reasons. First, the project partners wanted to see how drivers and users would behave and adapt to the new stop area. Secondly, they wanted to compare the behaviour recorded at this stage with that after a training session for drivers and users. The rationale for this approach was to evaluate the importance of training.

The film images were captured on the computer: still images (frame by frame) and dynamic images such as the approaching manoeuvre sequence. The images from the pre-training phase were analysed. Some of the photographs that appear in this chapter (e.g. Figure 5.44) show the results of drivers taking advantage of the guidance system to stop very close and parallel to the kerb, even though they had not been trained to use the guidance system. The pictures show that the ideal horizontal gap can be achieved and that this facilitates the access of users to the bus.

A very important point observed during the pre-training monitoring phase is the fact that private vehicle drivers seemed to be respecting the red bus stop cage. Although parking in the area where the two bus stops are located is not permitted, drivers are still parking illegally. However, during many hours of recording sessions only two events were registered with a car parked inside the cage and disturbing the whole approaching manoeuvre. During this phase it was also noted that the bus drivers were not confident that the guidance system would lead them to the correct stopping position when a vehicle was parked near to, but not within, the cage. This is one aspect that we would expect to improve after the training phase. Drivers need not only to understand exactly the function of each element implemented in the EXCALIBUR stops, but they also need to practice using them in order to keep the 'new' skills in good shape.

Consistent comparison can only be made after the training session step. Statistical analysis comparing the distributions of horizontal gaps and longitudinal stopping positions before and after training, passenger service times, dead times, dwell times and overall stop delay will be made. We will also be monitoring the ease with which passengers use the various facilities that have been installed at the stops (including the coloured and tactile surfaces, warning lines, raised platform). Initial outcomes suggest that the bus stops are capable of working as anticipated (see Figures 5.11, 5.24 and 5.44), but that the results would have been even better had more attention been paid during the construction phase to ensure that all the detailed aspects of the design were properly completed. We expect driver performance at the stops to improve with training and as more EXCALIBUR stops are constructed. We notice, for example, that driver performance seems to be better at EXCALIBUR stops in Brighton than in Newham, and this could be in part because Brighton has more EXCALIBUR stops in operation.

Conclusions

In this chapter we have described how we have taken the principles from earlier chapters and attempted to implement them in the form of some accessible bus stops. We worked with groups of elderly and disabled people to find out their needs in relation to the use of bus stops. For many of these people bus stops had been unusable because of the difficulties of boarding buses. It was therefore very useful that we could construct an experimental bus stop off-street so that we could explore with these users exactly what would make things easier or more difficult for them.

Bus stops should be designed to minimise the difficulty of changing from a pedestrian to a passenger, and vice versa. This means providing adequate space for passengers and their shopping and ensuring that this space is sufficient for those people who need more manoeuvring space than others. The relationship between the space taken by the bus stop and that used as a footway needs to be thought about so that the two activities can co-exist without loss to the ease of use in either case.

The first requirement for improving accessibility at bus stops is to bring the bus close to the kerb in order to minimise the horizontal gap between the bus and the raised bus stop platform. This requires development of skills on the part of the driver and the design of infrastructure and guidance systems can help to maintain a good and consistent performance in this respect. We need to work with both infrastructure and bus manufacturers to improve the compatibility and consistency between buses and infrastructure. This will make it easier to ensure that bus stops are consistent in their design, and thus easier for drivers to use. Only once buses can be expected to arrive consistently close to the platform at every bus stop can the value of other accessibility features be realised.

The EXCALIBUR project shows what is required to bring buses close to the kerb. One of the most difficult requirements to achieve in practice is the guarantee of sufficient kerb length. This should not be reduced, if at all possible: every metre less of platform length results in about 3 cm extra in the horizontal gap. The guidance system helps drivers to begin their approach to the bus stop earlier than would otherwise be the case, and thus to make it more controlled, safer and more comfortable.

It is quite clear from the experimental work, the on-street trials in London and the on-going implementation in Brighton that driver training needs to include detailed teaching of driving techniques at and around bus stops. This training needs to be completed before a driver starts work in service and needs to be updated regularly. We found that operators were generally weak on training after the initial period required for a driver to obtain their licence. Proper and on-going training will enable accessibility to be delivered more consistently on a long-term basis, and could also reduce damage costs because of the greater care with which drivers approach bus stops as a result. Brighton and Hove City Council has installed a 'training' bus stop so that drivers can learn and practice how to approach the bus stops properly before they need to do so in service.

Making a bus stop accessible usually involves reconstructing areas of footway. The opportunity can therefore be taken to ensure that the footway also meets accessibility needs. These include the provision of good crossfalls, smooth surfaces, correct and consistent use of tactile surfaces and signage.

There are three major actors whose needs have to be accommodated at bus stops: passengers, pedestrians and bus drivers. We need to ensure that these groups have an open communication channel with planners and highway engineers in the local authority and the bus operators and manufacturers. By having a continuing and constructive dialogue between all parties, better definition of priorities will result and thus designing better and more accessible bus stops will be possible. This will help to ensure that the bus system is designed, constructed and operated to the benefit of passengers, and thus to the community as a whole. There needs to be a conscious effort to achieve this, because different elements of the bus system are owned and/or controlled by different agents. Accessibility will not be achieved if the different agents only manage to work in isolation.

Bus stops are the gateway to the bus system, and thus to the activities that people wish to pursue. Everyone, including elderly and disabled people, should find bus stops easy and attractive to use. If this cannot be achieved, the bus system will be failing to meet the overall objectives of accessibility and independence that are so important to the equitable progress of society.

References

BARHAM, P., OXLEY, P. and SHAW, A. (1994). *Accessible Public Transport Infrastructure*. London: Department of Transport.

BUNDESMINISTERIUM FÜR VERKEHR (1997). *Bürgerfreundliche und behinderten-gerechte Gestaltung von Haltestellen des öffentlichen Personennahverkehrs*. Bonn-Bad Godesberg: Bundesministerium für Verkehr, 51

CERTU (2001). *Les Bus et leurs Points d'Arrêt Accessibles à Tous*. Lyon: Centre d'Études sur les Réseaux, les Transports, l'Urbanisme et les Constructions Publiques.

DETR (1999). *Disability Discrimination Act PSVA Regulations, PSV (Conditions of Fitness, Equipment, Use and Certification) (Amendment) Regulations, PSV (Conduct of Drivers, Inspectors, Conductors and Passengers (Amendment) Regulations: A Statutory Consultation*. London: Department of the Environment, Transport and the Regions.

DETR (2000). *Guidance on the Use of Tactile Paving Surfaces*. London: Department of the Environment, Transport and the Regions.

DOE/DTp (1992). *Residential Roads and Footpaths*. Design Bulletin 32. London: Department of Environment/Department of Transport.

EUROPEAN COMMISSION (1995). *Low Floor Buses*. Report 322, Cooperation Européenne dans la Domaine des Sciences et Techniques (COST). Luxembourg: Directorate General (XIII) Telecommunications, Information Market and Exploitation of Research.

IHT (1991). *Reducing Mobility Handicaps*. London: Institution of Highways and Transportation.

LONDON BUS INSTITUTE (2000). *Bus Stop Layouts for Low Floor Bus Accessibility*. London: Transport for London.

LONDON TRANSPORT (1997). *Guidelines for the Design of Bus Bays and Bus Stops to Accommodate the European Standard (12 metre) Length Bus*. London: London Transport.

ROGAT, U., BLENNEMANN, F., GROSSMANN, H. and KRÄMER, T. (1993). *Niederflur-Bussystem Anstandshilfen: Untersuchung von Möglichkeiten zur Erhaltung eines minimalen Anstandes zwischen Niederflurbussen und Haltestellen*. FE No. 387/92. Bonn-Bad Godesberg: Forschungsbericht für den Bundesministers für Verkehr.

TEBB, R. (1997). *The Unistop: Towards a Fully Accessible Bus Stop*. Discussion document. Firstbus Development.

TYLER, N. and CAIAFFA, M. M. (1999a). 'Design of fully accessible bus stops: infrastructure elements for buses and drivers'. *Proceedings of PTRC Conference*, Cambridge.

TYLER, N. and CAIAFFA, M. M. (1999b). *EXCALIBUR III Experiments: Performance of the Guidance System with different Low Floor Buses.* Working paper. London: University College London Centre for Transport Studies.

USTER, G., DEJEAMMES, M., HAYATS, S. and EDEL, M. (1994). *Proceedings of Seminar E – Public Transport Planning and Operations.* London: PTRC, Vol. P377, pp. 95–106.

USTER, G., KAPLAN, S., DESSAIGNE, M. and DEJEAMMES, M. (1997). 'Le développement d'une aide à l'accostage'. *Recherche Transport Sécurité*, Vol. 54, pp. 43–51.

Chapter 6

Information and Communication along the Journey Chain

M. Caiafa and N. Tyler

Introduction

Information is central to accessible bus systems. Throughout this book we have discussed and shown examples of information problems and solutions, especially in Chapters 5 and 8. Whether an information system is good or bad depends to a great extent on the way in which it allows people to make appropriate and timely decisions about their journey. This chapter complements the examples given in other chapters by discussing how to determine what is meant by 'appropriate' and 'timely'.

Accessible transport is irrelevant if the potential user does not know that there are activities to do and how the transport system enables these to be reached. Other issues might make the system inaccessible, even if everything else were known in advance (e.g. cost and fares systems might make the journey too expensive or too complicated, and thus impossible). Even if the journey is thought to be possible and the costs are within acceptable limits there is still the issue of ensuring that the journey takes place as planned and, if not, that the journey can still be made by an alternative route without undue stress on the traveller. Each of these issues can be a potential barrier for different users. The information role is to minimise the impact of these barriers.

Learning to identify what can represent a barrier is not sufficient. To deliver the information successfully it is also necessary to understand how the users think. This cannot be achieved without the active involvement of users: it is necessary to incorporate what they think and not what we think they think. This task involves learning not only how users acquire knowledge but also how they process it. Users need information that is consistent, clear and complete. More than that, it needs to be available at the right place and at the right time, so good strategies for diffusion and dissemination of the information must be formulated.

Identifying how users think is not enough either. We need to understand why the system that we have designed, considering all the recommendations to suit people with special needs, still does not work for some people. Understanding this will help us to design a truly accessible information system. Of course, just as with other accessibility issues, there will be a need for compromise when applying the thinking in practice. This means that we must judge what can or cannot be adapted or cut in order to know who will be affected by the resulting barrier and what this might represent to the community.

Specific users' needs

Information is needed at every stage of the journey chain:

- pre-trip information, to help the user plan routes and connections
- in-trip information, which assists users at each decision point during the journey
- supportive/confirming information, which repeats and informs data and decisions and helps users feel more confident while progressing towards their desired destination(s).

The first issue is to decide what information is needed at each point. Following Ackermann's approach (Ackermann, 1995), we can separate information into two basic types: *specific information* related to each stage of the journey and *orientation information* which directs people along the journey.

A person who wishes to make a journey must first identify where they will start and where they want to go. They will need to find the correct bus stop and bus service, board the right vehicle, alight at the right stop and find their way to the destination. However, this simple view of a journey oversimplifies the information needs. A lot of information is required in order to make a journey, and if the traveller has particular requirements (e.g. a deaf person) their information needs are even greater. A more comprehensive view of a user's information needs at various points in the journey chain is given in Table 6.1.

The table shows the information needs in terms of both specific and orientation information in relation to various stages of a journey: pre-trip, the walk to and from the bus stop, the wait at the bus stop, the ride on the vehicle and interchanges. A very important point we can draw from the table is the need to explain the functionality of the environments around a bus stop, inside a bus and at an interchange point. Knowing how a bus stop works, for example, means that a user can feel more confident, and thus more comfortable, about using it. We have seen in Chapter 5 that a well-designed bus stop places certain functions at certain places in the bus stop environment, and defines these very clearly (e.g. the boarding point, the alighting area). These definitions are useless if users do not understand what they are for and how to make use of them. It is essential that this information can be found at the bus stop. The same applies to other elements of the journey chain. For example, in a bus, information about which doors to use, where to pay the fare, where it is possible to stand, how to request the bus to stop and how to know where the bus is along its route would make it easier for passengers to make better use of the facilities in the vehicle.

Interchanges provide a more complicated environment in information terms because they consist of a convergence of different transport systems. Different bus lines or different modes could have different operational rules and different types of fare discounts for specific groups (e.g. elderly people, families, children). These 'rules' need to be explained so that people do not become confused while attempting to change from one service to another. Confusion translates into exclusion if the lack of understanding results in some people finding the system inaccessible.

In Chapter 5 we pointed out that a bus stop should provide information for people arriving on a bus. This information should indicate useful places within the local area, and the accessibility level of the pedestrian routes to local destinations. We have included this point in Table 6.1. The provision of such information is not only helpful to arriving bus passengers: it can also help other people, and for this reason the bus stop can become a valuable source of information about the local area. The area concerned should be large enough to include a reasonably comprehensive selection of likely facilities, but small enough that these could be easily reached from the bus stop. Indications of distances and accessibility levels would help people decide how best to continue their journey.

Balcombe and Vance (1998) suggest that the information upon which the majority of bus users depend is inaccurate and restrictive. Public transport information is usually provided by the operator or transport authority. Their perspective of the provision of information is often more to do with advertising their service and not really what is appropriate for users. The legislation discussed in Chapter 2 places a duty on the local authority to find and judge what is meant by 'appropriate'. This begs the question of what is 'appropriate'?

The users' information needs as described in Table 6.1 make up a list of what, where and when information is required, but we have not yet indicated how it might be made available. If the users' needs identified in

Table 6.1 *Information needs of the accessible journey chain*

Objectives of stages of the journey	Pre-trip information	The walk	The wait at the bus stop	The ride in the vehicle	Interchanges
Specific information system	(1) Locate the origin (2) Locate the destination (3) Identify the line(s) and service(s) (4) Locate the nearest bus stop (5) Verify the need for interchange (6) Have a preliminary view of the departure time, waiting time, duration of the trip and costs (7) Check accessibility of the vehicle (8) Verify the accessibility of the walk to the bus stop/terminal/station	(1) Identify and check the correct bus stop platform	(1) Be reassured of the bus lines that serve the stop (2) Have an estimate of the time to wait for the service (3) Be informed how the bus stop works – expression of the functionality of the bus stop environment (4) Be informed about the bus(es) number(s) as it approaches the platform (5) Have access to a service centre to ask for more specific information	(1) Identify the number of the bus line and destination (2) Know how the bus environment works	(1) Have reassurance about the onward service (2) Have an estimate for the time to wait for the onward service (3) Be informed how the interchange point works – expression of the functionality of the interchange environment (4) Have access to a service centre to ask for more specific information

| Orientation system | (1) Have access to information to reinforce the chosen path with important reference points (supermarket, hospital, churches, etc.)
(2) Be alert to any kind of situation that might represent danger (crossing point, cycle lane)
(3) Know locations of any resting facilities along the path
(4) Confirm a unique identification for the bus stop in use | (1) Be informed about the distance between the adjacent bus stops (upstream and downstream)
(2) Be informed about the kind of service facilities offered within a convenient radius of the bus stop (medical, educational, entertainment, food, market services)
(3) Be informed about the condition and access level of the infrastructure within a convenient radius of the bus stop (footway condition, rest facilities, etc.) | (1) Follow the route along the journey by announcing of bus stops and a route map display
(2) Have a general view about where the important destinations are along the route
(3) Know where to get off the bus
(4) Be informed about modal interchange points | (1) Leave the arrival point and reach the departure point
(2) Be informed about access to facilities (toilet, information points, lifts, help) |

Table 6.1 are to be met, it seems clear that all four of these requirements must be satisfied before any information can be considered appropriate. The first step towards this is to determine what methods are available for presenting each type of information listed in Table 6.1. Ackermann *et al.* (1995) suggest that information should be provided in the form of an information chain, which runs parallel to the accessible journey chain. This makes a useful starting point because the information chain concept emphasises the need for information to be provided throughout the journey. Some methods that could be adopted by the providers of information at each point in the journey chain have been suggested by Ackermann *et al.* and are shown in Table 6.2.

Tables 6.1 and 6.2 are linked. For example, the users' need for information about a bus line and its departure times (from Table 6.1) could be provided by a timetable (from Table 6.2). Table 6.2 is beginning to express the fourth requirement – the 'how' – but it does not show how we can be sure that the information, having been sent, is actually received and understood by the users. Whatever means of providing the information is chosen, everyone must be able to receive and make use of the information that is provided. For instance, a map which might be ideal for displaying a network diagram excludes blind people simply because it relies on visual capability in order for the user to be able to use it. In order for the bus system to be accessible, the information must also be accessible for everybody. Hence the information provider must be sure that their information is not only provided, but is also received, processed and understood by the users.

Table 6.3 is adapted from a guidebook on passenger information services for passenger transport systems in the USA (Transportation Research Board, 2000). The guidebook underlines what different kinds of information may and may not be provided. We have expanded their approach to include more specific types of information and two other classifications:

- the time and point of access to the information
- a description of the people who could be excluded by the use of each information type.

There can be many interferences between the source and the receiver of information. These interferences could be caused by the media (e.g. where information is presented only visually or aurally), the format (e.g. the way a timetable is laid out) or the content (e.g. the information is confusing). The interference problem permeates the entire information process and just one lapse can destroy the accessibility of an otherwise adequate information system. Much of the effort employed in designing an accessible information system needs to be directed towards the elimination of interference. Figure 6.1 shows an example of such interference. The timetable in the centre of the panel is barely visible

*Table 6.2 Elements of a continuous information chain**

Stage of a journey	Previous information (e.g. at home)	Way to/from the bus stop	Bus stop area	On/inside the vehicle	Interchanges
Specific information system	Timetable Network diagram Telephone service		Arrivals and departures board Network diagram Tariff information Announcement Service centre		Arrivals and departures board Network diagram Tariff information
Orientation system		Pre-orientation Signposts Guide strips (markings on the surface)	Signposts Map of bus stop and the environment Guide strips (markings on the surface)	Announcement Pictogram	Signposts Map of bus stop and the environment Guide strips (markings on the surface)

*Source: COST 322 (European Commission, 1997)

Table 6.3   General issues about forms of information*

Information type	What they could provide	What they do not provide	Time or point of access	Who is excluded
Maps (including network diagrams)	Spatial relationship of landmarks, routes and connections	Easy availability (the map is a physical object that must be obtained before trip planning can begin)	Pre-trip In-trip At interchanges	People with vision difficulties (unless provided in tactile form)
	Schematic view of the whole journey	Straightforward information (map reading presents difficulties for many people)		People having difficulties with spatial representation
	An overall picture of the transport system			People with learning difficulties
	Flexibility for changing trip plans			People with dexterity problems
	Supportive information during the trip			
	Portable information useful both pre-trip and in trip			
Timetables	Temporal relationship of bus stop locations (services schedule)	Easy availability (the timetable is a physical object that must be obtained before trip planning can begin)	Pre-trip In-trip At interchanges	People unused to timetable information
	Simple and narrow view of the specific route			People with vision difficulties (unless provided in tactile or audible format)

Portable information		Straightforward information (reading tables presents difficulties for many people)		People with learning difficulties People with dexterity problems
Oral instructions (telephone services)	Straightforward information	An overall picture of the transit system Reference material for future continued travel Flexibility or easy error correction	If equipment available, anytime, anywhere (including during a journey)	People with hearing difficulties People with learning difficulties People whose first language is not the local tongue
Signs	Supportive information Easy availability Straightforward information Permanent information	Detailed information and explanation An overall picture of the transit system Dynamic information Portable information	During the walk to and from bus stops and at bus stops	People with vision difficulties (unless provided in tactile or audible format)
Signposts	Directions and/or distance of specific points Supportive information Easy availability Permanent information	Detailed information and explanation An overall picture of the transit system Dynamic information Portable information	During the walk to and from bus stops and at bus stops In-trip, seeing from the vehicle	People with vision difficulties (unless provided in tactile or audible format) People with learning difficulties

Table 6.3 (Contd)

Information type	What they could provide	What they do not provide	Time or point of access	Who is excluded
Fare table	Detailed information about the price of the journey, type and discount Supportive information Portable information	Easy availability (the table is a physical object that must be obtained before trip planning can begin) Straightforward information (reading tables presents difficulties for many people)	Pre-trip In-trip At interchanges	People unused to fare information People with vision difficulties (unless provided in tactile or audible format) People with learning difficulties People with dexterity problems
Arrival and departure board	Detailed information about specific services Supportive information Easy availability Dynamic information Straightforward information	An overall picture of the transport system	At interchanges	People with vision difficulties People with learning difficulties
Variable messages, signs or oral announcements	Information about short-term changes (emergency or operational changes)	An overall picture of the transport system	At interchanges	People with vision (signs) or hearing (announcements) difficulties

				People with learning difficulties People whose first language is not the local tongue
	Easy availability Straightforward information Dynamic information Supportive information Stimulation for users' action			
Tactile surfaces (guide strips)	Permanent information	An overall picture of the transit system Information for people who are untrained to use it	At interchanges The walk (e.g. at crossings)	People with poor sense of touch
Service centre	Detailed information about specific services Straightforward information Information about short-term changes (emergency or operational changes)		In theory, this is the place where all information should be available	In theory, nobody should be excluded

*Source: adapted from Transportation Research Board (2000)

amongst the more colourful and eye-catching advertisements. Nobody we asked at the bus stop knew that there was a timetable there.

Whatever the type of information, the provider has to suppose that the user has a certain level of knowledge about the system. This presupposition can easily exclude some people. Figure 6.2 shows an example of arrival information for train services at Euston Station, London. This information requires the user to know which stations each of these trains has called at on its way to Euston, as only the starting station is indicated. This makes it difficult for people meeting someone from one of these trains to know which one to wait for unless the traveller started their journey at the station where the train started its journey. Even this does not help if the journey in question actually started at another station, with an interchange onto the train which is expected at Euston. In this case, there is no telling which train the traveller will arrive on, without a great deal of prior knowledge on the part of the person who is waiting to greet them. It is unlikely, for example, that a passenger will know in advance of making their journey where the train has come from (unless, knowing that it could be an issue, they ask when they book their ticket). Apart from

Fig. 6.1 Information interference: a bus stop timetable

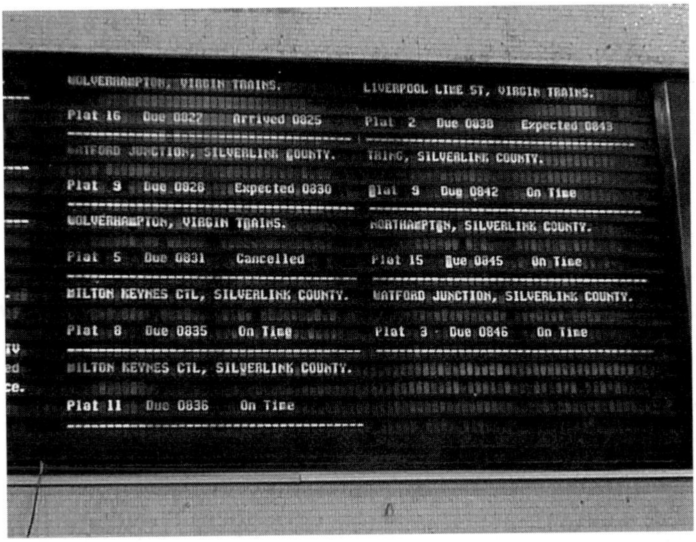

Fig. 6.2   The arrivals board at Euston Station

this, the information shown in Figure 6.2 indicates the platform at which the train will arrive, the time it is due to arrive (both scheduled and expected) and the train operator. Unless they have prior knowledge of the train routes, a person intending to meet someone at this railway station would need to seek further information in order to be able to know where they should wait. People for whom this sort of uncertainty is difficult will find this sort of experience frightening, and as a result they may decide not to meet anyone at the station. If the passenger needs to be met, either alternative arrangements would have to be made or they would not be able to travel. We discussed in Chapter 1 the difficulty encountered when trying to use a transport system which relies on personal assistance at a particular point in the journey. This is a simple illustration of the sort of problem that might be encountered due to a poor information system.

Table 6.3 identifies the people who would be excluded as a result of choosing a particular way of providing information. Combining the information in Tables 6.1 to 6.3 gives an insight into the need for providing information, not only at specific points in the journey chain, but also in suitable formats so that everyone can obtain the information they need in a way that they can understand. Ideally, information should be available in a variety of formats so that users can select the one which best suits their own needs. Table 6.4 illustrates some examples of users' groups and their media preferences. The table was constructed based on the advice given in Gregory (1996).

Table 6.4   Users' groups and media preferences

User group	Preferences
People with literacy problems	Television and radio Video and audio tape CD (multimedia) Telephone
People with hearing disabilities[*]	Text: printed information is acceptable, but English text must translate to BSL Television Video CD (multimedia) Television and video subtitling (with BSL) Teletext Textphones Typetalk Videophones
People with vision difficulties	Large clear print Tactile diagrams Braille Moon Television, video, audio description Radio Audio tape Electronic aids Telephone help lines CD (multimedia)
People with visual and hearing difficulties	Braille Large print Moon Tactile diagrams Clear speech in cassette Sign communications on video
People with learning difficulties[†]	Illustration Symbols/Makaton Television, video Audio tapes CD (multimedia)
Older people[‡]	The above, as required, plus oral and written information provided together

[*]Many learn and use British Sign Language (BSL) as their first language
[†]Repetition of information (visual or factual) is an important factor
[‡]Less likely to pick up information casually

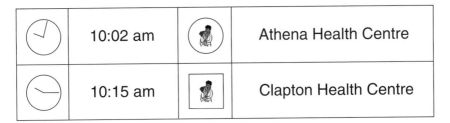

	10:02 am		Athena Health Centre
	10:15 am		Clapton Health Centre

Fig. 6.3   The Hackney Plusbus timetable

Examples

We have used the concepts described above when delivering information within a number of our projects. The following three examples show how we approached the problem of communicating information in an accessible way.

The Hackney Plusbus Timetable

When the Hackney Plusbus service started we had to produce a timetable so that people would be able to find out about the route and schedule. One of the potential user groups for the service consisted of people with learning difficulties, so it was important to make sure that a timetable was produced in a way that would be helpful to them.

Two issues are important in the production of a timetable: the names of the places for which times will be supplied and the representation of time. The first issue was to identify the points along the route that would appear on the timetable and how these should be described. The places named in the timetable were the same as appeared in the standard one, so that they would be compatible. We drew a number of simple symbols to represent the various places along the route, taking care to maintain consistency (i.e. all the health centres were denoted by the same symbol) yet trying to maintain differences (i.e. each health centre was framed by a different shape, such as a circle, square or triangle). An example of the timetable entry for two of the health centres is shown in Figure 6.3.

Shopping areas were indicated in a similar way (a shopping basket with the name of the area in clear text). The hospital was indicated by the conventional hospital sign (a capital 'H' in white on a dark background). Using this symbol meant that street signs near the hospital would match with the timetable information and thus help identify the location. Some places could be identified by an icon that represented their appearance (e.g. blocks of flats or a church).

We chose to use a representation of a clock face to present the scheduled times. The people with learning difficulties involved with this project asked for the times to be printed digitally in large type in addition to the clock face. They had two reasons for this. First, the digital representation added further information for those who could understand time in this form; and, secondly, they felt it was less stigmatising because other people would not know whether they were reading the clock face or the digital version. Both text and symbols were used to represent places, for the same reason.

The symbols (and names) used in the timetable were repeated on a simple line diagram of the route which accompanied the timetable. They were also reproduced inside the bus on a display which lit each symbol successively as the bus passed the associated point on the route. A user could therefore follow their progress along the route using the combination of the timetable, the route map, the information inside the bus and the view of the world outside.

The EXCALIBUR Timetable

We moved on to more complicated timetables in Newham, associated with the construction of our EXCALIBUR accessible bus stops. In this case, the bus services are not given as exact times, but as frequencies (e.g. 'every 8 minutes'). Working with people with learning difficulties, we devised a way of conveying frequency using the idea of a circular clock and its hands to mark a segment which indicated the interval between buses (Figure 6.4). The circle is placed on a black surround to indicate evening services. Clock face (and text) times are provided to indicate the times between which different frequencies apply.

The EXCALIBUR information also includes a simple route map showing the whole route with the bus stop names, the journey times between the stops and interchanges with other modes. The current bus stop is identified with a 'you are here' arrow. The journey times between each stop from the current bus stop are presented inside a bus symbol to reinforce the direction of travel. Another important point is the box that delivers information about intra- and intermodal interchanges available at the current bus stop. This information shows whether or not the onward service is operated with accessible vehicles.

This way of representing frequency was developed working closely with a worker from CHANGE (an organisation of people with learning difficulties), but has not yet been tested extensively. The composition of the timetable tried to incorporate symbols that are well used elsewhere (e.g. London Underground roundel, 'you are here' arrow, the general layout of bus stop timetables used by Transport for London) with information about accessibility. Thus the timetable contains a level of detail that is appropriate for different users and is presented in a way that makes it easier for people who prefer information in symbolic form.

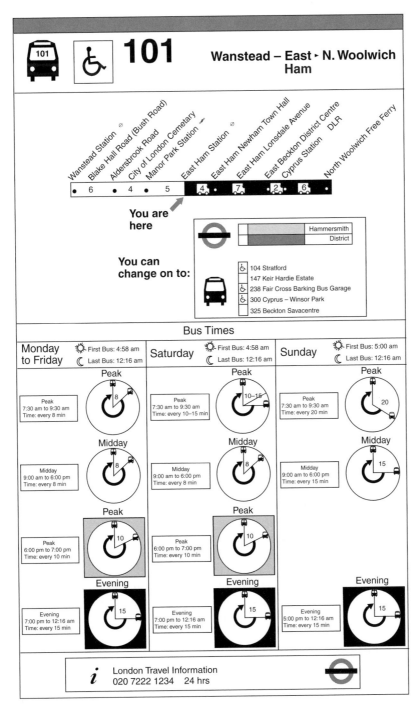

Fig. 6.4   *The EXCALIBUR timetable*

The Cumbria Plusbus Timetable

In Cumbria we have produced timetable leaflets in a format with a standard text of 12 point Lucida Sans Unicode (or Optima) (see Appendix 2), with timetable displays at bus stops set at 16 point. Although there is a simplified route map with the timetable, we have also produced simple maps of each village, showing where the bus goes, where it stops and some local landmarks (see Appendix 3). Importantly, every bus stop indicates where the bus stop is located for the return journey. We have also produced information about the bus service, including timetables in Braille (see Appendix 4) together with a tactile map (see Appendix 5). The Cumbria service also has a CD-ROM with audible information (departure times from each village, with information about the location of the stop, journey times to a selection of places and other useful information). These are all described in more detail in Chapter 8. The Cumbria information was not designed specifically for people with learning difficulties, although many aspects of the information are improvements on the usual information supplied to the public and will help some people with learning difficulties.

All the above examples are 'work in progress'. Our work in this area is continuing. We are looking at video maps, audible timetables and other techniques to help convey information so that people with learning difficulties can begin to increase their level of independence.

Conclusion

We have been developing methods of conveying information about public transport in an accessible way through a number of our projects. Our approach is always to work closely with groups of people so that we can try to respond to their needs. We realised the importance of establishing a channel of communication where the flow of information can made two way and at two levels: conception/design of information and delivery/ dissemination of information.

According to Balcombe and Vance (1998) the current formal information upon which the majority of bus users depend is inaccurate and restricted. We reinforce that view and add that the information flow is often conceived and delivered unidirectionally and is frequently poor in content and format. We have touched on the conception/design issue. For example, in the EXCALIBUR project we involved the community early in the process. But the challenge of delivery and dissemination of information is yet to be resolved.

New technologies (e.g. web-based material) might be able to help improve the delivery/dissemination problem. Cognitive sciences might be able improve conception/design issues. Together, and applied within an innovative context, they can help to establish the communication channel, putting the users at the centre, and thus improve accessibility. That is the way in which we are progressing or research in this area.

References

ACKERMANN, K. (1995). 'Low floor bus stops taking into account the situation in Eastern Germany'. Cited in European Commission (1995).

ACKERMANN, K., BLASCHKE, M. and FELLER, G. (1995). *Nutzungserleichterungen des ÖPNV für Ältere und Behinderte durch bessere Informations und Orientierungssysteme*. 70 444/94. Bonn-Bad Godesberg: Forschungsprojekt des Bundesministeriums für Verkehr.

BALCOMBE, R. J. and VANCE, C. E. (1998). *Information for Bus Passengers: A Study of Needs and Priorities*. Report 330. Crowthorne: Transport Research Laboratory.

EUROPEAN COMMISSION (1995). *Low Floor Buses*. Report 322. Cooperation Européenne dans la Domaine des Sciences et Techniques (COST). Luxembourg: Directorate General (XIII) Telecommunications, Information Market and Exploitation of Research.

GREGORY, W. (1996). *The Informability Manual – Making Information more Accessible in the Light of the Disability Discrimination Act*. London: Central Office of Information.

TRANSPORTATION RESEARCH BOARD (2000). *Passenger Information Services: A Guide Book for Transit Systems*. Transportation Co-operative Research Program Report 45. Washington, DC: Transportation Research Board.

Chapter 7

Involving the Public

N. Tyler, M. Caiafa and I. Brown

General Issues

Throughout this book we have advocated the involvement of the public in the process of making bus transport accessible. Public participation in this process is much easier to talk about than to do, and we need to explore the ways in which such participation can be achieved.

We have described the different perspectives of different participants in the design process, including the general public, the bus industry and local government. We summarised these in two diagrams (in Figure 5.1, which shows the common communication paths between these agents, and Figure 5.2, which shows a more participative approach). We have tried in this book to emphasise the need to encourage the inclusion of users (including current non-users) in the design, development and operation of bus systems. In the main, we have adopted this approach to bring the implementation of the bus system closer to the people – in terms of network, infrastructure, vehicle and information design – and to make it easier for everyone to use. This has meant placing the users and potential users at the heart of the development process rather than leaving them as an afterthought where they are left to put up with whatever has been designed on their behalf.

We have moved on from the idea that a 'successful' bus service is one with few empty seats (easy though it is to understand this concept). Rather, we are seeking to measure the success of a bus system using measures that reflect the needs of the community. These include the extent of social inclusion, the social and economic contribution that the service facilitates within the local community and the degree of independence that it generates. These characteristics may result in increased numbers of people using the service, but even so it is quite likely that society will have to accept some share in the financial support for such an outcome. This view of financial support is not, of course, just for the bus service as a transport resource. The bus service is merely the vehicle that brings about the level of social inclusion, cohesion and independence we seek. Society's support is, therefore, for the development and attainment of these objectives, which are only achievable if the service is truly and broadly accessible. Given the difficulty of achieving any of these without an accessible public transport system, the success of accessible bus services (as part of the public transport mix advocated in Chapter 2) in working towards these goals is good value for money. Chapter 8 describes a project which in its current form is looking at how some of these cross-sector effects might be measured so that we can learn how investment nominally directed towards public transport might obtain benefits in other sectors, including health and social services. However, seeing a bus service in this way requires a step change in thinking about public transport, not only on the part of bus system planners and operators, but also by the people who will be an intrinsic part of the system – the public.

It is fairly easy to see how planners, designers and operators of bus systems can set out and measure their achievements in conventional terms. They have data on residential areas, passenger numbers, fares taken and costs incurred to help them evaluate a bus service in these terms. As the public is indeed an intrinsic part of the system, it should become involved in the processes of planning, development, design and the provision of bus services.

In the UK, various governments have attempted to include people in the provision of various public services, mostly through some form of representative or political membership of the management boards of public authorities (such as police authorities, health trusts and passenger transport authorities). The trouble with this is that it is very difficult for the public to see this as representative of their interests. Membership of such bodies is often spread around the 'great and the good' and thus in practice it is available only to a subclass of people who are (a) too often highly unrepresentative of the public they are supposed to represent and (b) members of several such bodies. This calls into question the extent to which they form a clique of 'professional' representatives, which can too easily become very distant from the public that actually uses the services in question. We described in Chapter 2 how the Disabled Persons' Transport Advisory Committee (DPTAC) was set up under the Transport Act 1985. Members of the DPTAC are appointed for a fixed term by a Minister. Although the Minister chooses from a number of people who have applied to be members of the committee, it is still a ministerial appointment. The legislation ensures that at least half the membership of the DPTAC is supposed to be drawn from disabled people (currently, disabled people form about 70% of the membership). This is at least some form of control to ensure that disabled people have some guarantee of representation on this committee.

Public consultation and participation are increasingly being sought and required in public decision processes. We indicated in Chapter 2 a number of these requirements (e.g. in connection with the Transport Act 2000). However, legislation has not defined in detail what is expected in terms either of activities or of proof that a process, having been undertaken, really did result in better participation by the people.

The planning process is laced with opportunities for the public to be involved, from responses to formal public notices right through to the existence of, and their presence at, public inquiries. Indeed, the involvement of the public has recently been deemed to be so strong in the planning process that a consultation document has been released (DTLR, 2001) to consider controlling the extent and effects of public participation in the planning process. The reality of public participation in the planning process is hardly one of overt success: it is difficult to identify a case where a planning permission has been refused at a major public inquiry in recent years. The best that the public can really achieve is to cause a delay in the implementation of a proposed development project, which is hardly evidence of deep interest on the part of society in the concerns of the people affected by a proposed development. The planning process has become a rite of passage for the developer, an irritating necessity on the way to realising the ultimate goal of completing their project. Of course, the planning process does not seem this way on paper. The process is 'plan led' – that is, planning permissions for any development must conform to a previously laid down development plan which has been subject to public consultation and participation in its formation. What does this really mean? We can see one view of this approach in the case of public transport accessibility levels (PTALs).

In Chapter 3 we discussed the use of PTALs in the course of assessing development proposals in one London borough. The use of PTALs was published in the borough's development plan and was thus subject to consultation. Yet how many members of the public would realise the importance to them (or even the public at large) of the PTAL formula, understand the mathematical implications and difficulty of interpretation inherent in the way in which it is used (and thus the precise implications in particular cases) and raise questions about such a detailed issue in the context of the public examination of the plan? A developer would be extremely interested in such an issue and, if they felt threatened by such a method, would undoubtedly bring their resources to bear on the question with a view to changing it in their favour. The examination of the plan is thus likely to be a very unbalanced process, with the public being at a disadvantage compared with vested interests. Indeed, developers have long realised that their interests are best served by paying close attention to the broad structural and unitary development plans. The same applies to public inquiries, where the local people who oppose a proposed scheme (often for different and sometimes conflicting reasons) are often set against a developer with many resources and a single aim. When we take into account the costs involved (a developer may spend several millions of pounds on an inquiry), how many local communities could match such resources?

With a professed intent by different governments over the years to involve the public – some issues having been incorporated into primary legislation – why is it that the public feels so betrayed by the system? The DETR (1998) set out to find out how to encourage public participation in local government. The research team asked all English principal authorities about their attempts at public participation and carried out case study analyses in 11 areas. A wide range of public participation methods (19 in total) was revealed by the authorities, ranging from complaints schemes to user management of local services. It is not clear from the report how widely each method was used within each authority. Was the use of a given method a case of a one-off exercise or experiment in a single case, or was it a standard approach throughout all departments for all decisions? The survey methodology adopted in this study would not have revealed the answer to these questions. The questionnaire was sent to the chief executive of each local authority with a request to 'find a responding officer with the time and knowledge to complete the questionnaire' (DETR, 1998). The responses were, therefore, inevitably going to be a broad-brush description of the authority's various attempts at public participation: the detail involved in any single participation exercise would have been too extensive for easy summary in such circumstances.

The researchers also spoke to the public involved in the case study areas. Eight methods of public participation emerged from these discussions. These are listed in Table 7.1, together with a brief description of the public response to each method. For most people, the only method they really felt acquainted with was the public meeting (voting was also mentioned). People tend to assess the process in terms of outcomes rather than its intrinsic 'goodness'. It would therefore seem that there is some discrepancy between the perception of public participation held by the local authorities and that held by the public. There is still a lot of work to do on improving public participation and obtaining a higher participation rate from the public. Most people in the case study analysis had knowledge of only one of the 19 methods identified in the local authority questionnaire. If society really wants to include the public in the fundamental decisions about their bus system, it must examine with the public the methods by which this might be achieved in practice.

Table 7.1 Public perception of public participation methods and comments*

Public participation method	Comments
Public meetings	People would attend on 'issues that mattered' or protests against particular proposals. There was a feeling that the council's mind had already been made up
Questionnaires	People were sceptical: there needs to have been evidence of previous outcomes before people are confident about the value of a questionnaire
On-going forums (e.g. youth councils)	These were felt to be valuable
One-off deliberate exercise (e.g. citizens' jury)	Good for complex issues, such as local authority finance, where understanding was required
Small group discussions (including focus groups)	People felt that they were more likely to be heard than in a big public meeting
One-stop shops	Could act as a local focus for accessory services and 'having your say'
Citizen education (concerted programme to show people how local decision-making systems work)	Good for increasing understanding
Direct action	Some young people in an inner city area felt that the only way to be noticed was to make a noise, know their rights and protest outside the council offices

*Source: DETR (1998)

We distinguish between public consultation and public participation. Both are useful techniques in the process of involving the public in decisions, but they have different emphases in relation to the way in which the public are involved. Public consultation is the process whereby the public is approached for its views, which are then considered by the decision-maker, who then takes overall responsibility for and ownership of the ensuing decision. The public participation process seeks the views of the public, but encourages them to be actively involved in making the decision, for example by choosing options to be assessed for their technical merit and then choosing the one to be progressed to completion. In the public participation process, the public not only provide their views, but also take some share of the ownership of, and responsibility for, the decision.

We have brought the involvement of users into all of our projects. We have been particularly interested to include people for whom transport is difficult to use. We wanted to move away from the idea that participation would be covered if a questionnaire had been sent or a public meeting held. We were looking for a means by which people could begin to understand the underlying issues, including technical matters, of the decisions and to agree the extent and detail of the inevitable compromises between the ideal and the real world. We shall consider this here by describing the public involvement elements of six of our projects. These serve to illustrate the potential – and the difficulties – of involving the public in a variety of schemes.

Public Participation Case Studies

EXCALIBUR

Before starting the EXCALIBUR project, there was some connection between the public transport planners (both in the local authority and London Transport) and local users. However, this consisted mainly of data provision, such as passenger loadings surveys, rather than any direct approach to see what people – bus users or not – actually wanted. Similarly, planning permission processes 'involved' the public, but mostly in the sense of informing them prior to the implementation of a decision that had already been taken. There was also, mainly through London Transport, a connection between the public transport planners and the bus operators.

Some form of dialogue was apparently in existence between the transport planners and local disability groups, but this was rather dependent on the presence of one individual public transport planner and seemed to die away when he left the borough. Communications between public transport planners, general planners and the traffic and highway engineers were quite strong, but placed the public transport planners in a relatively weak position. This was because both the general planners and the engineers could call on legal powers if they needed, whereas the public transport planners had to rely on their ability to convince their colleagues by means of argument alone (Box 7.1). This is largely a result of the lack of clarity in the Disability Discrimination Act 1995 in relation to the bus stop environment (as discussed in Chapter 2).

The entry of the EXCALIBUR researchers introduced a new actor to the process. In addition to the university-based researchers, the project

Box 7.1   Relative powers within a local authority: responding to a complaint

A complaint was received by the general planners about one of the proposed bus stop designs. Conversations between the complainant and the research team suggested that the nature of the complaint was related to a supposed reduction in parking. Although the EXCALIBUR team had worked on the designs with the highway and traffic engineers, the intervention of the complaint meant that the public transport planners' proposal was suddenly turned down on the grounds of safety. Using this as a reason for deleting the bus stop from the project provided a 'legal' background for leaving the stop as it was. Nobody wishes to promote an unsafe scheme, but no analysis was carried out to establish whether or not the proposed design would be unsafe. The design was abandoned because it was politically unacceptable to offend the particular group represented by the objector. The planners' views (and, it must be said, those of the traffic engineers up to that point) were overridden. We would argue that, had the involvement of disabled people been stronger at this point, the argument might have turned the other way.

team included London Transport, the local authority, a commercial infra-structure components supplier and the local bus operator. Initially, the contacts with the disability groups in the area was the responsibility of the local authority. As noted above, this was problematic after a change of personnel at the local authority and the university had to take on the role of intermediary. We established direct contacts with current non-bus-users through local disability groups and with bus drivers through the local operator. In the local authority, apart from the public transport planners, we had direct, if not particularly strong, connections to the highway engineers.

Our connections with local disabled people enabled us to explore a number of issues with their help. These included questions and practical experiments concerning crossfalls, steps in the footway, different footway surfaces, manoeuvring space (for wheelchair users and ambulant disabled people), the use of bus ramps and the design of information systems. We incorporated many of the results of these practical trials and discussions in the final designs of the bus stops which were eventually built.

We have been slowed down in our attempts to involve disabled people in evaluating the outcomes because we wanted to carry out the evaluation by bus users (including ex-non-bus-users) after the drivers had received their training. Unfortunately, the delivery of the training has been problematic and we are still pursuing this with the operator. Post-training evaluation would enable us to include the assessment by local disabled people of the stops as they should work (i.e. with the minimum vertical and horizontal gaps). It is difficult to know if this was the correct approach in the circumstances. As far as the interface between the buses and the platforms is concerned, an earlier assessment would have shown us that the horizontal gap was not being achieved consistently enough by a sufficient number of drivers and that this was causing problems for some disabled people. In the event, we observed the number of drivers who managed to use the kerb properly at that time and we knew the problem caused by large horizontal gaps before we started the project, so not much would have been learnt from the evaluation by disabled people at that stage. Conversely, many of the features requested by disabled people during the course of the project were included in the bus stop design, and an earlier evaluation of these would have made clearer at an earlier stage the effects of these for disabled people. It is less clear if the performance of the buses at the stop would have coloured their views about other features, either in the short or long term. In fact, the best answer would have been to ensure that the drivers were properly trained at the right time and to carry out the evaluation at that stage.

With the benefit of hindsight, we consider that our attempt to involve disabled people in the project as a whole was weak. Although we discussed issues surrounding the details of the project and the bus stop design with disabled people from the local area and elsewhere, we did not involve them directly in the project team. Apart from including them in the ownership of the project, this would have strengthened our approach towards the selection of stops for treatment (including responses to local people – see Box 7.1) and in determining the best approach towards the evaluation of the bus stop performance. We found the local people generally open and willing to help and participate in the experiments. They would like to have a more active and explicit participation in the decision process. An increase in their participation will guarantee benefits for everyone, not just for them.

Perhaps the most direct connection between the actors, as described in Chapter 5, and the research team concerned the bus drivers. We discussed, tested, altered and analysed all sorts of ideas from the bus drivers about what would help them deliver the small horizontal gaps which are so critical to the physical accessibility of the vehicle. Outcomes of these discussions resulted in the guidance system described in Chapter 5. It has been harder to convince the bus operator to invest in a suitable training programme for the bus drivers so that they all, not just those directly involved in the project, would have the opportunity to learn how to use all the elements of the guidance system. The problem was that such training would require drivers to be withdrawn from the service roster for a day or so, and the difficulties of replacing them to maintain the contracted service (and thus the cost of the training programme) were too great to be possible for them. As a result, a less intrusive method was adopted – providing a set of informative posters for drivers to look at and discuss (with the opportunity for feedback to the research team). The training was not helped by the loss of access to the experimental facility used in the experimental phase of the project. This would have provided a safe and private location for drivers to learn how to use the bus stops. As it is, the drivers have to learn their skills at bus stops on-street (and possibly in-service), which does not help to ensure that the performance is adequate and consistent.

The driver training problem is related to the difficulties of recruiting drivers to work on buses in London. With a large number of vacancies and a high turnover of drivers between operators, the operators' reluctance to spend more time training drivers in details of using EXCALIBUR bus stops is understandable, even though it is not acceptable. Better resources within the project specifically for driver training would have helped. We found the operator open to talking to us about the problems, but that they did not seem able to afford the time and resources to act on implementing the solutions. Bus drivers were keen to help. They are governed by many rules – some regulations, some as a result of the training they receive and some because of commercial pressures. Many of these rules, although not all, work against them meeting accessibility requirements (e.g. waiting for passengers to be seated before moving away from a bus stop). Training would help this, if it could be made more appropriate (and actually done).

We also had a brief discussion with some bus manufacturers (about wheel, axle and rear-view mirror design). It was clear from these that the manufacturers had little knowledge of the interface problem and that they were prepared to consider changes in design that would help improve the vehicle–platform interface. However, unless the push comes from the purchasers of their vehicles for such changes, they will not invest in them. There is, therefore, a place for bus manufacturers being included more directly in the design of infrastructure – both the bus and infrastructure manufacturers say 'tell us what you want us to make and we will make it', but they do not seem to say it to each other. This represents an all too typical passive approach by such organisations. The implication is that things will remain as they are unless something is done by 'somebody else', and nobody is prepared to take the leading responsibility for the action: it is a recipe for doing nothing. People, including bus and infrastructure manufacturers, are not encouraged to think of new solutions in the abstract – it needs some sort of physical impetus before ideas begin to crystallise to the extent of developing new hardware. It took the reality of Kassel kerbs to make bus operators realise that buses could be brought close to the kerb without damage, but the need for redesign of buses to make this really effective has yet to be met by the manufacturers. Projects such as EXCALIBUR should be used to bring these parties together so that real progress can be made on standardising some of the awkward aspects of the interface (e.g. the relationship between the bus body and the horizontal position of the wheels).

In some ways the most problematic connection was between the EXCALIBUR team (including the public transport planners) and the highway engineers. We have already mentioned one aspect of this (see Box 7.1). Another was that, despite full involvement of the local authority from the start of the project, there was a failure to ensure that there was an associated increase in their understanding of what the project was about. They tended to see the project simply in terms of highway engineering and found it very difficult to include accessibility objectives as part of their stock in trade. This became evident when producing the detailed drawings for roadway markings and spilled over into difficulties during the construction period, where their lack of understanding resulted in some on-site decisions which reduced the potential accessibility of the bus stops. Some of these were recovered through actions of the research team, but others have had to remain unaltered. The complexities of the details involved in the construction of an EXCALIBUR stop, although not particularly difficult, were sufficient to lead the highway engineers to withdraw their support for constructing further stops as part of the project, and thus the number of bus stops actually constructed was less than originally planned.

Putting accessibility features in place requires changes in thinking by everyone. As we might expect, these changes are difficult to achieve. Strangely enough, it seems that the hardest part is to break the sets of 'rules' inside the technical departments within the local authorities and the bus industry. It seems that, because the rules are formalised and they have a routine and procedure for each action, the engineering and technical staff find it difficult to incorporate the new thinking required for accessibility. Routines and procedures are excellent devices for encouraging consistency, but if applied as an excuse for not looking at new objectives they can be a negative influence. The industry in general also needs to move on from the passive 'you tell me what you want and I'll do it' approach to a process in which they actively seek and act on the users' (as well as their customers') needs.

Accessible Bus Routes in Brighton and Hove

Brighton and Hove Council decided to set up a programme to design and construct accessible bus stops in 1997, soon after it became a unitary authority. The EXCALIBUR researchers were involved in the early stages of the project in showing the highway and traffic engineers what could be done at bus stops to improve accessibility. After a short while, we reduced this contact to an advisory role in one or two cases. In 2000, the council asked us to review the implementation of the programme after 2 years, and as part of this review we examined the connections between the actors.

The connections between the public transport team, the general planners and the highway and traffic engineers were quite strong, and representatives of all three groups were among the people involved in the project from the start. There seemed to be much more room for negotiation between these groups than we found in the EXCALIBUR case. Without a much more detailed analysis of the underlying structural reasons for such a difference it is difficult to determine why this should be, but it could be that at that time the Brighton and Hove organisation was based on local geographical areas rather than technical skills, thus encouraging a more interdepartmental approach to problem solving. The result was a much more rounded approach to the whole problem. There was also a strong relationship between the bus operator and the public transport team, which meant that it was relatively easy to obtain the direct participation of the company (if not of the drivers, as in the EXCALIBUR case).

Despite their best endeavours, the council seems to have found it quite difficult to reach the public with its communications about the bus stop project. It seems to have been particularly difficult for the council to engage with the local community of disabled people on this topic. This did not prevent the council from achieving a reasonable level of accessibility at the bus stops in terms of the infrastructure. However, it did stop the process of learning more about the needs of disabled people and meant that disabled people felt no sense of involvement in the project. Communications between a local authority and the public, especially disabled people, need to be active and continuing in order to maintain and improve the standard of accessibility into the future. As with the EXCALIBUR case, the direct, active and continuing involvement of disabled people from the outset of the project would help to make sure that the process and the resulting designs continue to be increasingly inclusive.

As part of our review, we spoke to several traders, residents, users and non-users of the bus services, asking them about their views of the changes to the bus stops. Not surprisingly, the bus users were enthusiastic about them. However, people working or living near to the bus stops felt that they had not been consulted about them and that they could not understand why the changes had been made. This was despite several articles posted in the local newspaper by the council. In many cases, people said that they had had no idea about the proposed changes until they had seen the official notices about planning permissions or (more commonly) they received the official notices about the forthcoming works 4 weeks in advance.

Communications with the bus drivers have been less direct than in the EXCALIBUR project, although we did speak to some drivers during our review. Driver training seems to have had a similar status at the bus

Box 7.2   Permanent and continuing vigilance over project design

It is important to ensure that accessibility standards are maintained. Two instances of recent bus stop construction can be used as examples of where the intervention of an actively involved users' group could have prevented a problem before it arose:

- There is a recent tendency to install cycle racks on bus boarders, sometimes in such a way that the racks, or the bicycles attached to them, obstruct the doorway of the bus if it stops correctly at the bus stop. This is clearly contrary to the EXCALIBUR recommendations that the platform be kept completely clear of obstacles and should not have happened. If the involvement of disabled people who were affected by access at such points had been more effective, the possibility of an alternative arrangement could have been found before the bus stop was built.
- We have found some bus boarders that have been constructed with a very large crossfall. This should have been avoided by appropriate reference to the recommendations, but would also have been spotted by local disabled people.

The conclusion is that, although the intervention by users should not be necessary in strict engineering terms, it serves to act as a check on the acceptability of the proposed design to disabled people. In this way costly mistakes can be avoided before they arise.

company in Brighton as in London. However, one interesting difference has emerged. As a result of University College London providing the bus company with a set of the poster displays used in the EXCALIBUR project, it became apparent that drivers were being encouraged to approach bus stops more carefully. This caught the attention of the claims manager in the company, who realised that there could be a potential saving to the company in terms of claims for damage resulting from careless driving near to bus stops. This brings a new actor into the process and emphasises that the introduction of accessible bus stops could, if introduced with the appropriate training package, result in a cost reduction to the bus operator. It is too early to be able to quantify this, but it is certainly an interesting area for further research. One result is that the council has constructed a training bus stop in a suitable location for the company so that the bus company has a training facility where drivers can learn and practice how to approach and use the accessible bus stops.

Box 7.2 gives some examples where it would appear that the design approach has failed to ensure that accessibility will be delivered. An active involvement by users' groups might have prevented these from being implemented. Continuing and active vigilance is needed by all parties, including the disabled community, to ensure that accessible design is obtained and maintained in every case. This suggests that the communication paths between all parties needs to be actively encouraged and not just assumed.

The council's concern with the public participation process was reflected in its decision to proceed with a small pilot public participation project so that impacts could be gauged for subsequent participation procedures. This project is called PUPPIT (Public Participation Processes in Transport) and is discussed below.

Cumbria Plusbus

A project called Accessible Public Transport in Rural Areas (APTRA) was established to investigate the effects of an accessible bus service in a remote rural area of Cumbria (this project is described in more detail in Chapter 8). As part of this project we attempted to address some of the public involvement issues that had arisen on other projects, including the EXCALIBUR and Hackney Plusbus projects.

The APTRA project was funded by the Engineering and Physical Sciences Research Council and the Rural Development Commission, and with the support of Cumbria County Council. As the project involved setting up a bus service in Cumbria it was potentially more invasive in political terms than were our other projects involving the design and construction of bus stops. The research team also observed how Cumbria County Council located bus stops along bus routes, a process in which the local people, including local residents and Parish Councillors, were directly involved as well as the more formal bodies such as the Police and Highway Engineers. All planning issues were dealt with at District Council level. This encouraged us to pursue an active public participation role in the APTRA project.

Prior to the start of the project, several surveys and questionnaires from the County and District Councils and the Rural Development Commission had made people very wary of more researchers in the area. One of the difficulties was that, although the public had been returning questionnaires, they felt that they had seen no action. There was, therefore, a fairly high level of scepticism about another research project. We had to break down the apathy about the various authorities before the local public would believe that we really did have a bus service for them and that we really did want to incorporate their views in the project.

The mechanics of the public participation process we devised for this project are described in Chapter 8; for now, we will simply comment on the various paths of communication. The first issue was that both the District and the County Councils considered that the correct communication path was through them to the local Parish Councils. This reflected, amongst other things, the political sensitivity of public transport in the project area. However, in the event it was agreed that we could contact the local Parish Councils, calling a meeting in each case to explain and discuss what we had in mind and to learn what they wanted from a bus service. In most cases, the public were allowed and encouraged to attend these meetings to voice their concerns and ask questions, so we eventually achieved direct contact with some of the local residents. Attendance by the public at some of these meetings was very high.

Subsequently, we returned to the villages to explain how we had attempted to incorporate their wishes and to discuss choices where their wishes resulted in some sort of conflict (e.g. including a particular village on the route resulted in the need to reduce the frequency). By this time the connection with the public had been established – they had a FREEPOST address by which they could contact the research team directly if they wished. Communications with the disabled people in the area proved to be difficult initially, possibly because they had made their own special arrangements for transport and had no immediate need for a new service. They could not imagine an accessible bus and so thought that the project was not for them. Also, they did not believe that the bus service would remain and were hesitant to change their current arrangements. Cumbria County Council Social Services department was involved in the project but found it difficult to introduce us to local disabled people. Interest among elderly and disabled people improved once they saw the bus in operation and believed that it would continue to operate for a reasonable period of time. Repeated attempts to engage local disability groups proved unfruitful. As with the EXCALIBUR and Brighton projects, we relied on information from disabled people elsewhere to help with aspects of the project such as the vehicle, route and schedule design, but we failed to involve local disabled people sufficiently in the project.

Arguably, one of the most controversial aspects of the APTRA project was the need to discuss with the local people how the bus service could be continued beyond the end of its initial funding. These discussions were wide-ranging: from asking the County Council to subsidise the service, to increasing the local precepts to cover the entire cost of the bus operation for local residents. We also discussed various means by which the local community could take some sort of control over their service, including options such as using volunteer drivers or setting up a community company to manage the service. The issue of control and responsibility arose. If they wanted to take control, would they be prepared to take on the responsibility for the service, and how would this be achieved? The outcome was the decision, taken at a well-attended public meeting, to create a company limited by guarantee, which would manage the bus service on behalf of the community.

Ideally, the community company assumes the responsibility for representing the local community's wishes and needs insofar as these can be met by the operation of the bus service. Incorporated in this responsibility is the need to set up the financial security of the service beyond the end of the current research funding. A company limited by guarantee cannot dispense benefits to its directors and it must work to the benefit of the community. The members of the community company are drawn from the local area and the management committee is elected from their number. Formal public involvement in the management of the bus service resides in the community-centred nature of the company.

A company limited by guarantee needs to have a constant reference back to the community to ensure that needs are really being met and, where necessary, to explain the reasons why they cannot be satisfied. Formally, the company needs to have an annual general meeting, but this may not constitute sufficient reference to the community to enable it to justify a claim that it is community-centred.

The interaction between the company and the community needs to be productive.

Relations between the community company and the County Council have been fairly weak. This is in part due to the nature of the project. It is a research project in which the funding has been obtained by the university and therefore the direct lines of communication between the project and the County Council have so far been between the university and the County Council (a similar situation exists with the Countryside Agency). This is now changing and the company is developing more direct communication paths with these entities.

In contrast to the relations with the local authorities, the communication path between the company and the bus operator is in place. This is helped by the fact that the operator has a reasonable understanding of the nature of the project and the ways in which this service is different from others.

In general terms, a community company needs a structure that makes the community-based approach central to its decision processes. The company's normal decision-making procedures should be such that the community is involved in taking major decisions. Notes of committee meetings should be publicly available and reasons for the committee's decisions explained in an understandable way to the community from which the company has emerged. There should be a concerted effort to ensure that users, including local disabled people, are actively involved in a dialogue with the company and thus can have a direct input to the way in which the bus operates. There has to be a very conscious and positive approach by the company towards the rest of the community to ensure that the company's decisions can be seen to be in the best interests of the community – including disabled, elderly, young and other socially excluded members – as a whole. One way of achieving this is to set up a users' group which is independent of the company but which has a formal means of reporting its views to (and receiving appropriate responses from) the company.

The public can, and should, be involved in the detail of projects as well as in the development of strategy. In the case of the APTRA project, a key example is the development of requirements for the passenger accommodation in the vehicle. Once potential users had been identified, the research team obtained their views and incorporated them in the specification of the vehicle. As we mentioned above, there was a difficulty in reaching local disabled people at the beginning of the project, but we were able to incorporate the needs of disabled people as expressed elsewhere. In this case it was the university, rather than the public, that communicated the requirements to the manufacturer, but now this would be a function to be facilitated by the community company. It would be beneficial if a similar approach could be adopted in relation to the longer term finacial viability of the bus service.

Hackney Plusbus

The Hackney Plusbus was an attempt to test the usefulness of a micronetwork, and for this project we worked closely with Hackney Community Transport (HCT). HCT is a company limited by guarantee but, unlike the community company in Cumbria, is a transport operator. The members of HCT are predominantly elderly or disabled people and thus we had a good line of contact with a large number of potential users who could help us directly by helping us to understand their needs. Sadly, the most common response we received was from elderly people and could be characterised as one of resigned acceptance of the limitations on their mobility. For example, we asked where they would like to go on the new service. The most common response to this was along the lines of 'You don't know where you want to go – you don't really want to go anywhere when you're old – it's just too difficult'. Nevertheless, we did receive a large number of helpful suggestions and useful assistance (which was often sufficiently general to help us in other projects). It became clear that the best approach would be to design a route and service on the basis of such information as we had, put it into operation, see how people used it and then find out why other people had not used it. The idea was that once people had seen the service in operation, its inadequacies would soon become apparent.

We held a users' meeting at the launch and again after 3 months of operation. This was an opportunity for users and non-users to raise issues of concern to them. One of these issues was the route. After some discussion it became apparent that the route should be changed to include a new supermarket that was about to open. Other matters raised by the

Box 7.3   Voting for technical changes to the Hackney Plusbus service

The Hackney Plusbus operated on a circular route, with two vehicles providing a service every half hour in one direction. Users pointed out that the problem with this was that it could be quite quick to reach their destination but it would then take a long time to return home. They asked why the buses could not operate in opposite directions so that the journey times would be the same.

We responded by pointing out that if the buses ran as they were suggesting, only one place on the route would receive a regular half-hourly service (albeit in two directions). Everywhere else would have an irregular service, where the irregularity would be different depending on where they were along the route. The worst case would be where the buses passed each other, where there would be two services at the same time but in opposite directions. This would make the service much harder to understand and would make it more difficult to remember the times at which the buses left each stopping point.

When put to the users' vote, it was decided to retain the route as a circular type. This became relevant to another vote at the same meeting about the route, in which it was decided to change the route to call at the new supermarket. When the new route was worked out, the route was reversed and became a figure-of-eight. When the users voted to accept the new route, they also realised that the point where the buses crossed in the new route would form an interchange where they could change from one bus to the other in order to reduce the journey time when necessary. The drivers now use radio contact to advise each other of such interchanges so that they can be co-ordinated.

users included the form of the route (Box 7.3), the drivers, the boarding and alighting methods, the design of the vehicles and eligibility for the service. The participation of the users in the project was, therefore, strong. Box 7.3 gives an example of our approach to responding to users' questions. We tried to explain the technicalities in a way they could understand so that they could vote on the decision having been informed about the issues concerned.

Users' meetings continue to be held about every 3 months. They serve as a check on the operator that they are operating as they should and that previously promised improvements are being delivered. Another type of decision can be quite strategic. Box 7.4 describes such an example, where the change of funder required some thought about what would happen to the route.

Communication paths with the local authority and health trust were good at the beginning, but funding and political problems served to reduce the effectiveness of this line of communication. One example of this was the removal of the complete upper management tier in the local authority, and

Box 7.4   Route length and frequency

The communication paths with the public were also useful when the funding body changed and the new funder required the route to be extended to reach a new area. For the reasons discussed in Chapter 3, this would mean removing the service from another part of the route. This was raised at another users' meeting, at which there was a vociferous expression of unhappiness about losing the service from that area. The operator then explained the technical reasons why the route would have to be cut at that point, especially that this would enable the frequency to be maintained. The discussion then arose about reducing the frequency in order to maintain the route. This would mean that people in the middle of the route who would have been unaffected by the proposal would now also be potential losers because of the reduction in frequency, so their views were sought. Eventually it was put to the vote that the frequency could be changed from one bus every 30 minutes to one every 45 minutes. An important element of this decision was that the users were given a simple description of the technical reasons behind the choices being put to them so that they could understand the issues involved in the compromise.

this prevented much contact after the bus service started. This was a pity, as it reduced the number of people referred to the Plusbus by the Social Services and education departments. The vast bulk of people using the service in the early stages were referred to the service by their GP. Similarly, the dialogue with the borough's public transport team has been small.

In the Hackney Plusbus project we involved the users, including disabled people, from the start, and this paid off in terms of the quality of the decisions that were, and are being, taken. The main reason why involvement worked in this case was that there was a pre-existing group which had an immediate interest in the project. Also, there was a membership list which made it easy to find people and to encourage them to attend users' group meetings. In addition, there was a trust between the users and HCT which meant that they believed what they were being told and that their complaints would be taken into account. Another important point is the fact that the meetings are scheduled to take place every 3 months. Thus unresolved business can be revisited and new issues raised on each occasion. This keeps the operator (and the research team) on their toes.

A special users' meeting was convened when HCT was awarded a contract to operate one of Transport for London's bus routes. This meeting was to determine which particular bus HCT should purchase from the three models identified as feasible by Transport for London. The three manufacturers concerned were invited to bring an example of their proposed vehicle for users to evaluate. This meeting resulted in some difficulties for the manufacturers. One asked 'What do these people (i.e. the users) know about buses?'. The meeting also resulted in choosing none of the vehicles on show. Instead the users identified the manufacturer who was most prepared to incorporate their needs. The resulting vehicle has seats located where elderly people wanted them, separate wheelchair and pushchair spaces, greater spacing between seats and, in order to accommodate all this the vehicle is 1 m longer than the one originally suggested by Transport for London. The result of this particular user participation process was a vehicle that is quite different from the one that was originally intended and a group of users who feel that they have had some ownership of the purchasing decision. The bus manufacturers should have returned to their factories with some thoughts about who their clients really are (the customer who buys the vehicle or the people who will be using it) and the way in which they should approach the users of bus services. It is too early to determine whether or not they have begun to make such a change in their perception of the industry.

Transport Co-ordination Centre

Perhaps the most novel change in communication paths came when we worked with Hackney Community Transport to design the Transport Co-ordination Centre (TCC) in Hackney. The TCC was one of the outcomes of our analysis of the transport problems for people using special education and social services in the borough. As part of this analysis we worked with users and carers to define a specification for a transport service which would be adequate for them, and then presented this to the local authority for their comments. We also discussed the feasibility of the users' needs with the borough's in-house transport department and various community and private sector operators. Eventually a service specification emerged which was used as the basis for two performance-based contracts: one between the local authority and the TCC and the other between the TCC and the transport providers. This approach changed the nature of the relations between the agents: in this design, the users are elevated to an equal footing alongside the local authority and the transport providers in the determination of the existence and quality of the transport they use. Previously, the quality and existence of transport was defined between the borough's purchasing department (e.g. social services) and transport. Now the users define the quality they want and the purchasers and providers respond. There is a channel of communication for users on transport matters, but the importance of the information that flows along these paths is elevated. In the definition of the service specification, the users really were at the centre of the process.

The users' involvement does not stop there. We also included in our structural design of the TCC an access forum, which consists of users, operators and local authority officers. The forum was designed to consider all aspects of operational and strategic decisions within the TCC and takes its place as an equal partner with the other actors in the decision-making process. A common problem when involving disabled people in this way is that it is sometimes difficult to ensure that the whole range of disabilities is represented in the decision-making body. The difficulty is that this would lead to having a forum that is too large to enable it to focus. It also makes it too easy for the technical members of the forum to override a group of people who happen to have differing (and sometimes conflicting) concerns. We therefore designed into the structure a users' group in which different users could discuss their needs between themselves. The resulting decisions would then be taken to the access forum by representatives elected from the users' group.

The TCC has been in action for about a year at the time of writing. In this time the service specification has been implemented, transport procured at a user-preferred quality and costs have fallen. User control over the strategic and technical management issues is in place, but the full access forum and user group are still in the process of being formally constituted. The TCC acts as a channel of information for local disabled and elderly people about all transport in the borough and elsewhere, as well as procuring the transport on their behalf. However, the hesitation in producing the formal access forum means that some users may still feel that it is difficult to become involved in the decision-making process. Now that the TCC is in operation, the access forum should be set up formally as soon as possible. It is too easy for an organisation which has good communications with its users to let this detail slip by: the access forum is a mechanism by which all users, whether they are on the management committee or not, can take their part in the making of decisions that affect them as equal partners in the process. This is quite different from being included in consultation where the responsibility and ownership of the decision rests with the local authority or transport provider. The access forum also provides the users with the opportunity to take their share of the responsibility for and ownership of the decisions which affect them.

The structure of the TCC within the local community is important because we wanted to ensure that it would retain its community-based roots once it was in operation. Figure 7.1 shows how the TCC exists as an enterprise within the local situation – the local authority, transport operators and potential sources of revenue. However, Figure 7.1 also shows the strong influence of the users, both indirectly through their respective purchasers and directly (independently, or through formal groups such as the access forum).

Figure 7.2 shows the functions carried out by the TCC. In addition to its role as a procurer of transport services, the TCC also uses its community-centred position to enable it to identify needs – of users, transport

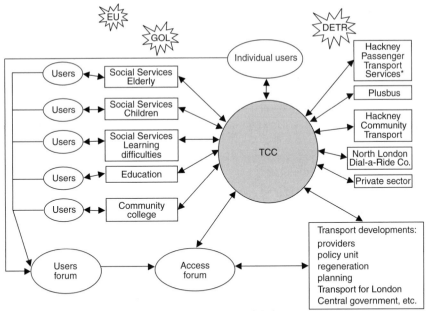

*The in-house transport department of the London Borough of Hackney
EU, European Union
GOL, Government Office for London

Fig 7.1   Transport Co-ordination Centre: enterprise perspective*

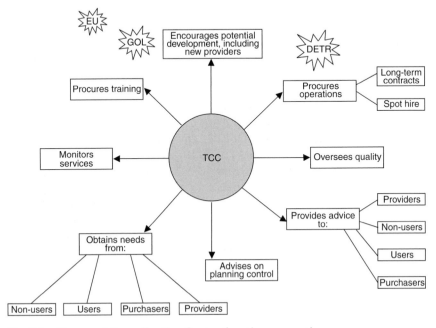

Fig. 7.2   Transport Co-ordination Centre: function perspective

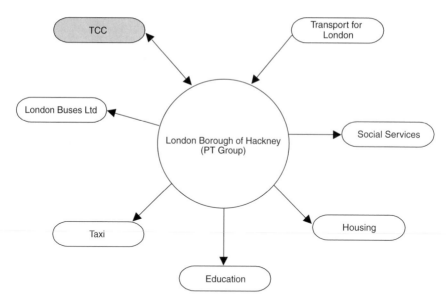

Fig. 7.3   Transport Co-ordination Centre: environment perspective

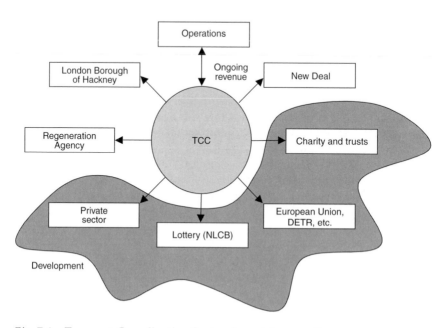

Fig. 7.4   Transport Co-ordination Centre: financial perspective

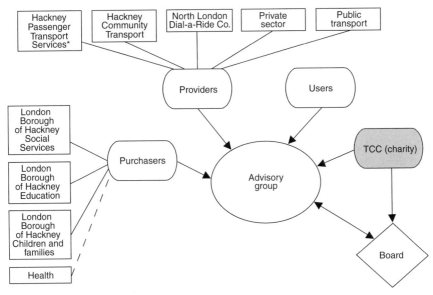

*The in-house transport department of the London Borough of Hackney

Fig. 7.5   Transport Co-ordination Centre: administrative perspective

providers and transport purchasers – in advance so that service quality can improve into the future. Figure 7.3 shows the TCC as a resource that could be used by the local authority's public transport group in the assessment of passenger needs. Figure 7.4 shows the way in which the TCC, as an independent body, has access to resources other than the direct income from its operations. The structure of its finances is thus a set of revenue streams from different sources which combine to maintain its independence of the local authority and transport providers so that it can act on behalf of its users. This includes the possibility for the TCC to finance development of transport services if necessary. Lastly, Figure 7.5 shows the administrative perspective. The TCC is guided by its management board, which in turn is guided by an advisory group. The advisory group consists of representatives of the providers, purchasers and users. Users represent over 50% of the TCC management board.

PUPPIT (Public Participation Processes in Transport)

The PUPPIT project is a pilot project designed to see how public participation might be incorporated in the planning and design process. A specific decision was chosen for the pilot project so that it could be monitored closely and compared with similar decisions which were being made at the same time. We hope to be able to compare issues such as costs, delays and general feelings about the projects being implemented with and without direct public participation. The specific decision used in the PUPPIT project was the reconstruction of a pair of bus stops as part of Brighton and Hove Council's Accessible Public Transport Routes project (for more details of this project see page 266).

The public participation process was formalised into a set of meetings between the public and the council officers, facilitated by the university acting as an independent arbitrator. The meetings were organised in pairs. The first of a pair provided the opportunity to explain the nature of the problem and the reasons why the council wanted to improve accessibility at bus stops. No solutions were presented to the public, but a sketch showing the basic principles in the form of a bus boarder at the relevant site was provided to aid discussion. The outcome of the first meeting was a set of requests from the public for a variety of solutions to be designed in more detail (three possibilities were chosen).

The council officers brought the designs to the second meeting, with the intention of discussing them with members of the public and coming to a decision about which one should be adopted. The meetings were duplicated so that people were not excluded because the meeting was held at a certain time of day. This provided a difficulty, as the final choice of each group was different. This meant that a third meeting had to be held to which both groups were invited and the final choice was made.

One problem with the project was that, although the local residents and traders were represented at the meetings, it had proved very difficult to interest non-local bus users (i.e. people who used these bus stops but who lived elsewhere) in the issue. Representation by local disabled people was very poor (although not non-existent). It is difficult to pin down the reason for this, but we wondered if perhaps previous occasions for joint discussion on other issues might have proved disappointing to the local groups of disabled people and they were reluctant to embark on another. This difficulty highlights the need for an ongoing dialogue between all actors, including disabled people, and that it is the responsibility of each actor to ensure that they take their part in the process. Work is in hand to try to repair this dialogue for future participation efforts.

In principle, the main differences in the communication paths after PUPPIT are the direct connections between the public transport planners and the non-bus-users and non-bus-drivers. Other paths could have been strengthened if it had been possible to attract more bus users to the meetings.

The other striking issue that arose from the PUPPIT process was one of attitude. People arrived at the first meeting saying that they were going to oppose the changes to the bus stops and that the council should act on their views. The first meeting started in a fairly acrimonious mood. The first action in the meeting was to explain the objectives of making a bus stop accessible, the nature of the standards that had to be achieved and the technical difficulties that arose in trying to achieve them. This was explained briefly, and in general terms, by the facilitator. The public were then asked to comment and raise questions about the topic before beginning to look at the specific issue of the bus stops in question. The meeting turned from being one of antagonism to one of trying to see how the objectives might be met with least negative impact on the local people. What this illustrates is the fact, mentioned elsewhere in this book, that if people are encouraged to understand the problem they will be much more able to discuss solutions in appropriate ways.

PUPPIT showed the value of public participation, but also the potential cost. We are currently working out a comparison of the costs of the public participation process and those incurred in the normal decision process, including the costs that arise as a result of public complaints, misunderstandings about the project or other interventions which occur at a later stage of the decision process.

The participation process as undertaken in the PUPPIT project was a research tool, designed to see what would happen if a more detailed participation by the public was incorporated in the decision process. We think that the process could be made shorter – for example, we would expect more than one pair of bus stops to be considered in such a procedure. We also believe that the process could be refined to include:

- One meeting with the public, broadly similar in principle to the first meeting described above (and duplicated to include people who are unavailable at certain times of day). The meeting should raise and deal with any conflicts and contentious issues between groups (e.g. conflicts over parking spaces) in the light of the objectives of the schemes under discussion. The outcomes of this meeting would be similar to those described above – a set of requirements to be worked through by the design team for the next exercise.
- The outcomes of this work would then be put on public display, staffed by technical staff so that the public could ask questions and receive understandable responses. One such display could present proposals for several schemes.
- The visitors would then be asked to vote for the design they prefer for each scheme in which they are interested, giving their reasons and the reasons why they did not choose the other designs.

The outcome of this vote would be the basis for the final decision, which would be reported back to the public – including a direct response to the people who had attended the display and initial meeting. This report would include a reasoned argument explaining why the final project appears as it does, why others were rejected and the extent to which the project meets the overarching principles of the programme of which the project forms a part.

Discussion

From all these experiences, we could see some common issues that affect the process of public participation. We can consider these issues in three groups:

- Subject matter:
  - the information being provided
  - the method of presenting the information
  - the timing of the process.
- Involvement process:
  - input by members of the public
  - the encouragement and facilitation of people to make informed judgements
  - the understanding and acceptance of appropriate compromise
  - the shared ownership in the resulting decision
  - the appropriate distribution of power and responsibility to include both the controlling authority and the local people
  - the use of votes to ensure equal and appropriate representation of all parties
  - evaluation of the effectiveness of the detailed project and the involvement process itself.
- Administration:
  - formal involvement, including reference back to the community when amendments are being considered
  - the users placed at the centre of the process
  - separation of control from the spending body to the users' body.

Subject Matter

We have seen that the subject matter can vary – for example, from the generation of strategy to the design of bus stops. Appropriate information must be made available and must be designed and presented to aid understanding. Under these circumstances, any subject involving people should be able to include the users' views as a central part of the process. Involvement should start at the very beginning of the project. The TCC and Hackney Plusbus examples indicate the benefits of this. The subject should be continually revisited and revised so that conditions continue to improve into the future.

Involvement Process

Involvement includes the active participation of the public in a decision, using many different processes, but we contend that they must be characterised by the factors listed above. All potential users should be involved in decisions which are likely to affect them, and the process should also ensure that the whole range of users is given the opportunity to provide inputs to the decisions if they wish. This means that a concerted effort has to be made to contact people from all potential groups as the project proposals are being developed, but at least as soon as the project itself starts. Talking to representative groups is necessary, but not sufficient. The process should ensure that everyone, no matter whether they are confident or diffident, can have their say and be taken seriously in the expression of their concerns in the matter. This could mean setting up ancillary groups to enable some people to discuss the issue and come to a collective view before discussion of the issues in public. This would be appropriate where specific interest groups are involved, but where they might have conflicting interests. Disabled people have many different, and sometimes conflicting, interests and it is important that they can come to a collective view about the issue at hand so that they can present a unified approach to the wider discussion. Otherwise it is too easy for other more single-minded groups to argue against them.

People should be encouraged to make judgements and to have them taken seriously, even if the majority disagree. With more involvement, personal judgements will become more informed and, in combination with better understanding of the issues, more directed to the problem at hand.

Understanding and acceptance of appropriate compromise means that principles and policies, technical matters and design issues must all be explained in plain accessible language so that everyone can understand well enough to make a sensible decision about the proposal. Again, continual reference to the public will make this much easier, but it is time that we all (including university researchers) made our knowledge plain to the public we are attempting to serve. Hiding behind jargon is not an option any more.

A key element of public involvement has to be the ownership of the resulting decision. Decisions should not be made by one group and imposed on another: they should be made by all parties and understood by everyone (whether or not they are agreed by everyone). With the shared ownership of the decision comes a shared responsibility, both over the decision itself and of its implementation. In the scenario of public involvement, decisions are not isolated events that can be forgotten, but are ongoing processes that need to be monitored and evaluated so that improvements can be made and mistakes rectified in good time. The sharing of ownership of and responsibility for decisions puts power in the hands of the community in which they are applied.

Voting regimes need to be established so that people feel that their views are taken into account in the decision process. In short, the involvement process needs to feel real as well as inclusive.

All decision processes should have an independent evaluation element to check that the decision outcome is working and that the effects are as desired. Involvement processes are no different in this respect, except that the outcomes of such evaluation should be more explicit and more widely available to the public than is currently often the case.

The involvement process should continue beyond the end of the project so that benefits are not lost simply because the particular project that brought them changed its funding regime or stopped altogether. Apart from changes in funding, the world changes and public participation is a good way of making sure that a project keeps up to date with progress (e.g. more general availability of accessible buses may alter the way in which other resources could be used).

It is important to have a schedule of meetings so that everyone knows when there will be an opportunity to re-evaluate problems and their solutions. The existence of a schedule provides the necessary power for the user to keep the pressure on the technical and political partners in the decision process. This prevents the meetings from becoming a superficial talking shop from which no practical solution ever emerges.

Better involvement during the EXCALIBUR project would have meant that the schedule could have been tighter, with a stronger input from disabled people helping to force through activities which other parties might perceive to be less important. An example of this was the driver training and subsequent monitoring process. Decision-makers also need to come to a view about the difference between wishing to include the public, including disabled people, young and elderly people and other typically excluded groups, and the practicality of doing so. Inevitably, involvement means setting up procedures so that these groups, which are typically very difficult to reach, are included in a way that makes their involvement real. This suggests the organisation of discussion groups, focus groups, public meetings and other diverse techniques to ensure that the involvement happens and is genuine. It is a very different world from the usual decision-making domain, where control is wholly in the hands of providers rather than the users of services.

Administrative Process

The process needs to be formal. The approach adopted in both the Cumbria Plusbus and TCC projects results in a community company. In each case this company takes responsibility for certain local decisions. Involvement needs to be incorporated formally into every process so that users are included as a norm at the centre of the process and not just in a series of meetings at the periphery. Participation is not a favour that can be dispensed with or withdrawn at will by anyone, whether they are a member of a community or a local authority. A central issue is the placing of control over spending. This is often retained by the spending authority on the basis of its legal responsibility for the proper use of public money. Users' involvement means that some of this control must pass to the users. This issue has already been addressed in the management of some social housing estates.

As long as the administration process is correct and the users are involved as stakeholders in the process, there is no reason to suppose that the involvement of users is any less 'proper' than an approach which does not involve them. In fact, we would argue that a process that does not include users at such a level is not a proper process at all: proper use of public money is surely to ensure that it is being spent wisely and to the greatest benefit of the potential user groups. Sharing responsibility for spending of public money in the social services area has already been started: the direct payments approach to funding a user's social-services needs delegates to the user the decisions about how the money is spent, even though the local authority has the legal responsibility for the resources. Involving users in the decision process as suggested here would work on a similar basis. Proper spending decisions have to involve the users, and the inclusion of users in the decision process is a necessary condition to enable such decisions to be made.

Conclusions

We have used examples from our own research to show some of the problems and benefits of involving the public in decisions about their local area. Different methods are useful in different contexts and it is important to have a full range of options available so that the best ones can be used in each case. It is important to review the process so that improvements can be made in the future.

Involving the public is an ongoing task, which means that procedures have to be set up to enable it to happen on a permanent basis. It is all too easy to forget the public once the service has been put into operation or the bus stops built. Once people believe they will be taken seriously they will become involved, and this involvement provides a project with a great benefit. Apart from the advantage of making sure that the project is appropriate for the local community, the public participation process lends the project's promoters a level of authority that is difficult to dispel. We use the word 'lend' in this context because the support of the public needs to be earned on a continuing basis.

Public participation carries with it some costs – costs of implementation (e.g. the cost of meetings) and of time (it requires enough time for the public's views to be heard and acted on). As discussed above, we feel that the number of meetings in the PUPPIT project could have been reduced without too much problem. This would reduce the time and cost of the exercise while retaining the public's involvement in the decision. It would not be appropriate to use the display approach instead of the first meeting as it is this meeting which enables the public to discuss the project in the light of its overall principles rather than in the fine detail of particular solutions. This aspect of the PUPPIT project was a success (we mentioned above the change in attitude of the public in the course of the first meeting) and shows that a more mature approach to such detailed issues is possible.

Involving the public is an essential element of a modern decision process. It is important that the public is able to participate fully throughout the process. Presence at meetings and completion of other consultation exercises, such as questionnaires or interviews, are basic forms of involvement. However, participation means that people must be informed about and understand the knowledge they need in order to be able to make a contribution. Many of the issues that cause members of the public to feel left out of the decision process arise because the reasons for the decision are not given or are not understood. For example, the solution that would be optimal from the public's point of view might be illegal, or technically impossible. In some cases, although the details of the design of infrastructure are constrained for technical or practical reasons, they could be adjusted to suit local preferences (e.g. moving a cycle rack from one side of a bus stop to the other). Explanations and discussions about what is possible mean that the public feel better about the outcome, even if their own preference has not been chosen, because the decision was made with, and at least to some extent by, the public rather than by somebody acting in apparent isolation at the town hall. Every decision is the selection of one compromise from a set of different suboptimal options. It is important that the rationale for this choice is understood by everyone.

It is important to ensure that the 'right' public is involved in a decision. Local decisions are clearly important to local people, but others may also have reason to have an input. Bus users, for example, might use a bus stop even though they do not live or work anywhere near it. A particular issue is the involvement of disabled people. We have mentioned the need to ensure that they have a voice in all decisions, sometimes with the opportunity to discuss the issues between themselves beforehand. Disabled people fill two roles in the public participation process: they provide their knowledge of their local area and they provide knowledge about at least some issues of importance to disabled people in general. It is essential that disabled people are included in every decision, even where it does not involve their immediate locality, so that the needs of disabled people can be included in every decision. This suggests that the initial publicity and associated information about the participation process must be made widely available before the process starts – if people do not know about the forthcoming issue, they cannot be expected to participate in helping to resolve it.

Formalising public participation by setting up a community company is an exciting and empowering way to enable people to take control of some aspects of their community life. The example of a community's control over its local bus service shows that this approach can work even where the operation concerned is complex. Such involvement requires a lot of time and effort. Comparison between the Cumbria and Hackney examples shows that implementation of full public involvement needs time and patience to establish a climate in which new initiatives can be easily established. Hackney as been developing formal user involvement procedures over the last 20 years, compared with the introduction of the Cumbria Plusbus just 3 years ago. This, coupled with the number of people living in the local area in each case, affects the range and depth of the available human resource and thus the rate at which public involvement processes can be introduced in different places. When devising public participation schemes, due account has to be taken of the available skills and the number of people able and willing to contribute to their local community in this way. When a full and inclusive public involvement programme is achieved, it can provide the most democratic way of making public decisions in the community's interest.

References

DETR (1998). *Enhancing Public Participation in Local Government*. London: Department of Transport, Local Government and the Regions.
DTRL (2001). *Planning: Delivering a Fundamental Change*. London: Department of Transport, Local Government and the Regions.

Chapter 8

An Accessible Rural Bus Service: The Cumbria Plusbus

I. Brown and N. Tyler

Outline

This chapter describes the setting up and outcomes of a research project – Accessible Public Transport in Rural Areas (APTRA) – in which we worked with the local communities in a remote area of England to specify, design and operate an accessible bus service that would respond to the needs of local people. The bus service started in April 1999, operates on a fixed route and schedule, reaches the heart of every village along the route, and operates every 3 hours on 6 days per week. The bus had to be specially designed as there was no vehicle available that was small enough to travel along narrow country lanes yet large enough to accommodate a reasonable number of passengers, including those in wheelchairs.

Objectives

The APTRA project, known locally as the 'Cumbria Plusbus Project', was devised at University College London to investigate ways of addressing users' needs for public transport in rural areas. The objectives of the project were as follows:

- to improve quality of life in a remote rural area for those unable to lead a full and independent life due to lack of accessible public transport

- to design an appropriate accessible public transport system for those with cognitive, sensory or mobility impairments, and especially for older people
- to test in practice the effects of accessible fixed-route public transport on the problems associated with accessibility in remote rural areas
- to provide guidance to planners designing public transport systems appropriate to the needs of older people in rural areas.

The project was funded principally by the Engineering and Physical Sciences Research Council (EPSRC) through its Extending Quality Life initiative (EQUAL), with a contribution towards the capital costs by the Rural Development Commission (now the Countryside Agency). The basic approach was to install some public transport in a remote rural area and observe the ways in which people made use of the new facility.

Background

General Issues

Public transport provision in rural areas of England has been 'few and far between' for many years. Frequently, it is only provided once a week on main roads and it fails to meet the needs of local communities.

People with mobility problems tend to become excluded from society because they have no access to suitable transport. The general assumption is that everyone living in a rural area has access to a car. The lack of public transport prevents some people, especially elderly residents, from making even simple shopping trips without asking a neighbour or family member for a lift (Tyler *et al.*, 1997). This situation is made worse where more wealthy members of the community use their car to travel to work, shops and facilities far away, leading to the isolation of the remaining members of their family at home without transport. This in time leads to the closure of local community shops and facilities due to lack of customers and support.

Thus many people living in remote rural areas, wishing to maintain a full and independent lifestyle, frequently become dependent on others who have access to a private car. This may be due to low income, being too old to drive a car, the absence of accessible public transport or the closure of the village shops. Those affected include young, elderly and disabled people.

Setting up the APTRA Project

The success of the project depended on several factors, as described below.

Box 8.1   Research considerations for the area to be chosen for the APTRA project

---

- *The area should not be inside a National Park.* This was for two reasons: (i) the level of tourism might unbalance the assessments of demand; and (ii) problems associated with the construction of any infrastructure, etc., within National Parks.
- *The area should contain some settlements, but not too many.* The project needed to investigate problems associated with accessibility (e.g. boarding and alighting) as well as movement between settlements (e.g. the distance and time it is necessary to travel). This meant that the communities being served should not be too far apart.
- *The area should contain at least one village with a village shop.* We wanted to look at the possibility of using the bus as a means of supplying goods to and from village shops. It was also of interest to see if the availability of good public transport would help to bring people to the village shop rather than take them to the market town.
- *The area should have a reasonable number of older residents.* The project was funded as an investigation into the effects of providing public transport that was easier to use for older people.
- *There should be little or no interference with bus routes registered as commercial services.* The service should not reduce significantly the number of passengers using existing commercial services.
- *There should be a suitable control area nearby.* In order to check the impacts of the service, it would be very desirable to have a control area nearby where travel patterns could be compared with those in the study area.

Location

In Chapter 3 we discussed issues relating to the location of bus services. As the APTRA project was principally a research project, there were other considerations that had to be taken into account in order to ensure that the research objectives could be met (Tyler and Brown, 1998). These are set out in Box 8.1.

Cumbria was chosen as the area in which the study could be carried out because:

- Certain parts were very sparsely populated (under 0.5 people per hectare). This was important because we were trying to find out what the costs and benefits would be of providing accessible public transport in such areas, where the number of people is small and the distance between them very great.
- Several rural areas of Cumbria were inadequately served by public transport (34% of parishes had no public bus service (Voluntary Action Cumbria, 1992)).
- Many older people lived in the area (7.8% of the population is aged 75 years or over (Office of National Statistics, 1991)). We were

particularly interested in the choices available to people as they became older. Often they have to move away from the area they have lived in for many years because they cannot tackle basic activities (e.g. day-to-day shopping) without assistance from others.

The selection of the actual location was determined in association with the local authorities, and is dealt with in more detail in a later section.

Accessible vehicle

It was essential to ensure that the public transport service would be accessible and would present as few barriers as possible to potential users, especially older people and those with difficulties travelling around. The development of a suitable vehicle for the project is treated later in this chapter (see page 293).

Involvement of the local community

Another key ingredient of the project was to ensure that the needs expressed by the local people would be addressed. This required extensive consultation with the local communities and their active participation in as many of the strategic decisions as possible.

Funding

The EPSRC funding paid for the research, the vehicle and the operating costs for a little over one year of operation. The Countryside Agency provided a contribution towards the vehicle cost through the Rural Transport Development Fund.

Liaison with Local Authorities, Funding Agencies and Bus Operators

At the start of the project a steering group was set up to deal with strategic issues. It consisted of representatives from the County Council, District Council, Countryside Agency, University College London and a potential bus service operator. As the time approached for letting the contract it was no longer felt appropriate for the bus operator to attend the steering group, which continued as a strategy group. Thus operational matters were discussed between University College London and the chosen operator under a separate contractual arrangement.

Issues discussed by the steering/strategy group included, among other things, the following:

- the project vehicle, service operation, contracts and programmes
- route location and timetable
- consultation process, publicity, marketing and public relations
- planning issues, bus stops and shelters

- details of user surveys for the Plusbus and nearby Community Bus Service
- funding issues
- post-project strategy.

Initially, liaison with local Parish Councils was carried out in conjunction with the County Council, but later we organised and discussed issues directly with representatives from the local parishes and the general public along the lines discussed in Chapter 7.

Project Vehicle

Specification

Perhaps the most visible evidence of the Cumbria Plusbus is the vehicle. Early in the project it was established that there was no public service vehicle on the market that could provide accessibility similar to that required of large buses and at the same time be suitable for use in narrow rural lanes. This meant that a vehicle had to be designed and constructed taking account of our requirements for accessible passenger accommodation based on experience from previous projects and comments obtained during the consultation process. Our requirements for the vehicle are summarised in Tables 8.1 to 8.7 and discussed below.

Overall Considerations (see Table 8.1)

Basic type of vehicle
The first issue to consider when attempting to meet the user's needs was the basic nature of the vehicle. For easy access it is necessary to provide either a lift or a ramp. We have found throughout our research that the users' views are evenly split between a preference for lifts or ramps. Although lift equipment is often used on door-to-door and other social services or health-related transport services, it is not adequate for public transport. This is because the time taken to board and alight would upset a service timetable (or would mean that a large amount of slack would have to be incorporated in the basic timetable, resulting in unacceptable journey times). We found that some users felt exposed when using a tail lift in a public environment, so we concluded that lift access would not be the best option for a public service vehicle operating on a local bus service. We also found that the main source of discomfort in using ramps was the process of walking on an incline and the general difficulty of using them if the ramp were too steep. On balance, and given that level entry would be impossible in the country lanes and in most villages because of the lack of

Table 8.1 Cumbria Plusbus: overall considerations

Feature	Requirement	Actual construction
Basic type of vehicle	Low floor, fully accessible minibus (ride height of passenger saloon 320 mm)	Requirement achieved: coach built, based on Renault Master, low floor chassis cab with 2.8 tdi engine
	Maximum overall vehicle length 6.1 m	Requirement achieved
	Maximum overall vehicle external width 2.2 m	Requirement achieved
	Minimum headroom in vehicle 1.98 m	Requirement achieved
	Vehicle to meet DPTAC recommendations as far as possible	Requirement achieved
Seating capacity	Maximum of 13 passengers, including up to 2 wheelchairs	All requirements achieved
	12 seats, 425 mm wide, double/single, maximum 8 fixed	
	Minimum seat pitch 650 mm	
	Minimum distance between seat cushion and rear of forward seat 250 mm at knee height	
	One combined seat/ wheelchair restraint	
	2 wheelchair spaces (1 occupied by combined seat/wheelchair restraint which can be removed)	
	Flexible seating arrangement	

DPTAC, Disabled Persons' Transport Advisory Committee

Table 8.2   Cumbria Plusbus: specification for passenger access

Feature	Requirement	Actual construction
Front entrance door	Powered plug door	All requirements achieved
	Minimum unobstructed opening width 850 mm	
	Minimum headroom 1.98 m	Door in two halves, opening outward
	Anchorage points for ramp	
	Handrails	
Rear entrance door	Two quarter-width, fully glazed doors	All requirements achieved
	Minimum unobstructed opening width 850 mm	
	Minimum headroom 1.98 m	
	Lockable door checks (90°)	
	Anchorage points for ramp	
	Handrails	
Steps	No internal steps in passenger saloon	Requirement achieved
	First step height 200 mm from road level when lowered	Requirement could not be met without complete redesign of chassis. Actual height of first step achieved 240 mm
Aisles	Minimum width 850 mm	Requirement achieved (subsequently altered)
Wheelchair ramps	Two entry/exit ramps: one 900 mm long; one 1800 mm long	Requirement achieved, except that carrying handles not supplied
	Minimum width 850 mm	
	Locking mechanism to secure ramp when in use to vehicle	
	Upstands on sides	
	Carrying handles	
	Suitable for use at both doors	
	Secure stowage for ramps when not in use	
	Safe working load: 300 kg weight	
	Signs stating restriction on use visible to user	

Table 8.3   Cumbria Plubus: specification for vehicle equipment

Feature	Requirement	Actual construction
Suspension	All-round lowering and raising air suspension (relative to normal ride height)	Vehicle supplied with separate front and rear lowering facility only
Brakes	Antilock Braking System	Not supplied on standard Renault Master chassis cab. Cost of retro-fitting was in excess of £800, so not fitted
Steering	Power-assisted steering	Requirement achieved: standard on Renault Master
Driver's door	Separate door on right-hand side of vehicle in driver's cab	Not fitted
Interior lighting	Four interior light units	Requirements achieved
	Working light for driver to cover change giving, ticket issuing, etc.	
Accessories	Tachograph	All requirements achieved
	Luggage pen with mounting for ticket machine, moneybox and cash tray to suit operator requirements	
	Clock	
	Stowage for ramps and wheelchair-restraining straps	

Table 8.4   Cumbria Plusbus: specification of vehicle finishes and ancillary equipment

Feature	Requirement	Actual construction
Wall and ceiling covering	Soft trim carpet throughout	All requirements achieved
Windows	Tinted glass Hopper ventilation	All requirements achieved
Seats	Style: semi high back Fabric: vandal-proof	All requirements achieved
Heating	Fan-assisted, diesel, recirculatory heater	All requirements achieved
Ventilation	Two rotary ventilators Coach-style, lift-up roof ventilation	All requirements achieved
Colour of bus	High visibility, acceptable to the local community	All requirements achieved

Table 8.5   Cumbria Plusbus: specification for passenger safety and related equipment

Feature	Requirement	Actual construction
Passenger restraints	Integral lap and diagonal seat belts anchored to seats to M2 standard	All requirements achieved
Seat fittings	Padded head rests High-visibility, corner grab handles on all aisle seats to DPTAC recommendations	All requirements achieved
Seat fixings	To be anchored to the floor by bolting where fixed; quick-release fasteners where attached to floor tracking; all to M2 standard	All requirements achieved
Wheelchair passenger restraints	Included in combined seat/ wheelchair restraint	Requirement achieved (integral restraint supplied)
	Three-point installation to be fitted if combined seat/ wheelchair restraint removed	Two-point restraint supplied only

Table 8.5   (Contd)

Feature	Requirement	Actual construction
Wheelchair fixings	One combined/wheelchair restraint seat	All requirements achieved
	Four-point webbing restraints for two wheelchairs	
Floor covering	Slip-resistant vinyl	All requirements achieved
	High-visibility door edges	
	Radius corners and kickplates	
Floor tracking	Low-profile longitudinal rail at 330 mm spacing laid parallel and (1) centred to wheelchair space and (2) suitable for anchoring removable passenger seats where required	Rails not fitted parallel or in correct position initially. This was corrected
Handrails	High-visibility handrails (vertical and horizontal) in front of the left-hand seat and at the rear of the driver's partition	Requirement achieved
Side wall tracking	To provide third anchorage point for wheelchair passenger restraint	Not fitted due to misunderstanding of requirement
Other safety details	Fire-retardant cavity wall/roof insulation	All requirements achieved
	First aid kit	
	Two fire extinguishers (one at front, one at rear)	
	Life hammer/seat-belt cutter	
	High-level brake lights	
	Step lights	
	External loading light	

DPTAC, Disabled Persons' Transport Advisory Committee

infrastructure, we opted for a low floor vehicle with ramps from ground as well as kerb level. Specifying the ride height meant that we could be reasonably sure that the vehicle would be able to cope with the local roads without causing problems with the suspension.

The vehicle needed to be small enough to travel along narrow country lanes, but wide enough to accommodate manoeuvring space for

Table 8.6   Cumbria Plusbus: specification for communications equipment

Feature	Requirement	Actual construction
Location of vehicle	Global Positioning System to track vehicle position to ±50 m	All requirements achieved
	Mobile phone	
Destination display	Illuminated destination sign equipment in accordance with current proposals (DETR, 1999)	All requirements achieved
	Destination board for left-hand side of vehicle	
Audio equipment	Radio cassette sound PA system	Requirement achieved
	Induction loop incorporated into PA system	Independent PA system supplied for hearing-aid users only
	Bell pushes fitted to each seat bay and wheelchair space	Requirement achieved

wheelchair users within the vehicle. We also wished to avoid the problem of height restrictions so that people could stand upright inside the vehicle. This point is important in a public service vehicle, where people need to move around easily to board and alight.

We wanted to meet the Disabled Persons' Transport Advisory Committee's (DPTAC) current recommendations for large public service buses (DPTAC, 1997) as far as we could. The rationale for this was that we should aim to ensure that the accessibility standards were as near as possible to those of a large bus. The recommendations concerned included door widths and entry height, floor height at the doorway, floor slopes, seat spacing, ramp angles, floor markings, spacing between grab handles and handrails, surface and colour of handrails, destination boards and wheelchair spaces. In some cases (e.g. seat spacing, bell-push positions, number of wheelchair spaces and the provision of an induction loop) we managed to exceed the recommendations. The Public Service Vehicles Accessibility (PSVA) Regulations 2000 came into force during the course of the project. Had they applied to vehicles of this size, this vehicle would have satisfied most of their requirements. It also satisfies the DPTAC recommendations for small buses, which were published in December 2001 (DPTAC, 2001).

Table 8.7   Cumbria Plusbus: specification for technical compliance criteria

Feature	Requirement	Actual construction
PSV certificate	Vehicle to be delivered with appropriate certificates for public service vehicle operation	Requirement achieved
Draft technical approval procedures	Draft technical approval procedure for the design and construction of the vehicle modification including, among other things:	
	• Approval in principle to proposed design criteria including structural form, loading and analysis	Only partially successful
	• Vehicle design to comply with the regulations, etc.*	Requirement achieved
	• Vehicle supplier to provide certificate of compliance with appropriate British Standards, regulations and departmental requirements	Requirement not achieved
	• Design of vehicle modification to be checked and certified by an independent qualified automotive/mechanical engineer	Requirement partially achieved
	• Statements concerning standards for construction and quality control to be provided by vehicle supplier	Requirement not achieved
	• Manual (operation and maintenance) for all non-Renault equipment	First draft received
	• Vehicle supplier to provide 24 month/120,000 mile transferable warranty for parts and labour	Requirement achieved

*Public Service Vehicle Regulations, SI 1981/257; Road Vehicles (Construction and Use) Regulations, SI 1986/1078; Department of Transport Vehicle Standards Engineering Codes of Practice, Nos 87/1 and 2/96; Disabled Persons' Transport Advisory Committee Recommendations for low floor buses (1997); Department of the Environment, Transport and the Regions proposals for buses and coaches to meet the Disability Discrimination Act 1995 (1997)

Seating capacity

The number of seats was dictated by the space within the vehicle, ensuring adequate manoeuvrability for people in wheelchairs. Figure 8.1 shows the seat layout as supplied and as in current use. The current configuration arose because we wished to test in practice a seat which was designed to operate either as a normal seat or as a wheelchair restraint. The main effect on the layout is that the aisle width is reduced at this point (see below). Figure 8.1(b) also shows that the rear single seat has been

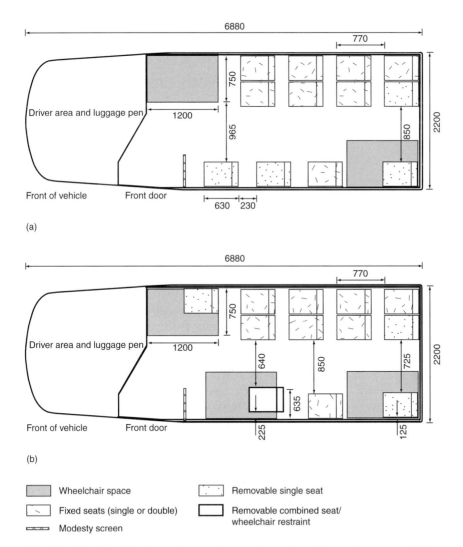

Fig. 8.1 Cumbria Plusbus vehicle seating configuration (dimensions in mm): (a) as supplied; (b) as in current operation

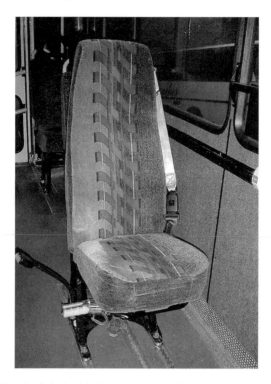

Fig. 8.2   Combined seat/wheelchair restraint

moved slightly away from the side wall of the vehicle. This is because the tracking to which it was secured became slightly out of line and the seat had to be moved to the parallel tracking in order to maintain safety standards. The current configuration can also be seen in Figure 8.4.

We had to allow for passengers, including wheelchair users, to board and alight from either the side or rear of the vehicle, due to the lack of available width of some roads. This meant that the aisle had to be wide enough to allow a wheelchair user to pass through the bus, thus limiting the number of seats that could be accommodated. However, this approach allowed us to have a choice of location for wheelchair users: they could choose to sit near the front or the back, knowing that they could board and alight easily from either position.

The seat pitch was specified as 650 mm (as is now required in the PSVA Regulations for priority seats).

In order to make the process of securing a wheelchair more comfortable for the wheelchair user (and to speed up the process of anchoring and releasing wheelchairs in the vehicle) we installed a combined seat/ wheelchair restraint (Figure 8.2). This acts as a normal seat, but can also act as the basis for restraining a wheelchair if required. Thus it is much easier for both the wheelchair user and the driver when making sure that both the wheelchair user and their chair are secure in order to comply with the law. There is a corresponding time advantage as well. The disadvantage is that this type of seat has to be set some distance from the side of the vehicle to allow the wheels of the wheelchair to pass alongside the seat when the wheelchair is secured. As a result, the gangway, which in the original layout had a minimum width of 850 mm, is now reduced to 640 mm alongside the combined seat and wheelchair restraint. Although 640 mm is still much wider than the 450 mm required under the PSVA Regulations, it would only allow a little over 50%, as opposed to 95%, of wheelchairs to pass if another wheelchair were secured to the wheelchair restraint (Stait and Savill, 1995). So far, the width reduction has not apparently given any problems, and the fact that it is easy to secure the wheelchair and the passenger has been appreciated by both wheelchair users and drivers.

Passenger Access (see Table 8.2)

Front entrance door

We specified a plug door for the front entrance to enable people to hold onto handrails inside the vehicle. This provides adequate clear width when open and does not intrude into the interior of the vehicle. Apart from allowing easy access for people in wheelchairs the wide unobstructed opening allows people to enter the bus with children in pushchairs, heavy shopping or other encumbrances. The disadvantage is that the door opens outwards and the effective unobstructed width is reduced a little by the door opening mechanism. It requires clear space outside the vehicle and means that passengers waiting to board the bus have to stand clear of the opening doors. On balance, we consider that the plug doors are probably the right solution. Figure 8.3 shows the entry door of the vehicle.

Figure 8.3 also indicates the headroom achieved at the entry doors. Ensuring that the doorways are high enough to permit entry to the vehicle without worrying about headroom is important for everyone. It also contributes to the feeling of space inside the vehicle and makes it easy to manoeuvre into a safe position for the journey. The impression of space inside the vehicle can be seen in Figure 8.4.

Rear entrance door

The second entrance door acts as the emergency door and is located in the rear face of the vehicle rather than on the right-hand side. Although it allows boarding and alighting through the rear door if necessary, it reduces the seating capacity by one. The rear door is large enough to enable people to assist others in evacuating the vehicle if necessary (e.g. some ambulant

Fig. 8.3   Cumbria Plusbus: entry door

Fig. 8.4   Cumbria Plusbus: interior

passengers or wheelchair users would need a doorway that is wide enough to allow them and any assistant(s) to pass). The interior view of the rear door can be seen in Figure 8.4.

Steps
In order to make movement around the bus easy for everyone, we required that there should be no stairs inside the vehicle. We specified the floor height with the bus lowered to 200 mm. This has, so far, proved impracticable and we are content to work with the 240 mm that has been achieved.

Aisles
For the reasons stated above, we specified a minimum aisle width of 850 mm.

Wheelchair ramps
Short (0.9 m) and long (1.8 m) ramps were provided to give access from either kerb or road level, their lengths enabling the slope to be not more than 12.9%. We specified the handrail to help support people who feel uncomfortable walking on an inclined surface whilst on the ramp, which has to be long enough to reach ground level at an appropriate angle. The ramps as specified are manually operated. Although this means that the driver has to set up the ramp before use, we were not satisfied that motorised ramps would be able to deliver the reliability we required of the facility.

Vehicle Equipment (see Table 8.3)

Suspension
Table 8.3 shows the requirements for the various items of equipment on the Plusbus. We had wanted raising as well as lowering suspension as a precaution against difficulties with road conditions, such as sudden changes in gradient. Although the vehicle is equipped with the appropriate valves and switches to raise the suspension from the normal ride height, this was disengaged by the manufacturer because of potential lack of performance reliability. One of the problems of installing air suspension in a small vehicle with a low floor is the limited space available for the air reservoir. In the event it was only possible to fit a small reservoir. This increases the time required to raise the vehicle once it has been lowered at a bus stop. Although it has not proved to be a problem in reality, it could do on a busier bus route.

Driver's door
There was already good access to the driver's compartment from within the vehicle. The space was used for switches, etc., located on the driver's right.

Interior lighting
Good internal lighting is essential for both passengers and the driver.

Accessories
The luggage pen as fitted is rather small. However, the space provided appears to be sufficient for people's needs, especially as the rest of the vehicle is quite spacious.

Vehicle Finishes and Ancillary Equipment (see Table 8.4)

Seats
The seats had to be high enough to provide good back support. In fact, the seats also had seat cushions that were slightly longer than usual, which provide better support for the thighs (this being particularly important for taller people).

Colour of bus
The local community was asked for its ideas before settling on the colour scheme. The light beige colour with dark green lettering chosen met with their approval. We wanted the bus to be easily identifiable and to have the operator's telephone number displayed prominently to make it easier for people to contact them (e.g. for information).

Passenger Safety and Related Equipment (see Table 8.5)

Passenger restraints
We required all seats to be fitted with seat belts. Apart from being required if the vehicle were to be used for the carriage of children under 14 years of age, this provides the opportunity for everyone to be more secure in the bus.

Seat fittings
The seats have integral headrests, which are designed so that it is possible to see through them. This reduces any feeling of claustrophobia caused by only being able to see as far as the seat in front. High-visibility grab handles are fitted to all seats that are adjacent to the aisle (with the exception of the combined seat/wheelchair restraint). These can be seen in Figure 8.4.

Seat fixings
Where seats are removable, quick-release fixings to M2 standard are fitted.

Wheelchair passenger restraints
Only two-point restraints were supplied, because no side-wall tracking was supplied (see below). Although the two-point system is in common use, we felt that there was a risk of compressing the spine when in use. We

did not consider this to be satisfactory and this was one of the reasons why we investigated the combined wheelchair and passenger seat (which has an integral three-point passenger restraint).

Wheelchair fixings
Although the combined seat/wheelchair restraint is designed to accommodate the vast majority of wheelchairs, there are some that will not be able to use this restraint system. The bus therefore is required to carry standard four-point webbing restraints.

Floor tracking
The floor tracking was aligned so that removable seats could be fitted in two wheelchair positions in addition to the alignment required for the combined seat/wheelchair restraint. With hindsight, it might have been better to provide more tracking so that more flexibility in the seating arrangements would have been possible.

Handrails
Ample handrails, stanchions and grab handles mean that support is available for those who need it, whether the vehicle is stationary or in motion. Some of these can be seen in Figure 8.4.

Side-wall tracking
We had specified tracking to be positioned in the side walls of the vehicle for the three-point passenger restraint to be used in conjunction with the four-point wheelchair restraint system. This would have avoided the passenger restraint being fixed over the shoulder to the floor tracking. Unfortunately, there was a misunderstanding with the manufacturer about what we actually wanted and the side-wall tracking was not installed. In the event, this issue has been resolved for most situations by the use of the combined seat/wheelchair restraint, which has an integral three-point passenger restraint. This is similar to the seat belt arrangements in the other seats, in terms of both safety and comfort.

Other safety details
We specified high-level exterior loading lights. With hindsight we feel that these should have been more powerful and moveable than the system that was installed.

Communications Equipment (see Table 8.6)

Location of vehicle
The Cumbria Plusbus operates in a remote rural area and we therefore had to consider several communication issues (e.g. contacting the bus,

being able to see the vehicle destination equipment, problems encountered by people with hearing difficulties in communicating with bus drivers).

We specified a global positioning system for the vehicle. This worked fairly well, but was extremely costly to operate because of the number of calls required to provide suitably frequent information updates. In the event, the service has run to schedule and thus there has been little need to update information about its location in this way. The vehicle is equipped with a mobile phone, which can be used to establish current location and in emergency.

Destination display

We specified a dot-matrix destination sign system for the front of the bus. There is some dispute about the clarity of such systems, but we were encouraged to adopt it in case the vehicle had to be used elsewhere. In practice, the system has worked well and there have been no complaints about legibility.

We specified a destination board for the left-hand side of the vehicle (as is now required by the PSVA Regulations). We did not require a route/ destination sign for the rear of the vehicle, but we would do so if specifying a similar vehicle now. This is useful for passengers approaching a bus from the rear. A rear route-number display is required under the PSVA Regulations 2000.

Audio equipment

An induction loop system was installed so that people with hearing aids could find it easier to hear the driver. The system was retro-fitted because we had to establish that it was possible to use the system in a vehicle where construction materials and electrical equipment might cause interference. In this case the body frame was constructed of stainless steel with aluminium panels and a glass-reinforced plastic (GRP) roof. However, the installation has proved to be successful and, as the induction loop is switched on when the ignition is switched on, the system is always in operation when the vehicle is in use. The microphone for this system is located above the driver. As this microphone is very directional, it picks up very little ambient noise and thus when the driver is not talking, no other sound can be heard. A complete lack of sound could cause some discomfort in a moving vehicle. If specifying such a device now, we would consider fitting a wide-area microphone in addition, to provide better background sounds. This is because when a hearing aid is switched to the telecoil position, the only sound that is processed is that picked up by the microphone. The additional microphone would also enable hearing-aid users to converse more easily with other passengers. The system has to be tuned in order to ensure that enough sound is picked up by the microphone(s) without unnecessary noise from elsewhere (e.g. from outside the vehicle). The system was tuned to provide a strong signal near to the front entrance and at head height for passengers sitting in the vehicle. The former is intended to help with conversations with the driver related to paying the fare or other enquiries. The latter is to make it easier to hear announcements in the vehicle. A good balance between the volumes of any speech signals and ambient sounds needs to be achieved. The best way of checking that these issues have been properly addressed is to ask users of hearing aids to test the system. We are also looking at ways of making automatic announcements about the location of the bus en route. These could be added to the vehicle in due course.

Bell pushes were positioned so that it would be unnecessary for a passenger to leave the seat in order to communicate with the driver. Even though the vehicle is small, this is a good principle to adopt and the cost of additional bell pushes is very small if fitted during original manufacture.

Technical Compliance Criteria (see Table 8.7)

Procurement

We have already touched on the problem of obtaining a suitable vehicle. In the event a total of seven possible vehicle suppliers, converters or coach builders were asked to quote for the supply of the minibus based on the specification given above, which was provided on proformas originated by West Sussex County Council for accessible minibus design purposes. Also, in the light of previous experience and in order to help future purchasers, we were keen to initiate a draft technical approval procedure for coach-built modified vehicles. Only one organisation was prepared to supply the vehicle as specified. A contract was drafted and, after discussions, was awarded early in 1999. The vehicle was delivered and commissioned 12 weeks later.

Draft technical approval procedures

This was a new approach to the provision of custom-built minibus design, which was unfamiliar to and resisted by the vehicle supplier.

For the purposes of this project we required compliance with some documents that would not have normally applied to a vehicle of this size. We also referred to other regulations which were still in draft at the time of ordering the vehicle. However, the requirement was requested because we were intent on having a suitably accessible vehicle.

We wanted to ensure that all appropriate standards were being met in the design and construction of the vehicle. This would include, for example, the certified competence of welders and provision of appropriate materials (including, for example, bolts and nuts). The idea was to ensure that the vehicle was being constructed to acceptable standards and that we would know what materials had been used in the construction in the event of failure later on. Stress checks were carried out by an independent chartered mechanical engineer.

No information was provided by the supplier in response to a request for statements concerning the standards for construction and quality control. This reflects the lack of regulation of the industry.

Manufacture

Base vehicle and modification

The vehicle converter chose a Renault Master 2.8-litre tdi, low-floor chassis cab as the basis for a 13-seater, fully accessible public service vehicle (Figure 8.5). In order to meet the vehicle specification the original vehicle underwent extensive modification, being cut transversely behind the driver's cab and discarding the chassis to the rear. However, the trailing arms for the rear axle, the rear stub axles and hubs, and the brakes, lights and wheels were retained for future use. New longer channel section chassis members were fitted to the rear of the original box section chassis forming part of the cab using spigot and socket bolted joints. The new part of the chassis was braced with transverse channel sections, including out-riggers to form a 'ladder' structure. Other modifications to create a platform chassis frame included new mountings for trailing arms and suspension units, a new rear axle with brackets to support air-bag suspension units, air-bag units to replace front springs, an air pump, a reservoir and control gear, a new fuel tank and a new exhaust system. The superstructure comprising a stainless steel frame was then fabricated and welded to the chassis frame, followed by a marine plywood floor and all the coach work. The finished vehicle is shown in Figure 8.6.

Fig. 8.5   Renault Master, 2.8-litre, chassis cab

Fig. 8.6   APTRA low-floor bus: exterior view

Technical approval procedure and check calculations

In the light of previous experience, the serious nature of the modifications and the use of a largely untried design, we were concerned to avoid, as far as possible, the risk of mechanical breakdown of the Plusbus once it had been put into service. To this end we adopted a technical-approval approach toward the design and manufacture of the vehicle modification. However, this proved to be too difficult to complete fully, mainly because the vehicle converter was unfamiliar with the procedures. It was not possible for them to adapt fully to the situation in the short period available for the design and manufacture of the vehicle.

In the event, we provided the requirements for the passenger accommodation and supplied a list of chartered mechanical engineers to the converter. The converter then chose an engineer to define the loading regime and to carry out stress check calculations based on a finite-element analysis of the chassis frame, which had already been built. As a result of this work, the size of the main longitudinal chassis members was increased and several joint details were strengthened.

Development of the Bus Service

General Considerations

We have already discussed how the vehicle was designed to be fully accessible so that people with mobility problems and older people were able to use it without difficulty. Now we discuss the choice of location, route, information provision, the scheduling and general nature of the service. Although we were committed to locating the project in Cumbria for geographical and funding reasons (Cumbria County Council had supported our application for funding), it was important to choose a study area which would enable us to have a reasonable chance of success at the operational level and to carry out useful research at the investigative level.

It was also important to the project to ensure that service frequency was as high as possible, because this would allow people the greatest possible choice of travel times. Daily scheduled operation would also allow people to make regular tips (e.g. to or from work). Another important ingredient of the project was to bring the Plusbus route as close to the people as possible. It therefore goes right into villages rather than bypassing them and operates on a hail-and-ride basis. Careful thought concerning the design of the route and schedule means that an individual passenger's journeys need not take too long in practice.

Choice of Area within Cumbria

Options
As a first step, in order to assess the transport needs in this rural area among socially excluded groups, we referred to various data, including *Cumbria in Figures* (Cumbria County Council, 1995), the Population Census (Office of National Statistics, 1991) and full details of existing bus services

Table 8.8   Characteristics of the areas examined for study

Area	Size	Settlements	Boundaries		
			Daily buses	No very frequent buses	Outside National Park
North of Carlisle	Large	Very few		✓	✓
West of Carlisle	Medium	Few	✓		✓
South-east of Whitehaven	Small	Several			
East of Barrow-in-Furness	Small	Several	✓		✓
South of Appleby	Medium	Several	✓	✓	✓
South of Carlisle	Medium	Several			

in Cumbria. All bus routes in Cumbria lying outside the National Park areas were plotted on 1:50,000 Ordnance Survey Maps. The service frequencies were noted and a number of possible study areas identified.

Three areas – Allerdale, Eden and South Lakeland – were examined initially due to their very low population density (<0.8 people per hectare), with up to 9.7% of the population being aged over 75 years and about 40% of all households with pensioners, but it became clear that some areas around Carlisle also needed to be considered.

On the basis of the above information, three areas were examined in more detail (Table 8.8):

- North of Carlisle (centred around Brampton)
- West of Carlisle (within the area bordered by Wigton, Maryport and Silloth)
- South of Appleby-in-Westmorland.

The North of Carlisle area (Figure 8.7) is large and characterised by a distinct lack of settlements and bus services. This is a difficult area to serve in terms of public transport and would not have been a suitable challenge for the project. The settlements are too small and the only local centre (Brampton) is too large relative to the local communities. Also, the travelling distances would be too great to demonstrate the accessibility benefits of the project. In addition the choices of destination would have been rather limited.

The West of Carlisle area (Figure 8.8) is not too large and is bounded on one side by the sea and on the other two sides by major bus routes. However, the number of settlements is small. The three towns of Wigton, Maryport and Silloth could dominate the project by drawing too much between them from the outlying communities. The frequency of the buses on routes to Silloth and Maryport (and consequently to Wigton) is too high to analyse the interchange habits of passengers on the APTRA service. We would therefore have had difficulties isolating the effects of the new bus service.

The South of Appleby-in-Westmorland area (Figure 8.9) in the Eden Valley has several villages which are of a reasonable size for the project. The area is bounded by Appleby in the north, Kirkby Stephen to the south and South Stainmore to the east. There is a commercial bus service running weekly into Great Asby, which the project should avoid. The size of the towns (Appleby and Kirkby Stephen) relative to the size of outlying villages is reasonable. Although it is believed that there may be a historic attraction between some villages and one town or the other, this should present no problem for the project. The frequency of buses along the A66 (4 buses/day) was a little high for our purposes, but it was considered that this would not present too much of a problem as the new route would be serving villages off the main road. In addition, opportunities existed for

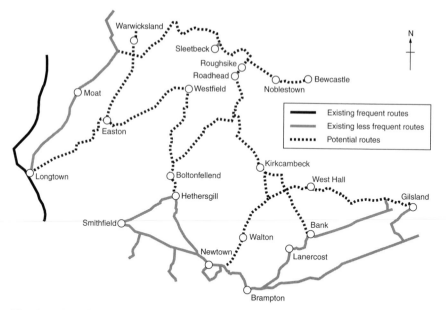

Fig. 8.7   North of Carlisle area. (Reproduced from Ordnance Survey mapping on behalf of The Controller of Her Majesty's Stationery Office © Crown Copyright. Licence Number AL 100016520. 2002)

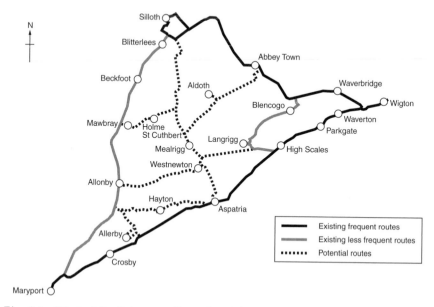

Fig. 8.8   West of Carlisle area. (Reproduced from Ordnance Survey mapping on behalf of The Controller of Her Majesty's Stationery Office © Crown Copyright. Licence Number AL 100016520. 2002)

Fig. 8.9   South of Appleby-in-Westmorland area. (Reproduced from Ordnance Survey mapping on behalf of The Controller of Her Majesty's Stationery Office © Crown Copyright. Licence Number AL 100016520. 2002)

connections with trains and lower frequency bus services towards the west of Kirby Stephen.

Chosen locality, town and villages

In view of the various drawbacks listed above, the South of Appleby area was selected for further investigation. Provisionally we included settlements such as Appleby-in-Westmorland, Sandford, Warcop, Great Musgrave, Brough, South Stainmore, Kaber, Rookby, Winton, Kirkby Stephen (and station), Soulby and Waitby. However, this list had to be reduced in order to provide a frequent service within a smaller geographical area. Following our public consultation exercise, the final choice agreed with the local community was an area around Kirkby Stephen containing 12 villages: Warcop, Little and Great Musgrave, Brough, Church Brough, Brough Sowerby, Kaber, Winton, Hartley, Nateby, Soulby and Crosby Garrett, and a few houses near the railway station at Kirkby Stephen (Figure 8.10).

Based on the criteria discussed in Chapter 3 and earlier in this chapter (see Box 8.1), it was felt that the area selected was appropriate for the following reasons:

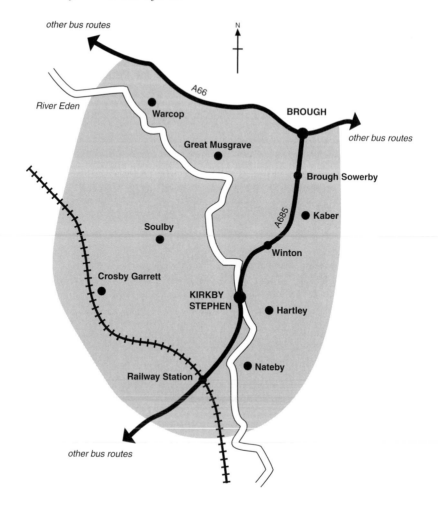

	Size of population served (Register of Electors, October 1999)
Surrounding settlements	1820
Kirkby Stephen	1407
Total	3227

Fig. 8.10 Map of Eden Valley, north of Kirkby Stephen

Geographical and social aspects:

- It provided a local market town, the focus for many of the basic services.
- There was a health centre in the market town with a satellite in one of the villages. The only secondary school in the area was located in the market town.

Operational features:

- The villages were not connected to the existing public transport network (except in a few cases where services were available on the main road which normally bypasses the villages).
- There were opportunities to interchange with other public transport services (including trains).
- The area was not too large for analysis, but was large enough to provide an example of a remote rural area.
- There were several isolated villages within a fairly small area.
- There were a few local bus operators in the area, as well as one larger operator.

Research considerations:

- The chosen area was not inside a National Park.
- Ten of the 12 settlements surrounding the market town were not directly served by an existing public bus service and were within manageable distance for the proposed new frequent service.
- Three villages had retained a post office and two had a few shops.
- Twenty-one percent of the population was of pensionable age.
- There was 'forced car ownership' for 60% of pensioner households in Eden district.
- Twenty percent of people in Eden had limiting long-term illness.
- Eight settlements had more than 40% of lone-pensioner households.
- Cumbria County Council was sympathetic to innovative public bus services and agreed that the chosen area would not interfere with other commercial bus operations.
- We needed a control area so that we could compare how the people travelled in the Cumbria Plusbus area compared with elsewhere. One possible control area was identified nearby to the west of the proposed study area. This was bounded on the east by the Settle–Carlisle railway line; to the west by Maulds Meaburn, Orton and Tebay; to the south by the A685 and to the north by the easterly part of the B62600. For political reasons, this control area proved to be impracticable and another area was chosen for comparison (see below).

Route Selection

Factors

The next step was to examine possible routes for operating a bus between settlements in the proposed study area. The main considerations were:

- physical constraints
- journey times
- traffic issues
- bus stops, bus shelters and connections.

Physical constraints were checked initially by travelling around the study area by car and checking the features of the local roads. This revealed that some roads were too narrow with very few passing places and thus were unlikely to be feasible for bus operations with the size of vehicle being proposed for the project.

With regard to journey times, we divided the road network in the area into distinct sections between junctions, noting the road width and likely travel speeds. Some junctions were treated as separate sections so that we could calculate the time required to make a turn (this being particularly important when a right-hand turn into a major road was required). We also treated any point where the vehicle might have to turn around as a separate section. We then travelled along each section in a van with dimension, weight and power characteristics as similar as possible to those of the vehicle we anticipated would be used for the bus service, at a speed that would be used by a bus. The length of each section was measured and timed. This enabled us to 'construct' any feasible route within the study area by joining together the relevant sections, and enabled us to compare journey times for the various route options.

While carrying out the timings, we also noted points at which traffic issues could be a problem (e.g. difficult right-hand turns and school bus arrival or departure points).

We were keen to go right into the centre of each village so that people did not have to walk far to get on a bus. Therefore the principal bus stops to be settled included village sites and at the Kirkby Stephen railway station. We noted potential bus stop locations and the few bus stops that already existed. Once the route had been identified in more detail, the new bus stop locations were investigated and agreed jointly on site with the local parish representative, local authority planning office, the highway authority and the police. Possible sites for bus shelters were also selected.

Features of the selected route

The Cumbria Plusbus route as implemented is shown in Figure 8.11. The route is fixed and serves 12 villages around the market town of Kirkby Stephen. It also includes the railway station (which is some 2 km from the town). In order to ensure that journey times are not too long, the bus calls at the market town after visiting a small number of villages, then goes to another small group of villages before returning to the town, and so on. This results in a frequent service at certain points in the town – the bus

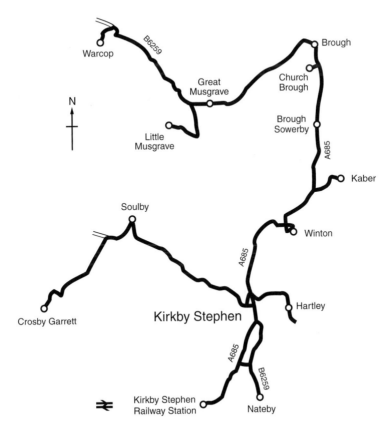

Fig. 8.11   The Cumbria Plusbus route

calls 24 times/day at one of the supermarkets, which has since constructed an accessible bus stop for the service. The bus route approaching this stop also gives access for ambulant people to the health centre, thus helping to provide a good service for visits to the health and social services facilities located there. Further details of the route are given in Appendix 3.

Infrastructure: Bus Stop Shelter and Platform

Cumbria County Council constructed one rural bus shelter on the APTRA Plusbus route at Crosby Garrett based on the space requirements mentioned in Chapter 5, as a model for the Lake District National Park. However, the council decided, without consultation, to reduce some of the dimensions and also repositioned the entrance. The effect has been to place the seating in a rather inconvenient position (see Figures 8.12 to 8.15). The reduction in the dimensions has also made the footways on the platform rather narrow for turning manoeuvres and there is no dedicated wheelchair space inside the shelter. This shelter would not meet wheelchair users' requirements, except for the near all-round visibility it offers. On the other hand, the difficulty perceived by the local planners was that the shelter would look too large in the village, thus spoiling the local visual environment. This is an example where a compromise was sought between two conflicting requirements and has resulted in a loss to some disabled people.

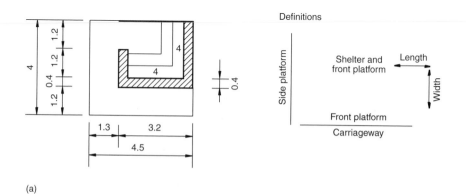

(a)

Fig. 8.12   Crosby Garrett bus shelter: (a) layout dimensions (in m); (b) external view, including platform

Fig. 8.13   Crosby Garrett bus shelter: platform

Fig. 8.14   Crosby Garrett bus shelter: entrance

Fig. 8.15   Crosby Garrett bus shelter: seating

Preparation of the Timetable and Fare Tables

Timetable

It was decided during the consultation exercise that the service should run on Mondays to Saturdays providing four services in each direction each day. The service is scheduled to run every 3 hours, starting at 6.30 a.m. and finishing at 6.30 p.m. The actual times at each official bus stop were determined as described above. Any slack in the timetable was put at the end of each journey to allow either time for catching up, time to start the next journey on time and/or to give the driver a short break. It also allows the timetable to be simple – it is the same every day so there is no need to remember different schedules for different days.

Connections are made with some of the train services at Kirkby Stephen station. It is possible to connect with only a few trains because of the irregularity of the railway timetable, and because there is only one vehicle on the Plusbus service. Nevertheless, it has been possible to provide identifiable connections which allow enough time to reach the platform in time for the train or for the train to be late without missing the bus. This means that passengers may sometimes have to wait for a fairly long time at the station, but the service has been designed to allow older people and others with mobility problems to reach the train (or bus) without stress.

Given the difficulty of making connections with the train services, we sought to get passengers to the early morning train to Carlisle for work or early hospital appointments, to the mid-morning train to Carlisle for afternoon hospital appointments or visiting, and to catch the late afternoon train back to connect with the Plusbus for the journey home. It was more difficult to connect with trains to Settle and Leeds, although there were some connections on Saturdays. The bus meets three trains a day from Carlisle and one from Settle (two on Saturdays). Further details are given in Appendix 2.

Fare tables

Having recorded all the incremental distances between official bus stop locations on the route, as described above, a table was prepared showing the route mileage between stops. Where the Plusbus followed the same route as other bus routes a rate per mile for existing services was determined for longer distances (i.e. more than 2 miles). This rate was applied to the fares to be charged for the Plusbus, regardless of distance, subject to rounding up to the nearest 5 pence, and a minimum charge of 10 pence for an adult fare. In addition, 10-pence flat fare zones were created for Kirkby Stephen and Warcop to encourage short cheap shopping trips in these areas, particularly for those with mobility problems. We wished to respond to the need expressed by people for the bus to be accessible for short journeys – even a ride of 50 m could provide a welcome relief for someone having difficulty walking in poor weather or with heavy shopping. We were particularly interested in whether this approach would benefit elderly people. Further information about the fare table is contained in Appendix 2.

Information

As discussed in Chapter 6, the provision of accessible information is essential to obtaining an accessible public transport service. In many cases this is seen only in terms of real-time information. However, as we showed in Chapter 6, this is only a part of the information system. It is also necessary to have information available before starting on a journey. The various types of information provided for users are described below.

Printed material

Leaflet giving timetable and fare table.   As with most public transport systems, the main source of information is through printed timetables and other published 'static' information. We tested a number of timetable formats to check legibility and clarity for people with varying degrees of visual impairment. The font was chosen on the basis of advice from the Royal National Institute for the Blind, and the paper quality and colour were selected to provide sufficient contrast without too much glare. The county-wide timetables produced by Cumbria County Council are comprehensive, but the small print size makes them inaccessible to people with poor eyesight. The provision of information via the Public Transport Information 2000 project will help with the dissemination of information, especially on a regional or national basis. However, this will not remove the need for clear printed information about local services or the need to provide legible information at bus stops. For further details see Appendix 2.

Leaflet describing locations of official bus stops. We produced simplified maps of each village on the route. These show the exact location of the official bus stops in relation to identifiable points within the village (e.g. church, pub, river, prominent house, other feature). Appendix 3 shows maps for the villages on the route, including the complete route in a normal geographical format. However, the development of a map which represents the major geographical aspects of a route but which is simplified to make it easier to follow was recognised many years ago by the operators of the London Underground system. We therefore produced a simplified, schematic version of the map for the Cumbria Plusbus service, reducing the route to straight lines with a limited number of angles to indicate changes in direction. Part of the printed information is shown in Appendix 3.

Timetables (large print) for display at bus stops. A timetable case was attached to the pole erected at each official bus stop. The internal dimensions of the cases (740 mm by 320 mm) allowed plenty of scope for producing legible information, and to make the service more inclusive we provided large-print timetables for people with visual problems. This takes the form of timetables in each direction, rail connections, a large schematic route map based on that developed for the leaflet (see above) and other information. We had in mind that the bus stop display should be easily readable from 1 m away, and set the font size, print style and background accordingly. Details concerning the legibility and durability of these timetables are as follows:

- Thin card: chromomat white, weight 230 g/m^2.
- Print: black, main text, bold, font size 14 pt, font type Helvetica.
- Encapsulation: glossy plastic, thickness 75 μm.

The prepared sheet was encapsulated to prevent condensation, which would make the ink run and, finally, rot the paper. At the time of writing, these timetables are still in use, and have neither faded nor rotted, so we can conclude that the above specification is an appropriate starting point for such displayed material.

Tactile schematic map of route and Braille timetable (Appendices 4 and 5). We took the opportunity afforded by the Cumbria Plusbus service to consider the provision of a tactile map with Braille timetables for blind people. This information is produced on paper which can be folded and carried about. Thus it is no longer necessary for blind people to memorise the entire timetable. The tactile map shows the spatial arrangement of the villages on the route and how the bus travels between them. The form of the map is the same as the schematic map described above and so would be recognised by someone who had access to a copy of the simplified map even though they would not be able to read the Braille text.

The blind person who tried out the first draft was amazed to discover where the villages were located in relation to each other (even though he had been born in the area and thought he was familiar with the district).

Audio information: timetable and general user information recorded on CD
When presented with a timetable, a sighted person sees the whole arrangement at once (e.g. the rows and columns, and the route number and destination). This is a characteristic of the eye – it is extremely good at taking in a whole range of information simultaneously, leaving the brain to sort out what is actually useful. The user of a timetable searches for the appropriate place in the rows of the timetable and then looks across the columns to find the most convenient service. People who cannot adopt this 'overview and search refinement' strategy have to receive information piece by piece, one piece after another (e.g. a person who cannot see, or who can see only at very close range, cannot see enough, or any, of the document to make a judgement about how to refine the search). This has a serious effect on the way in which we deliver information to people with sight difficulties. To consider this effect, a sighted person has to imagine that they can only read a timetable character by character. Answers to simple questions such as 'Where do you start to read the document?', 'How do you know what the document is?' or 'How is the information arranged?' are essential to enable a blind person to understand the document. If the information can only be received serially, each question (and answer) has to be explained in this way (i.e. serially).

We realised that simply translating the normal timetable text into Braille was not sufficient. Apart from the issues raised about the nature of the information, the number of people who can read Braille is quite small. Information delivered orally is also serial. To make the timetable accessible to a wider body of people with visual impairments, we had to provide the information in an audible format. Conventionally, this is done by recording the information onto tape and playing it back through a cassette recorder. This would be attractive for a timetable in the sense that a tape player could be used to make the information portable. However, the major difficulty with tape is that it is very difficult to locate the relevant information. Recorded books make use of a tone to mark the beginning of, for example, a chapter. This tone can be detected while the tape is being wound forward or backwards, so that by counting the number of 'beeps' the listener can find the correct chapter. We therefore had to break up the oral information so that we could define suitable divisions that could be marked in this way.

We therefore had to work out how to break up the oral information so that it could be obtained in memorable pieces without being so broken up that it would be too complicated to join the pieces together. We decided to deliver the information place by place. This follows the strategy described above – look for the place and then find the times. The Cumbria Plusbus has 22 stopping points in each direction. If each place were recorded as a separate 'chapter' there would be 44 chapters. Trying to find chapter 42 on a tape would be complicated, even with the tone system described above. We therefore used a different technology.

CDs are becoming more popular and cheaper. The advantage of a CD is that it provides random-access memory. Therefore, any point on the disc can be reached independently of what has been recorded before or after it. This is, of course, used to great effect with computer data, but also for acoustic CDs where different pieces of music are recorded on different tracks and each track can be selected as required by the listener. We therefore recorded information on a separate track for each stopping point noted on the published timetable. The information includes the times at which the bus calls at the stopping point, an indication of journey times to a few places along the route and in some cases information about the location of the bus stop. In the case of the railway station we also indicated the train connections and how to reach the platforms from the bus stop. Figure 8.16 shows an example of what is said on the CD for one of the stops. The voice used is a 'tenor' voice, as this is the pitch which provides the best clarity. Ideally, a local accent should be used, but this should not be so strong that someone from outside the local area would not understand what is being said. The text should be read slowly, with a clear gap between separate elements of the information (although these breaks should not be so long as to make the listener feel that they are missing something, the track has finished or the machine has broken down). Indicating the end of a track is a good idea so that people know when they have reached the end of the information for each stopping point. Testing with potential users is clearly important.

There are three tracks on the CD that simply indicate how to use the CD. The first track (i.e. the one that would play automatically when the CD is started) explains what the CD is and that there is an index track which will indicate which track number relates to each stopping point. It also suggests that more general information about the bus service is available on a separate track. By separating the tracks in this way the information within each track is kept fairly short, so it is not necessary to listen for a long time in order to find the required detail.

CD technology is becoming more common, both in the form of players in houses and in a portable form. The technology is robust and, unlike a

Track 8 ..... Buses from Christian Head Health Centre.

Buses leave Christian Head Health Centre for Kirkby Stephen town centre and Warcop at 6.41, 9.41, 12.41 and 3.41.

The bus takes 14 minutes to reach the town centre via Hartley. The journey to Nateby takes 19 minutes, the journey to the Railway Station takes 24 minutes and the journey to Warcop takes about 1 hour 10 minutes.

Buses leave Christian Head Health Centre for Soulby and Crosby Garrett at 9.15, 12.15, 3.15 and 6.15. The journey to Soulby takes 4 minutes and the journey to Crosby Garrett takes 9 minutes.

End of Track 8.

Fig. 8.16   Example text from the Cumbria Plusbus audible timetable

cassette tape, maintains its clarity throughout its life. Once the initial effort has been made to write and record the text, the reproduction costs are quite small. There will not be a requirement for large numbers of these CDs and it would not be difficult to place the data on a web page so that it could be heard over the internet by people with suitable cards in their computers (which many blind people have).

Other types of information

Prior to travel.   Posters were produced to publicise the bus service. These were displayed on parish notice boards, at the Kirkby Stephen Council and Community Centre, the Tourist Information Centre and at health centres. Other publicity was provided in the form of numerous press releases and photo opportunities, including items on local television news. These were kindly arranged through the Countryside Agency.

In addition, a global positioning system (GPS) device was fitted to the vehicle. Although basically a management tool, this was also developed as an information source. We managed to put the real-time GPS information onto a web page so that the bus could be located using the internet.

In-bus.   An induction loop was fitted in the passenger saloon of the vehicle to improve communication between the driver and passengers with a hearing aid. The conducting wire around the compartment was operated at mains voltage using an inverter connected to the 12-V vehicle supply. No stray magnetic fields interfered with the reception inside the vehicle because the passenger saloon had a non-magnetic stainless steel frame with aluminium and fibre glass panel covering.

Community Involvement

Local consultations

In October 1998 we distributed leaflets about a new rural bus service to each parish in the area. We then asked parish councils to set up meetings in several local communities to explain the proposals, discuss how the service could meet their needs and to receive potential users' views on the route, frequency, operating hours and vehicle specification. Following these meetings a route and schedule were prepared, checked on site and presented at village meetings. In most cases people's wishes were met. Where this was not possible, explanations were given. This consultative process was designed to help people feel a real sense of community ownership of the service.

The basic principles of public participation have been discussed in Chapter 7, and we give here some of the issues that arose during this exercise (Tyler and Brown, 2000). At first, people were surprised to be consulted on such a matter and it was helpful that the parish council had called the meeting so that the community's attention was drawn to the issue. This gave the ownership of the meeting to the local people – it was not a case of some outsider calling local people to listen to a set of their ideas. The reaction to the exercise varied between parish councils, from a friendly dialogue between the university and the assembled people, to a formal presentation by the university with special dispensation to the public to ask questions. Nevertheless, the project was being 'promoted' by a university rather than a political body, the advantage being that the university was not involved in the local politics and so the meeting could proceed without the need to bring previous political decisions into the discussion. This is one of the reasons why we have suggested that an independent facilitator is useful in public participation meetings.

For the first round of meetings, we had prepared a leaflet which explained what we were trying to do and approximately where we were thinking of doing it. Among other suggestions, we received strong representations from one small village that it should be included in the route. This enabled us to open up the discussion about the interaction between journey length and frequency. We were pleased to receive the views of the meetings about their issues and took away various suggestions for a bus route. These were investigated to see how many could be included and at what cost. We also discussed aspects of the specification of the vehicle with the public, including seat width and spacing, headroom, aisle width and colour scheme.

We devised several options for routes and services on the basis of these initial consultation meetings and tested them for operational feasibility. We then returned to the villages and presented them with options for their comment. This series of meetings also permitted examples of timetable and other information about the service to be discussed. In most cases it was possible to satisfy the wishes of the communities. Where this was not possible, we provided explanations for the choices we had made.

Kirkby Stephen Secondary School

During October 1999 we were invited to talk to the lower school classes about the Plusbus project. As a result, the children in the school began to explain how useful this bus was to them and their friends. At the same time we learnt more about how they and their families used the bus. This was a very valuable and useful exchange: young people have much to say about their local environment (including the transport system) and their views should be taken into account in the same way as for other members of the public. After all, young people are significant users of the transport system and the habit of using public rather than private transport needs to be started early. As we can see from the user survey (see below), the Plusbus has been particularly successful in this respect.

Development of a succession strategy

The community knew that the project would end in August 2000 but did not wish to lose the bus service. In September 1999 we held a meeting with representatives from all the parishes to discuss various options for the future. The majority felt that community management of a local bus service was possible, but they did not want a service operated by volunteers.

Community management of the bus service

Following several public meetings the local people realised that they needed to do all they could to secure additional revenue over the next few years. They would also need to develop links with possible funding bodies in order to continue to own and manage the community bus service in their area beyond the end of the university project. As a result, people in the community came forward and set up a management company limited by guarantee, registered at Companies House. The community has also agreed to provide £5000 each year towards the operating deficit of the bus service and £2000 each year towards administration costs for the first few years. Some parishes have raised the money by Precept, but one decided to provide their share by holding fundraising events.

Procurement of the Bus Operator

Once the route, service frequency and a tentative timetable had been agreed with the local people, we went ahead with the process of contracting an operator and registering the service with the Traffic Commissioner.

Level of bus service provision

Contract documents for the bus service were drafted on the basis of providing an accessible public local bus service, hail-and-ride plus official bus stops, going right into villages, and using drivers who had received training in disability awareness and first aid. There would be clock face operation at intervals of 3 hours from 6.30 a.m. to 6.30 p.m. Monday to Saturday, excluding Bank Holidays. The bus would also be available for private hire outside its scheduled operating times. The service was to be operated under a full operator's licence; the operator contracting to provide the service as specified by the university. For a list of topics included in the contract see Appendix 1.

Tendering procedure

Initially, it was proposed by the Steering Group that the bus service should be run by the major bus company in the area. However, following significant and unacceptable price rises, expressions of interest were sought from small local bus operators in the area. Subsequently, on the basis of competitive unit labour and mileage rates, a contract was given to a bus company located in one of the villages on the Plusbus route.

Registration of the bus service

The bus operator, as part of his contract with the university, applied to the local Traffic Commissioner to register the Plusbus as a new local commercial bus service between Crosby Garrett and Warcop (No. 571). The application included a copy of the agreed timetable in both directions, indicating connecting services and the hail-and-ride facility. The service started on 19 April 1999.

Monitoring of the Plusbus Service

Three separate methods were used to monitor the performance and to generate sufficient data for studying how the community used the new Plusbus service.

Bus ticket machine

A manually operated Wayfarer MKII ticket issuing machine (Figure 8.17) was installed on the Plusbus to record all tickets issued. The removable module retains details of each ticket, including driver number, journey number, stage number, time, ticket number, fare and class of ticket Examples of a bus ticket and driver's waybill are shown in Figure 8.18.

At the end of each shift the driver removes the module and the ticket machine issues a waybill recording the time, module number, running total money recorded, number of tickets issued and number of tickets cancelled. At the end of the working day the module is downloaded into

Fig. 8.17   (a) Wayfarer MKII: (a) machine; (b) module

a Depot Reader machine, which issues a driver's receipt (Figure 8.19), recording the time, driver number, module number, tickets issued, tickets cancelled, total money and date and time that the module was last zeroed. The operator can then generate at the end of each week a printout showing complete details of all tickets issued during the period. These details were input manually into an Excel spreadsheet. Following initial checks of the output to confirm that the data were consistent with the waybills and drivers' receipts, derived information included, among other things:

- a graph of the total number of boarding passengers per week
- a graph of the total revenue generated per week
- the number of tickets issued at each stage, journey and day of week
- the number of tickets issued at each stage and possible destination per week

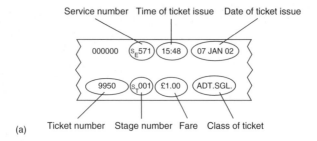

Service number   Time of ticket issue   Date of ticket issue

Ticket number   Stage number   Fare   Class of ticket

(a)

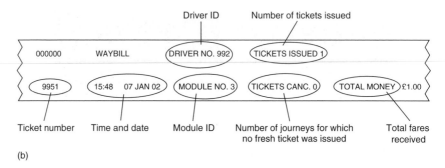

Driver ID   Number of tickets issued

Ticket number   Time and date   Module ID   Number of journeys for which   Total fares
no fresh ticket was issued   received

(b)

Fig. 8.18   (a) Bus ticket; (b) waybill

- the revenue generated at each stage, journey and day of the week
- the revenue per class of ticket sold and the total fare per passenger for each direction of travel and day of operation
- the revenue per passenger trip for the service as a whole and for each stage, if desired.

Other data were generated as and when required.

User survey

As part of the APTRA project a 10-week questionnaire survey of users was carried out in April, May and June 2000. This survey supplemented the regular monitoring of usage. At the same time a similar survey was carried out of the long-established Fellrunner Community Bus service operating under Section 22 of the 1985 Transport Act in an area nearby. The questionnaires sought to find out how users had altered their travel habits as a result of the two different bus services (new and established), including information about transfers from car (as ex-car-passenger or ex-car-driver), use of the bus, effects of the accessibility measures incorporated in the bus service, reasons for travel and the nature of journey purposes.

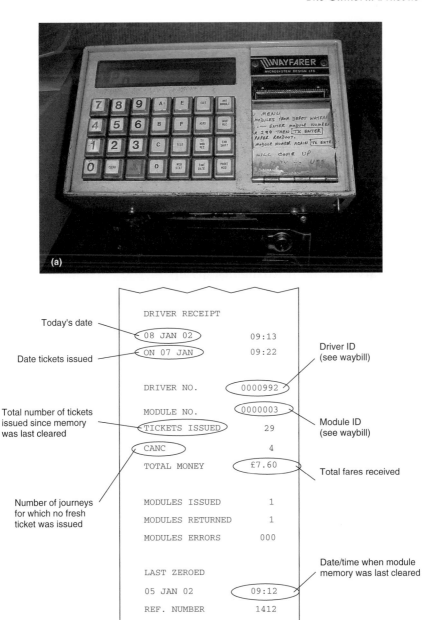

Fig. 8.19 (a) Wayfarer Depot Reader; (b) driver's receipt

Essential features of the surveyed services.   These were as follows:

The APTRA service:

- the bus is accessible (e.g. low floor, no stairs, satisfies most DPTAC requirements for large buses)
- the two or three local drivers are fully licensed for passenger-carrying vehicles, trained (including in disability awareness) and well known to the passengers
- about 280 trips per week on one bus
- journeys are spread throughout the day and over 6 days of the week
- the service is hail-and-ride plus bus stops, and carries newspapers in bulk to several of the villages.

The Community Bus service:

- the bus is less accessible than the APTRA vehicle (e.g. high floor, entry steps, restricted internal space)
- the drivers are all drawn from a large pool of volunteers (>30)
- about 110 trips per week on two buses
- there is little choice of day or time to travel, the bus visiting each village mostly once on a particular day each week.

Objectives of the surveys.   These were:

- to learn more about the people using the bus services
- to find out how people made similar journeys before April 1999
- to compare and contrast the APTRA service with a Community Bus service operated by volunteers providing shopping trips from different villages on different days of the week to one of two large towns in north Cumbria
- to record the purposes of journeys made using the bus services
- to identify passenger needs not met by the bus services in the local context, and to help inform the development of rural policy.

Survey form.   On-bus questionnaires were used. The survey form was designed to be read easily (i.e. large print, clear typeface) and to be short in overall length. This approach limited the form to 15 questions on four sides of A4 paper but increased, we believe, the number of people prepared to participate in the exercise.

Survey sample size.   The number of responses to the surveys and the approximate level of weekly use of each service are given Table 8.9.

Results of the surveys.   A selection of the results and their interpretation are presented below. For further details, including the methodology

Table 8.9   Survey sample size

Bus service	Sample size	Approximate number of trips per week
APTRA	59	280
Community	58	110

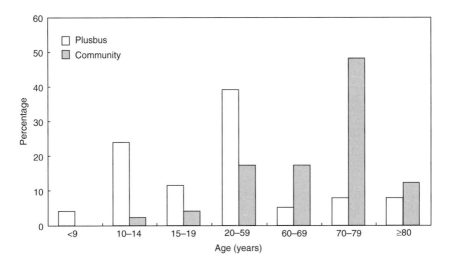

Fig. 8.20   Survey results: age distribution of users

adopted for the analysis of the information, the reader is referred to Brown and Tyler (2001).

Age distribution.   The results of the surveys (Figure 8.20) showed that the APTRA Plusbus service carried passengers of all ages, 36% of passengers being in the 10–19 years age group. The Community Bus service, however, appeared to cater mainly for elderly people. There were very few young users. However, the age demographics for the two areas are broadly similar. The reason for this apparent anomaly may lie in the difference between the timetables adopted by the two services.

Occupation. The survey results (Figure 8.21) indicated that the APTRA bus service was used equally by school children, working and retired people and only a few holiday-makers. However, the Community Bus was used predominantly by retired people, again because the timetable was designed to carry people into the local town at a time convenient for shopping.

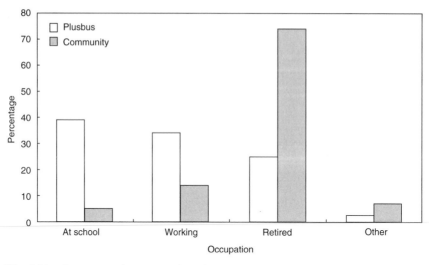

Fig. 8.21   Survey results: occupation of users

Journey purpose.   The survey responses (Figure 8.22) showed that the APTRA service provided transport for shopping, education and work in roughly equal measure, but twice as many (42%) used it for social purposes. The Community Bus tended to be used for shopping (79%), which is not particularly surprising as this was its original purpose many years ago. This service does not seem to have set out to widen its appeal to other types of user.

Distribution of outward journeys throughout the day.   The survey results (Figure 8.23) show that outward journeys on the APTRA service, which has a 3-hour frequency, have a fairly even spread throughout the day, although the demand is low during the mid-morning and mid-afternoon periods. The distribution for the Community Bus relates to a timetable having a single journey each day and is therefore constrained by the departure time of the bus service.

Mode of outward journey before April 1999.   The survey responses (Figure 8.24) showed that 79% of APTRA service users would have made similar journeys using different transport before April 1999 (when the service started). Of those who did travel, over 40% (32% of the total) received a lift by car, over 30% (27% of the total) drove a car and others used a bus or taxi, cycled or walked. The situation with the Community Bus service was rather different, as this had been in existence for nearly 20 years. Of the people who made the journey before April 1999 (91%), 45% (41% of the total) used the bus, about half received a lift or used their car and others used the train or taxi. There were no cyclists or walkers, probably due to the age of the travellers or the distance of travel. The percentage of people who did not travel previously shows the extent to which a lack of public transport acts as a barrier to social inclusion.

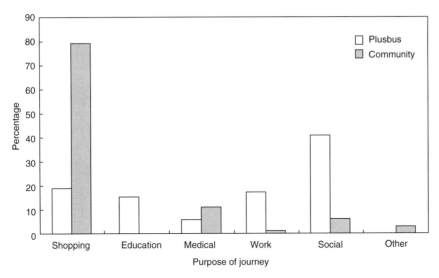

Fig. 8.22   Survey results: purpose of journeys

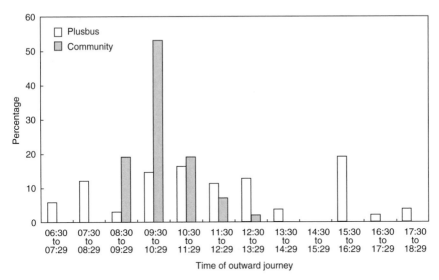

Fig. 8.23   Survey results: time of outward journey

Increased use of bus services. Both surveys asked users whether they made more journeys in April 2000 than in April 1999. Between two-thirds and three-quarters of all current users reported that they were making more journeys in April 2000 than in 1999. In both cases, most of the additional journeys were being made using the bus services in the survey. The details are given in Table 8.10.

Additional journeys. For the people making more journeys on the bus services, the relationship between their occupation and their journey purpose is as follows. The survey showed that APTRA bus users made additional journeys mainly for social, work and educational reasons if they were below retirement age, whereas retired people made additional trips mainly for shopping and medical purposes (Table 8.11). Community Bus users of all ages surveyed were interested in visiting shops more frequently and, if retired, made more medical trips. They reported no additional social trips (Table 8.12).

Reasons for using the bus services. The responses to the surveys showed that APTRA users were interested equally in the proximity of the bus service to their home, the low cost of the bus fares and that there was no need to ask for a lift from relatives and/or friends. The Community Bus users were most interested in the proximity of the service, followed by the helpfulness of the driver and a convenient timetable. The answers given in the surveys may reflect differences in the age distribution and financial situation of the users of the two services (Figure 8.25).

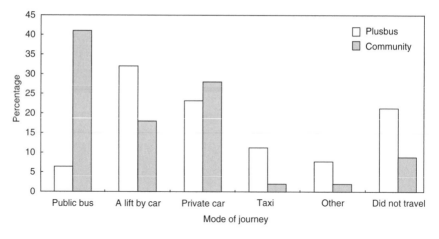

Fig. 8.24   Survey results: mode of outward journey before April 1999

Table 8.10   Increased use of bus services

Bus service	Made more journeys in April 2000 than in April 1999 (% of total)	Journeys made using the bus service (% of total)
APTRA	71	62
Community	63	61

Table 8.11   Additional journeys on the APTRA bus service

Occupation	Purpose of journey (%)					Total (%)
	Shopping	Education	Medical	Work	Social	
At school		11		3	26	40
Working	3			6	20	29
Retired	14		11		6	31
Other						
Total (%)	17	11	11	9	52	100

Table 8.12   Additional journeys on the Community Bus service

Occupation	Purpose of journey (%)					Total (%)
	Shopping	Education	Medical	Work	Social	
At school	6					6
Working	12		1	1		14
Retired	57	1	10	4		72
Other	7		1			8
Total (%)	82	1	12	5	0	100

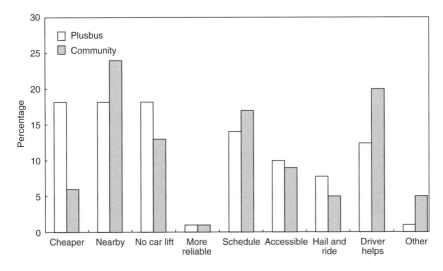

Fig. 8.25   Survey results: reasons for using the bus services

Inter-village trips.   Users were asked whether or not they used their service to travel between villages (Figure 8.26). The survey showed that 17% of the APTRA service users did so. Of these, the majority gave their reason for travel as 'social'. The remaining 83% travelled to and from the small market town in the area. The opportunities provided for inter-village bus services were taken up by people of all ages. The Community Bus survey did not show any inter-village journeys. This reinforces the view that users were only interested in shopping trips, not social activities within the community.

Frequent users and purpose of journey.   The APTRA bus service survey showed that 41% of users made regular journeys (e.g. for work, education, shopping) once or more times each week (Table 8.13). Assuming that all these journeys need to be made it is clear that people will adapt to make daily use of a cheap and frequent bus service where it is provided. The survey results showed that the service was able to respond to people's needs. The percentage of regular weekly journeys made on each day of the week is shown in Table 8.14. The table indicates that a greater than average number of journeys were made on Mondays, Tuesdays and Thursdays, and thus journeys were not restricted to market day (Monday) in the town. This clearly shows that people want to travel on most days of the week. A similar analysis of the survey data from Community Bus users revealed that 27% of users made frequent journeys (Table 8.15). The maximum number of journeys recorded by a user in a week was three. However, this figure may hide a suppressed demand because the bus service does not operate on the same route every day of the week. Of the

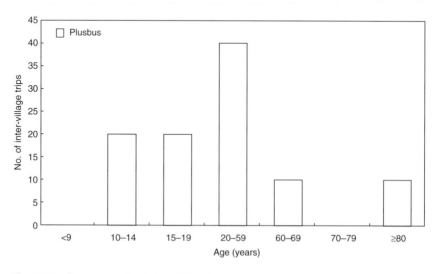

Fig. 8.26   Survey results: inter-village trips

Table 8.13   APTRA bus service: the purpose of frequent journeys

No. of journeys made by each user each week	Purpose of journey						Users	
	Shopping	Education	Medical	Work	Social	Total	Total No.	% of survey sample
1	2					2	2	3
2	2	2		4	2	10	5	9
3	5	1	4	3	5	18	6	10
4				8		8	2	3
5		15		10		25	5	9
6	6	6		6	6	24	4	7
Total	15	24	4	31	13	87	24	41

Table 8.14   APTRA and Community Bus services: days of week on which frequent journeys were made

	% of journeys					
	Mon.	Tues.	Wed.	Thurs.	Fri.	Sat.
APTRA	22	18	14	21	16	9
Community Bus	0	44	0	22	19	15

journeys made regularly each week, the percentage of journeys made on each day of the week is shown in Table 8.14. It is worth noting that the Community Bus is not in service on Mondays. The most frequent purpose given is shopping on Tuesday, the market day in the large town to which the bus travels on most days. This contrasts with the APTRA user survey, and may reflect the different age profile of the users of the two services.

Proximity of bus service to home.   A key principle of the APTRA service was that it should be routed to the centre of each village along the route. However, one village was less well served than the others in this respect. In response to user feedback, the route was extended by 500 m in mid-November 1999 to resolve this. Figure 8.27 shows the resulting change in patronage as derived from ticket-machine records.

Users' unmet needs.   The questionnaires asked users to suggest improvements to the two bus services, under four headings. A summary of the responses is given in Box 8.2. In addition, the Community Bus survey asked users what features they would like in a new bus. Putting this into context, the existing bus service made use of a conventional 23-seat, high-floor vehicle. The responses (50), expressed in order of popularity, are given in Table 8.16. The most popular feature desired was a low step. This reflects the greater age and lack of mobility of users of the service and that the buses were not low-floor vehicles. The next most popular features – the wide aisle and storage for shopping – reflect the main use of the service (i.e. shopping). Some users were also anticipating increased infirmity with age by selecting the need for a flat floor and space for one or two wheelchairs. However, they did not show much interest in an induction loop, easier seat belts or pushchair storage.

Tracking facilities

The vehicle was fitted with equipment to enable it to be tracked by satellite using the GPS. The satellite system gives the location of the vehicle as it travels along the route. This was used to provide information about the whereabouts of the bus and to check on service reliability. However, the cost of obtaining the location data was so high that for a one-vehicle

Table 8.15 *Community Bus service: the purpose of frequent journeys*

No. of journeys made by each user each week	Purpose of journey						Users	
	Shopping	Education	Medical	Work	Social	Total	Total No.	% of survey sample
1	6			0.5*	0.5*	7	7	12
2	10		1		3	14	7	12
3	4.5*		1.5*			6	2	3
Totals	20.5	0	2.5	0.5	3.5	27	16	27

*More than one journey purpose.

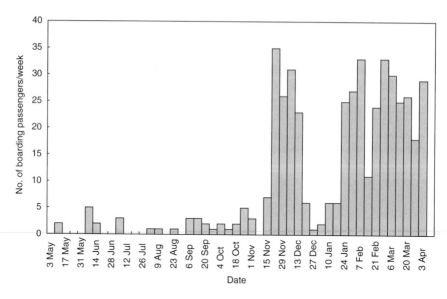

Fig. 8.27   Survey results: proximity of bus service to home and service usage

Box 8.2   Users' comments in relation to unmet needs in the APTRA and Community Bus services

---

Timetable
- Several APTRA users wanted the bus to run on Sundays, during the evenings and to make better connections with the local train services
- A few Community Bus users wanted the service to run more frequently (i.e. from each village on more than one day each week)

Route
- Several APTRA users wished that the bus ran on a more extensive route
- One Community Bus user wanted to have a bus stop at a medical centre

Information
- Two APTRA users said that they could not use the timetable
- No suggestions for changes were made by Community Bus users

Other
- One APTRA user suggested that weekly tickets could be issued
- Two Community Bus users said they needed footrests

Table 8.16   Community Bus service: interest in accessibility features

Feature	Responses (%)
Low step	37
Wide aisle	19
Storage for shopping	19
Flat floor	9
Space for one or two wheelchairs	7
Wide seats	4
Induction loop	2
Easier seat belt	2
Storage for pushchairs	1

service it was not considered to be providing a sufficient benefit to justify the costs. The location data would cost the same for a much larger fleet operation, so this type of system could become worthwhile for large-scale bus operations. The reality in this case was that the Plusbus service was generally very reliable. In any event, a potential passenger could contact the local bus operator by telephone to enquire about the whereabouts of the bus.

Other Uses

When the Plusbus was not being used for the scheduled service (i.e. on weekday evenings, Sundays and Bank Holidays) it was available to the communities it served on a private-hire basis. This had two objectives. First, it allowed the communities to have a transport resource which they could use for journeys outside the scheduled route and timetable. Secondly, it gave the opportunity to identify specific journeys that might be incorporated in a schedule at a later date. However, this aspect of the service has not been taken up as had been hoped. This is partly because the bus is in service for so much of the working day that it is difficult to make it available at the times that groups would want to hire it and partly because the small capacity of the vehicle makes it rather expensive to hire.

The Plusbus also carries goods. It is currently delivering newspapers in bulk to many of the outlying villages and has delivered leaflets for the Kirkby Stephen Community Centre. Some traders have used the bus to deliver packages and the trend is expected to continue once people have learnt how to make best use of this service. The bulk delivery of mail (i.e. letters and or parcels) has been discussed with Consignia, but problems such as insurance, security and labour relations have to be addressed before further progress can be made. Other possibilities for generating revenue, such as delivery of prescriptions, advertising and sponsorship, still need to be explored.

Discussion

Vehicle

Procurement

Several issues of interest arose during the process of procuring the vehicle. Most vehicle converters approached were unwilling to consider constructing a vehicle to the required specification. The one manufacturer who was prepared to meet the requirements (see earlier in this chapter) probably did not realise the full implications. Bearing in mind the actual approach the converter took towards 'design' problems, it is now clear, with hindsight, that it was too ambitious to expect the proposed technical approval procedures to be implemented fully within the limited time period available. Formal technical approval procedures would have been useful for two reasons.

First, it became clear that the vehicle converter did not have enough qualified technical staff in house capable of carrying out engineering calculations to support the design process. It was their custom to fabricate the chassis, measure up the completed structure and produce drawings. Then, when urged to calculate the stresses in the structural members, they would employ a separate organisation to check the adequacy of the 'design'. This procedure meant that there was a very real risk that the chassis would have to be modified at a later date, after work had started on the assembly of the passenger saloon superstructure. This actually happened in the case of the APTRA vehicle, the disruption delaying completion and creating problems in commissioning the vehicle.

Secondly, during construction it was obvious that there were few quality-control procedures in place. There was no monitoring of welding procedures and no proper certification of welders for the types of structural welds being produced. There was also a worrying reluctance to think about the implications of removing structural material, which had been found to be highly stressed in check calculations. In this instance the converter removed the material to increase the clearance between the steelwork and the rubber airbag suspension unit, which was fretting against the edge of a gusset plate. The result of this action is noted below. Eventually, the converter had to modify, remanufacture and fit a new rear axle subframe to the vehicle. We believe this sequence of events could have been avoided if proper design and construction procedures had been adopted initially.

The issues mentioned above were of particular interest, because in this case the university had the time, knowledge and resources to insist that the structural quality of the design be checked. These facilities would probably not be available to most organisations purchasing modified vehicles in this market at present. It would appear, therefore, that current design and construction procedures could be improved.

For the future, it would be beneficial to introduce a formal technical approval procedure for vehicle conversions. However, the regulation of the design and construction process would need to be based on the results of a national survey of mechanical problems arising from modifications by vehicle converters. In the short term, clients could provide a detailed specification based on their users' needs over the design life of the vehicle and insist that the vehicle converter provide a signed statement setting out the design criteria proposed to satisfy the client's specifications. The client or their technical adviser could approve these criteria in principle. The designer would then be expected to have his design calculation checked independently before construction went ahead. This procedure would also act as a check during the construction of the vehicle. Apart from anything else it would force the vehicle converter to think through the implications of the specification for the detailed design of the vehicle.

Costs

The cost for the supply of the vehicle, including the induction loop and pedestrian ramps, was approximately £54,000 at 1999 prices.

Vehicle component reliability

The maintenance regime for the Plusbus was subject to several constraints:

- The original manufacturer's warranty was valid for 12 months from the date of registration and related to the Renault components only, the routine maintenance schedule being based on mileage intervals.
- The vehicle converter's warranty (in this case only) was transferable and valid for 24 months or 120,000 miles, whichever was sooner, from delivery of the vehicle, and related to non-Renault vehicle components built, modified and/or supplied by the converter.
- The bus operator was obliged to carry out routine maintenance of all his public service vehicles at monthly intervals as a condition of his licence from the Traffic Commissioner.

Records of all maintenance work and vehicle breakdowns were kept by the bus operator. These records showed not only the regular servicing carried out, but also the short life of certain components. Several welding defects in the rear axle subframe developed into fatigue cracks. These arose from inadequate design and detailing on the part of the vehicle converter before he began construction of the modified rear axle. As noted above, adopting a more rational approach to design and construction would have saved the vehicle converter money (they carried out the remedial work free of charge). Also, it would have avoided disruption to the bus service. Despite proper maintenance, eight drive shafts have had to be replaced in 150,000 miles (up to the end of October 2001). The original components supplied do not, therefore, appear to have an adequate service life. Faults have also developed in other components, such as front door bearings, the gear change cable and the electrical wiring.

Overall Observation about the Bus Service

Community involvement

A major issue was to ensure that initial consultation was undertaken and feedback obtained from the communities before final decisions were taken. This allowed adjustments to be made on the basis of the discussion with potential users. Apart from helping to make sure that the subsequent service matched their needs, it also helped to make the people feel that they had a real say in the development of the service and was essential if there were to be a sense of community ownership. It was also important to see this as a two-way process rather than as an example of giving out information. We kept options open for as long as possible, so that choices were really in the hands of the local people, giving them a true sense of ownership of the bus service.

The service has presented several challenges to the local communities, which are beginning to work out how to use the transport resource. A key issue seems to be that the service runs every day. This allows for regular trips (e.g. to work) to be made. Services which run only on certain days of the week will never be able to provide for this sort of journey. The frequency is important because it offers some sort of choice to people about when they travel.

The design of the service has taken account of the needs expressed by local people. Conventional public transport services tend, however, to be viewed in terms of what an operator or local authority can afford to do rather than what people need. Clear differences in the outcomes of the two approaches arise when considering frequency, journey times, routes and some aspects of vehicle design. It was important that the local people and businesses came to regard the Plusbus service as 'their' resource. People talk of it as an entity in its own right rather than just as a bus service. The sense of community ownership of the resource is highly dependent on the feeling that the service will be responsive to their needs. So far the design of the route and service timetable have both reflected the wishes of residents. It is clear that the value of working with the communities in this way is something which proves to be beneficial in designing public transport services.

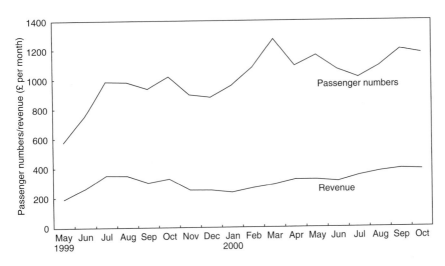

Fig. 8.28   Plusbus usage

The main effect of the Plusbus service has been to increase travel opportunities, especially for elderly, mobility-impaired and young people in the community. It has removed the need to rely on a lift (when available) from neighbours, parents or other family members. The local people have reported that the bus service has increased the sense of independence of all age groups in the area, especially of parents at home with their children during the day but without access to a car.

Survey results
The results of the survey show that the Cumbria Plusbus service is seen as a community resource rather than an 'old people's bus' and is being used for many reasons, including work journeys. Inter-village travel amounts to about 17% of the trips (impossible by public transport before this service was introduced). There are no records of such inter-village travel on the nearby Community Bus. In contrast, nearly all the journeys on the Community Bus service are from a village to the large town for shopping on market day, and it would appear that the age profile of the people using the service has remained static throughout its 18-year history. It is not clear from the survey why more young people do not use the Community Bus, but the timetable, which suits the needs of elderly people, might be inconvenient for the needs of others.

Usage of the Plusbus
During the 12-month period ending 31 October 2000, the number of passenger trips including delivery of newspaper bundles was 12,900. By September 2000 up to 300 tickets were being issued per week. Figure 8.28

shows the monthly totals of passenger numbers from May 1999 to October 2000. The yield (revenue per passenger trip) has varied over the period, but is fairly stable at about 30 pence/trip. In part, this reflects the use of the flat-fare zones in Kirkby Stephen and Warcop, which have enabled people to travel within these areas for a very low price. Kirkby Stephen is long and thin in shape and there is considerable benefit in using the bus service to help keep people at the extremities of the town in touch with the centre. Nevertheless, there is now a case for reviewing these fares, particularly in the light of the national concessionary fare scheme defined in the Transport Act 2000 (see Chapter 2 for more details) and which came into effect in June 2001.

Considering the absence of any bus service in the villages prior to the start of the Plusbus service, the passenger numbers grew quickly. This, together with the evidence of modal shift identified in the user survey, shows the need for such services in rural areas. We should also note that this project has indicated that there are three 'hidden' effects in the modal shift behaviour that are not included in any of the formal demand models but which are important in remote rural areas. These effects arise because of the lack of transport provision other than the private car:

- If a person has no car of their own, they need to have access to one belonging to someone else. This means having to ask for a lift when they wish to go out, thus making them dependent on a 'lift-giver', reducing their chance of making journeys without others and precluding the possibility of being able to make a journey without other people knowing its destination or purpose. This may not matter in some circumstances, but in others it could have adverse effects. For example, the Institute for Rural Health has noted this as one of the reasons for people failing to present themselves for early treatment or preventive consultations, especially in relation to particular medical conditions.

- The root of the second effect lies in the fact that the provision of a lift carries with it implications of 'doing good' on the part of the lift-giver. Changing from accepting a lift to using the bus carries with it the implication that the offer of a lift is being turned down and this may have consequent effects on the future relationship between the lift-giver and the lift-taker. As a result, there is a reluctance on the part of current lift-takers to change to the bus unless they have confidence that the bus service will continue for a reasonable time into the future. This reluctance to transfer to the bus from current transport arrangements is one of the reasons why measures that are perceived to be short term often fail. It seems that a bus service needs to be ensured for a time horizon of at least 3 years in order that people can feel confident that a transfer to using the bus would not compromise other personal arrangements in the short term.

- Some people feel unable to ask for a lift in the first place. This is often the case where the potential lift-taker is already socially excluded for some reason. This results in the people concerned not travelling at all.

The bus service can respond to these hidden effects because it is more anonymous than private cars or taxis and thus removes the need for someone to ask for a lift or be placed in a situation where they feel obligated to the lift-giver.

Total costs and revenue

The gross cost was approximately £46,000 during the 12-month period ending 31 October 2000 of Plusbus operation. This figure is based on 1999 prices, i.e. 35 pence/mile, labour (£6 per hour) and a competitive tender for the operating contract. The total fare revenue was approximately £3,700 during the same period (based on the published fare table and bulk delivery of newspapers at 50 pence/bundle). It can be seen that the net operating cost was approximately £42,300.

Other derived statistics are as follows:

- average gross cost/passenger trip £3.60 (to the nearest £0.10)
- average net cost/passenger trip £3.30 (to the nearest £0.10)
- average revenue/passenger trip £0.29 (to the nearest penny)
- revenue/gross operating cost 8%.

We have commented above on the yield per passenger trip and the effects of the policy of low flat fares in Kirkby Stephen and Warcop. The net cost per passenger trip compares quite favourably with other types of public transport in rural areas, including dial-a-ride type services. It is more constructive to work with this figure than the revenue/operating cost ratio because this makes comparisons easier with specialised transport provision for health, education and social services (which are usually costed on a per-trip basis). Income from other sources, such as conveyance of goods or advertising, would be included in such an analysis because it would reduce the net cost.

It is unrealistic to expect the revenue to equal or exceed the gross cost per passenger trip in rural transport services. The question is how the income can be generated from other sources (e.g. realising the effects of cross-sector benefits in terms of income) so that the net cost per passenger trip falls to a level that can be supported through transport grants and subsidies. The financing of a bus service in a remote rural area would thus comprise a package of revenue streams, one of which would be the fare income and another would be subsidy. This requires entrepreneurial ingenuity on the part of those charged with managing the finances of rural bus services, but should not be beyond the whit of suitably skilled and imaginative people.

Conclusions

Community Involvement

Detailed participation by the local community in the development, funding and operation of local public transport engenders 'ownership', meets their needs as far as possible and encourages greater use of the service. The community ownership continues to date in two forms:

- a community-based management company, which has been set up to maintain, enhance and develop the service into the future
- the local parish councils support the service by contributing 10% towards the operating costs of the service.

However, there is a need for the management of the service to refer back to the public (in addition to the parish councils) on specific issues such as changes to the service, fares or local contributions towards the overall cost of the service. It is very easy for the public to be forgotten amongst the complexities of the operation and management of the service, but it is the public that form the users, and non-users, of the service. The annual general meeting of a community company affords an opportunity for regular feedback to members of the company and, if invited, to the community as a whole. There is a case for more frequent feedback than this, but if there is a clear means of providing this information and receiving the community's views informally, it may not be necessary to hold more formal feedback meetings. It is important that the public has the opportunity to know and understand the problems and management issues as well as the good news. The support of the public cannot be guaranteed and it is very easy for ill-informed dissenters to spread misinformation. Public participation is one way of dealing with this problem at source.

Bus Service Route

The route should pass through the centre of each settlement, link settlements to each other and to the local market town. This, together with a presumption of hail-and-ride operation, tackles the problems caused by excessive access distances by bringing the bus service nearer to the people it is intending to serve. Formal bus stops are necessary in addition to the hail-and-ride operation because they provide points of information about the service and act as identifiable stopping points for people who are unfamiliar with the area.

Bus Service Timetable

The frequency of the service should be such as to enable daily travel to work and educational facilities. Daily services are important in rural areas if the aim is to enhance access to employment and other frequent activities. The frequency should be a high as possible. Earlier research at University College London (Brown, 1996) showed that there was likely to be a benefit from the provision of choice across the day and that two services in the morning and two in the afternoon would be a reasonable start. It is also evident that the availability of reliable bus services every day makes other services possible. For example, the delivery of newspapers and the linking of the bus service to health centre clinics and other facilities are only practical if they can be achieved on a daily basis.

Bus Service Operator

The use of the Plusbus service by young children unaccompanied by adults is due in large measure to the service being run by a local bus operator known to the local people. The drivers are locally known, and have been police-checked and trained in disability awareness, manual handling and first aid.

Social Inclusion

It would appear that the provision of both an accessible bus and services throughout the week reduces social exclusion because they provide frequent, independent access to work, education, social activities, health and social services. Reducing the frequency to one or two days of the week limits the range of activities (e.g. work, education) that can be reached and reduces the direct benefit of the service to the community as a whole. There is a form of 'multiplier effect' which arises as a result of the provision of a bus service of this nature. For example, the employment of local drivers brings money into the local area. The fact that it becomes easier for local residents to do some shopping in Kirkby Stephen rather than other towns also provides additional income for local businesses. This is one way of helping the local economy, which in turn helps to reduce social exclusion.

It is important not to see the Plusbus as just another bus service. It is the means by which local communities can become more cohesive and helps to ensure that people are able to be included in mainstream society. The bus provides independent travel for young people – the user survey shows how important this is – thus enabling them to develop their identity and social groups, which will enable them to be less isolated (and thus less at risk of being excluded) in the future. The bus also provides other opportunities. For example, using the bus, rather than using specialised dedicated transport, to reach health and social services activities means that people have the opportunity to combine medical trips with other activities. This is difficult to achieve with dedicated transport, for legal as well as practical reasons. This, together with the financial implications of such use of public transport is being investigated in the ELIXIR project.

Postscript

We have discussed the APTRA project in this book in relation to its operation up to October 2000. At that point we handed over the day-to-day management of the service to the Upper Eden Plusbus Company. The project continues to receive funding from the EPSRC and the Countryside Agency in relation to the ELIXIR project, in which we are investigating the direct and cross-sector impacts of accessible bus services in remote rural areas. The ELIXIR project will be completed in August 2003.

References

BROWN, N. L. C. K. (1996). Buses and accessibility: a qualitative approach. MSc Thesis, University of London.

BROWN, I. E. W. and TYLER, N. A. (2001). *APTRA and Fellrunner Bus User Surveys 2000*. Working Paper. London: University of London Centre for Transport Studies.

CUMBRIA COUNTY COUNCIL (1995). *Cumbria in Figures*. Carlisle: Cumbria County Council.

DETR (1999). *The Public Service Vehicles Accessibility Regulations: A Statutory Consultation*. London: Department of the Environment, Transport and the Regions.

DETR (1999). *Access and Facilities for Disabled People*. The Building Regulations 1991 (updated 1999). Approved Document M. London: Stationery Office.

DOE/DTP (1992). *Residential Road and Footpaths*: Design Bulletin 32. London: HMSO.

DPTAC (1997). *Recommended Specification for Low-floor Buses*. London: Disabled Persons' Transport Advisory Committee.

DPTAC (2001). *Accessibility Specification for Small Buses*. London: Disabled Persons' Transport Advisory Committee.

INSTITUTION OF HIGHWAYS AND TRANSPORTATION (1991). *Reducing Mobility Handicaps*. London: IHT.

OFFICE OF NATIONAL STATISTICS (1991). *Population Census*. London: Office of National Statistics.

STAIT, R. E. and SAVILL, T. A. (1995). *A Survey of Occupied Wheelchairs to Determine their Overall Dimensions and Characteristics*. Research Report 150. Crowthorne: Transport Research Laboratory.

TYLER, N. A. and BROWN, I. E. W. (1998). *Accessible Public Transport in Rural Areas: Choice of Study Area for the Project*. Working Paper. London: University of London Centre for Transport Studies.

TYLER, N. A. and BROWN, N. L. C. K. (2000). 'Public participation in transport decisions'. *Traffic Engineering and Control*, Vol. 41, No. 3, pp. 88–92.

TYLER, N. A., BROWN, N. L. C. K. and LYNAS, J. R. (1997). 'Improving accessibility to bus systems for elderly people'. *Proceedings of Ville et Vieillissement*, Arles, France.

VOLUNTARY ACTION CUMBRIA (1992). *County Wide*, Vol. 4. Penrith: Voluntary Action Cumbria.

Chapter 9

Conclusions

N. Tyler

So where have we come to at the end of this book? This chapter collates some of the ideas we have rehearsed through the course of the book and seeks to draw some overall conclusions about accessibility and its place in society.

An inaccessible society fails all its members because it prevents some people from realising their full potential. Not only is an individual excluded from society (with all the resulting problems that this entails), but society fails to benefit from their inclusion: how can they make their contribution to society if this necessitates travel but the means of transport is inaccessible? When society has to prioritise its use of resources for transport, one of the decisions it has to make is to choose between different groups of people: those whose objective is to obtain access to the transport system (an accessibilty-based objective) and those whose objective is to travel more (a movement-enhancing objective).. We pointed out that these objectives were often conflicting and that, whereas the latter group could be inconvenienced by a failure to meet the objective, failure on the part of the former group would result in their being prevented from carrying on the life they would like to live. Why is this important?

Rawls (1971) took the view that the expectations of increased benefits to a relatively well-off group cannot be increased if it would cause a consequent decrease in expectations to a worse-off group, because this would result in a reduction in social justice. To be just and fair, we need to apply a social justice 'filter' to a decision before other considerations can be taken into account. If the outcome of a decision is going to worsen social justice or fairness for some group relative to another group, then it should be rejected at this point before any consideration of other benefits and costs is taken into account. We believe that this philosophy applies, not only to the world of economics used by Rawls to explain the concept, but also to the subject of accessibility. It is important to have a clear philosophical basis for decisions affecting accessibility because sometimes accessibility objectives conflict with others (e.g. allowing for increased time for elderly people to board buses could increase operating costs). We need to be clear whether or not a decision is just and fair.

Many decisions designed to enable people to travel further and faster reduce accessibility for others (e.g. the removal of pedestrian crossings to improve traffic flow). As prevention of travel is likely to be more unjust and unfair than a reduction in the attractiveness of a journey, it seems clear that accessibility objectives should come ahead of movement-based objectives when priorities are being chosen for the use of resources. This is important because we are dealing not only with a transport system, but also with society as a whole. A society in which some people are excluded, whether deliberately or unwittingly, and for whatever reason, fails to be civilised. We therefore need to find ways of ensuring that people are not prevented from being included in society and one aspect of this is the accessibility of the transport system.

The intention of this book is to encourage people to think about the way in which the transport system could be designed to make society accessible to all its members. One of the difficulties with accessibility is that, although it is a broad concept, the way in which it is achieved depends on the fine detail of each element in a system. The achievement of the broad concept can fail simply because one of the details of one of the elements has rendered the rest of the system inaccessible. For example, the bus system can be a barrier to people by virtue of:

- the design of the network, services and operating systems
- the pedestrian- or bus-related infrastructure
- the design of vehicles
- the attitude and skills of drivers and other transport staff
- the location, style, content and form of information provision
- the way in which the bus system relates to local people in its design and implementation.

Each item in this list has many constituent parts, making a huge number of details that have to be made right in order to achieve an accessible system. Designing for accessibility is made a lot harder by the fact that many of the items in the list are in the hands of different entities, which are often in conflict with each other. These include not only statutory bodies but also public and private companies responsible for designing and constructing vehicles or infrastructure, charitable bodies representing various interests and individual members of the community. As with any problem in which people may hold different views, the outcome will depend on the attitudes held by the various parties involved about the principal problem, in this case accessibility, and about each other.

Accessibility is not going to be achieved unless there is a fundamental shift in the way in which different agents in society view and work with each other. The most accessible bus system can be disabled by careless design and construction, weak or faulty legislation or, perhaps most easily of all, by thoughtless actions by individuals. Examples such as failing to allow enough space, poor quality surfaces, legislative loopholes, parking across dropped kerbs, obstructing bus stops or thoughtless use of the space inside a bus come to mind in this respect. The fact that so much effort expended on making society accessible can be ruined by such small and otherwise inconsequential actions means that the wider task of educating and sensitising society as a whole to the details of the issue is a vital component of any improvement to the accessibility of the bus system itself.

Accessibility is about dealing with barriers, whether these are physical, sensory or cognitive. It is also about the social and psychological barriers put up, often unwittingly, by society. We have discussed the relationship between accessibility and independence and the ways in which changing either of these can have effects on the other.

The way in which a network, vehicles and service style are designed would be radically different if the system as a whole were designed to meet users' needs rather than the requirements of operators and planners. A key element of a user-centred network is that people need to reduce the distance it is necessary to walk to meet the service. A user-centred network, therefore, should be routed to bring the service nearer to the people who will use it. This was clearly important in both Hackney and Cumbria.

For some people, the only transport they can use is provided by health, social services or education departments (specialised transport) and is subject to a set of eligibility criteria. To the user of specialised transport, this is their 'public' transport. If a person is not eligible for specialised transport and is unable to use the public transport system, they fall into the accessibility gap and are excluded from both the transport system and the activities they may wish to undertake. Making the public bus service more accessible reduces the number of people in the accessibility gap and can enable some people who currently use specialised transport to travel more independently by using public transport. We must ensure that specialised transport services are integrated in the design of the overall mix of public transport so that nobody is excluded because they do not have a transport service which is accessible to them. The Transport Co-ordination Centre in Hackney shows some evidence of how this can be done by finding the most appropriate, least-cost means of transport and including public buses in the mix of available transport to be considered. In Cumbria, we can see how, when an accessible public bus service is available, users of health and social services take advantage of the less stigmatising (and easier to use) bus.

However friendly and local the bus route and service, it is still necessary to ensure that the act of entering or leaving the vehicle does not present barriers to intending passengers. This means thinking about the interface between the pedestrian network and the bus network, namely the bus stop. We have used the bus stop as one particular example of how infrastructure should be conceived, designed and constructed in order that it constitutes as little of a barrier as possible. Few people currently think about bus stops even as infrastructure, and even fewer consider them as infrastructure that needs careful and skilled design. Although our choice of the bus stop as an example is of course related to the research we have carried out on this topic, it is a good choice to use in this book because it enables us to open up discussion about more general issues related to accessibility:

- The bus stop is an interface between people's needs, the constraints and opportunities afforded by infrastructure design and construction and the requirements of vehicles. It thus contains many of the conflicts between these requirements that have to be resolved.
- The bus stop is a physical manifestation of the hype and argument about public versus private transport. How one prioritises the competing aspects of bus stop design is an expression of one's view about this debate.
- Bus stops are of concern to many people, including bus users and drivers, residents and traders who live or work near to bus stops, pedestrians and users of the general traffic systems, commercial enterprises (e.g. bus companies, advertising companies, suppliers of utilities) and political entities. The consideration of bus stops encapsulates the conflicts between these groups and thus the way in which the design for enhancement of accessibility would affect each party.
- Making bus stops accessible opens up the whole network to people who are currently excluded from activities which necessitate making a journey. Our discussion about network design deals with this issue and forces thought about how the network can be made to work (including the contribution made by good design of the bus stops, with sufficient capacity of buses and adequate accessibility for passengers).

The EXCALIBUR project shows what the requirements are for a bus stop which would make the bus system more widely accessible. It may be that the resulting dimensions cause concern in some quarters. However, we should emphasise two points in relation to EXCALIBUR stops:

- The dimensions for EXCALIBUR bus stops result from the physical characteristics of buses. A bus is a rigid object that requires certain space for certain manoeuvres. If this space is not available, the manoeuvre cannot be completed. The bus operates in a traffic stream and cannot have two attempts to reach the bus stop, so we have to ensure that the design allows buses to dock successfully at the first attempt.
- EXCALIBUR bus stops highlight the need to make buses and infrastructure work together. Inconsistency in the design of buses reduces the accessibility available at a bus stop. There is a desperate need to encourage the bus manufacturing industry to design and construct vehicles to a consistent set of dimensions relative to the bus stop infrastructure. By working in conjunction with infrastructure manufacturers a much more consistent performance of both vehicle and infrastructure could be achieved, to the benefit of passengers, drivers and operators. Until the detailed requirements necessitated by the attempt to achieve overall accessibility objectives had been established, these details were not of overriding concern to bus manufacturers. Now the situation is different and vehicle design has to be scrutinised. The Public Service Vehicles Accessibility Regulations 2000 are not the end of the matter for vehicle manufacturers, and there are many small but significant changes to vehicle design that could yield many benefits in terms of accessibility improvements. Examples include the lateral gap between the body and the tyres/ wheels, axle length, ground clearance on the nearside of the vehicle and the need to maintain a consistent ride height in the suspension system.

It is not always feasible to construct the ideal solution, whether in terms of infrastructure, vehicle, service or any other aspect of the bus system. The size of a bus shelter, the length of a bus stop and crossfalls are all examples of where pressure to reduce accessibility is applied. However, each reduction from the ideal results in more people being excluded, and thus needs to be scrutinised in the context of the social justice and fairness criteria discussed earlier. It is essential that those responsible for the specification, design, implementation and operation of the bus system have a clear understanding of the implications for accessibility of each decision that moves the solution further away from the ideal. They need to be aware that this is not just about whether or not someone can board a bus, but that failure in any of the various elements of the system will mean that they will be condemning someone to be unable to reach the objective of their journey. Such an outcome presents many problems for, and includes imposing unnecessary costs on, other parts of society, such as health, education, employment, the local economy or other characteristics such as social cohesion. Each of these is affected by the inability of a person to travel independently, to use, take part in, contribute towards or enjoy them. Apart from the cross-sectoral cost implications, all of society is diminished by the impoverishment in the quality of life of people who are excluded as a result of inaccessible transport. Before the Hackney Plusbus came into operation, one of its current users used to be taken to his outpatient appointment at the local hospital and brought home in hospital transport. Even though his appointment took only half an hour, he had to be dropped off at 9 a.m. and taken home at 4.30 p.m., regardless of the time at which the appointment was scheduled. After the Hackney Plusbus came into operation, this user found that he was able to go to his appointment, arriving half an hour before and leaving half an hour afterwards. This means that he can now decide what to do with his day instead of being forced to spend it in the waiting room of an outpatient department. It also means that hospital transport is available for people who are excluded from other transport and the hospital does not incur the costs of providing accommodation for people who are simply occupying space and other resources in the hospital while they are waiting.

What may seem attractive for some may result in a severe loss of independence, health or quality of life for others. There is often a pressure to provide more car parking spaces rather than to sterilise the kerb space so that buses can come close enough to the kerb to enable elderly and disabled people to use the bus system. However, the issue is not just one of allocation of space near to a bus stop. Such decisions are often influenced by political inputs and become a comparison between the 'pro-car' lobby and 'pro-disabled people' lobby. By favouring one group over the other, the decision inevitably opposes the other group.

Political expediency and technical compromise drive many decisions, but the exclusion of even one person as a result of a decision means not just a small increase in inconvenience: it constitutes the segregation of that person from the rest of society. Those who make such decisions must therefore take the responsibility for that exclusion. We have raised the question of how many people are included or excluded as a result of the network design. We have also discussed who these people are and how the bus system might need to be rethought in order to improve the extent to which it could include a greater proportion of the community. It is not clear how ready society is to take up this challenge (the reluctance to cede a parking space to make a bus stop accessible is a case in point). There is a need for education of the public as a whole so that the need and rationale for such compromises is understood and absorbed into the daily view on life. This goes beyond the scope of legislation and design thresholds and cuts into the deeper reaches of society.

The provision of accessible information is a huge problem which is still in the early days of investigation. Research has yet to show reliable and general ways of ensuring that information is accessible. Translating the mix of marketing hype and deep research in cognition into meaningful frameworks for information providers to use is yet to be achieved so that people with learning difficulties, sensory problems or other sources of confusion in unknown situations (i.e. most of the population at some stage or other) can readily understand what they need to know. Research into these issues is on-going, not least in the Accessibility Research Group, but we really need some good answers very soon.

Education is vital. Not only do engineers, architects, designers and other professionals need to be skilled in accessibility issues, but the citizenry as a whole needs to be made alert to the subject. This is particularly important in the field of public participation in decision-making processes. We noted that participation is different from consultation. Whereas consultation requires some conversation with the public but no shared ownership of the resulting decision, participation not only actively involves the public during the decision-making process but also includes them in the ownership of, and responsibility for, the decision. Active involvement of the public in this way means that they need to understand not only what they want but also why they may be unable to achieve it. Dialogue between people as equals is crucial to the development of acceptable compromises that are inevitably necessary as we push the frontiers of universal accessibility ever forward. It is in the relationships between different members of the public that the real advances in accessibility will be generated rather than in the government department, designer's studio or engineer's workshop. This is because without the public's understanding of the problems, solutions and compromises, advances in accessible design will not be generally accepted and, therefore, will not work.

We need to think about several design issues. For example, wheelchairs were designed to facilitate movement around an institution. Since the early 1990s society has been encouraging people to move into the wider community. Has wheelchair design caught up with this? Although specialised design of sports wheelchairs has become relatively common, it is less easy to find evidence of wheelchairs that have been designed to make it easier to use public transport. We came across medical practitioners who were unaware that wheelchairs could go onto buses and thus had never thought about what they should prescribe in terms of wheelchair design (e.g. wheel diameter) that could make this easier or more difficult. Changes in wheelchair design could help to reduce the effect of different barriers and thus increase the feasibility of eliminating them altogether. This could help in all sorts of areas, not least the design and use of dropped kerbs, buses and the pedestrian infrastructure in general.

Are we making the right decisions about street infrastructure when an increasing number of people are extending the range of their activities through the purchase of an electric scooter? What are the implications of this for the design of pedestrian infrastructure? What should we be encouraging the designers of such vehicles to incorporate in their products? How should we determine the rules of engagement for users and non-users in order that scooters do not act as a means of exclusion for people who do not have access to one? This will not be easy (we have not yet managed to achieve it with that other icon of individual movement – the car).

The nature of our research is to develop concepts and then test them in the real world. One example of this is the Cumbria Plusbus project. This has involved us in a wide range of interfaces – physical, sensory, cognitive and political. We needed to obtain an accessible minibus, but found an industry unwilling to provide one. Indeed, the vehicle manufacturer has been joined by only one competitor in the production of low-floor minibuses since then, even though regulations are just around the corner which will require minibuses to comply with regulations similar in extent to the requirements for large buses. Other manufacturers seem to be reluctant to enter this market. This is worrying because the technical difficulties of providing low-floor accessibility in a small bus are difficult and will take time to resolve.

Some of the material in this book should have been familiar to some readers. We hope that the book has helped to change ideas and thinking, and to develop different perspectives of the links between concepts, theory, design and implementation to make a practicable and accessible whole. A civilised society brings with it the responsibility to construct, among other things, an accessible bus system. This in turn requires that compromises be resolved. Dealing with compromises requires understanding of the fundamental principles underlying the need for accessibility. We hope that the associated technical information and evidence from practical implementation needed to put this into practice is helpful and that we have shown the need to deal with compromises in the full realisation of their impacts on society.

Nevertheless, there is still a lot to do. More work needs to be done on the measurement and evaluation of accessibility: exactly how much better is option A than option B? This includes the determination of what constitutes a barrier, for whom and the extent to which such barriers result in exclusion. Only with this information can sensible decisions be made about network design, limits of tolerance beyond which pedestrian infrastructure is impassable, the need for more accessible design of information, or other accessibility enhancement issues. We need to understand a lot more about the ways in which people move around and interact with pedestrian infrastructure. This requires comprehensive and rigorous study of the effects of different characteristics (e.g. gradients, crossfalls, surface conditions, including weather conditions) on the ease with which people can move around. Policy needs to be responsive to need and active in promoting resolution of accessibility problems. Policy formulated and implemented on the basis of knowledge, geared to performance rather than standardised inputs and subjected to on-going independent evaluation, also stimulates the need for a proper and objective method for evaluating accessibility.

This book is not a textbook that explains how to do things, neither is it just a set of examples of best practice that shows what has been done in selected cases. We have tried to show why a clear picture of the society we wish to live in leads to a particular approach to the problem of how to increase accessibility. This approach leads to the determination of needs and the subsequent design specification for every element of the transport system. The book takes a few examples from our own research projects and follows the logic:

- the characteristics of a civilised society lead to
- the way in which activities are consequently located leads to
- the role to be taken by public transport (in this case the bus system) leads to
- the design of the bus network leads to
- the design of the service style, infrastructure and vehicle needs of the bus system leads to
- the implementation of information systems leads to
- the wider availability of activities to a wider range of people leads to
- the design of a monitoring and evaluation system leads to
- the formal incorporation of improvements in the bus system leads to
- the enhancement of accessibility and independence leads to
- the characteristics of a civilised society … .

There are many feedback loops within and between the items in this list, but the overall concept is that we are really interested in achieving a society in which people are not excluded by the design of the bus system from leading as full and independent a life as they wish.

We also try to open up the realisation that there are some aspects of accessible design that are essential, and failure to incorporate them results in people being excluded from society. We acknowledge that in many cases there is no alternative other than to implement something which is less than perfect. However, the overarching 'no exclusion' requirement means that a reduction in independence arising because one element of the transport system cannot be made accessible has to be compensated for by the provision of an accessible alternative.

The book aims to encourage a style of thinking that will question the way in which skills are applied to the specification, design and implementation of bus systems. We aim to show that when the thinking is different the solutions are different, but not so different that they are unachievable. The resistance to change is political as well as technical and requires both politicians and their technical advisers to think differently.

For politicians to take such a radical step, it is necessary for the general public to be convinced of the merits of the accessibility case and then to apply appropriate pressure on the political decision-makers. We hope that this book will show a way forward – that thinking about accessibility means a change in perspective, that the change in perspective leads to a change in specification, design and operation and that these changes are wholly possible if the will is there to make them happen. The outcome should be a more complete, satisfying and civilised society in which every person is able to live as full and independent a life as they choose.

Reference

RAWLS, J. (1971). *A Theory of Justice*. Oxford: Oxford University Press.

Bibliography

Acts of Parliament, Regulations, Statutory Instruments, Codes of Practice

Chronically Sick and Disabled Persons Act 1970
Public Service Vehicle Regulations, SI 1981/257: Conditions of Fitness, Equipment, Use, Certification (and subsequent amendment regulations)
Code of Practice: The Safety of Passengers in Wheelchairs on Buses, VSE 87/1
Transport Act 1985
Road Vehicles (Construction and Use) Regulations, SI 1986/1078 (and subsequent amendment regulations)
Disability Discrimination Act 1995
Advice on Retro-fitting Seat Belts to Minibuses and Coaches, VSE 2/96
The Building Regulations 1991 (updated 1999), Approved Document M: Access and Facilities for Disabled People
Transport Act 2000
Public Service Vehicles Accessibility Regulations 2000, SI 2000/1970
Public Service Vehicles Accessibility (Amendment) Regulations 2000, SI 2000/3318

Acts of Parliament, Regulations, Statutory Instruments and Codes of Practice are available from the Stationery Office, London

Publications and Working Papers from the Accessibility Research Group

Below is a list of articles produced by the Accessibility Research Group between 1996 and 2001. These, together with current information about the group, its research and current publications, are available via the group's website: http://www.ucl.ac.uk/transport-studies/accessib.htm.

2001

BROWN, I. E. W. and TYLER, N. A. (2001). 'Users' responses to the implementation of an innovative accessible bus service in a remote rural area'. *Proc. Ninth International Conference on Mobility and Transport for Elderly and Disabled People*, Warsaw, July, pp. 143–52.

CAIAFFA, M. M. and TYLER, N. A. (2001). 'Evaluation of changes to bus stop design to benefit elderly and disabled people'. *Proc. Ninth International Conference on Mobility and Transport for Elderly and Disabled People*, Warsaw, July, pp. 219–28.

CAIAFFA, M. and TYLER, N. A. (2001). 'Provisión de información en el ambiente de paraderos para omnibuses totalmente accessibles'. *Proc. II Simposio Internacional sobre Facilidades de Transporte y Tránsito para Personas Discapacitadas*, La Habana, September [in Spanish].

CEPOLINA, E. M. and TYLER, N. (2001). 'Explicit model of pedestrian behaviour'. Annual Convention: *Metodi e Tecnologie dell'Ingegnaria dei Trasporti*, Reggio Calabria, Italy, December (full version in press).

FERNÁNDEZ, R. (2001). Modelling bus stop interactions. PhD Thesis, University of London (unpublished).

GILLINGWATER, D. and TYLER, N. A. (2001). 'Specialised transport'. In: K. Button and D. Hensher (eds), *Handbook of Transport Systems and Traffic Control*). Oxford: Pergammon Press.

SILVA, P. C. M. (2001). Modelling interactions between bus operations and traffic flow. PhD Thesis, University of London.

SILVA, P. C. M. and TYLER, N.(2001). 'Sobre a validação de modelos microscópicos de simulação de tráfego'. *XV Congresso de Pesquisa e Ensino em Tranportes (ANPET)*, Campinas, Brazil, November [in Portuguese].

SILVA, P. C. M. and TYLER, N. (2001) 'Avaliação de projetos de paradas de ônibus'. *XI CLATPU – Congreso Latino Americano de Transporte Público*, Havana, Cuba, September [in Portuguese].

TYLER, N. A. (2001). 'Politica britanica de transportes: transporte publico y accesibilidad'. In Monzon, A. (ed.), *La Politica Britanica De Transportes, Jornadas Sobre Politicas Nacionales De Transporte En La Union Europea*. Madrid: Ministerio de Fomento [in Spanish].

TYLER, N. A. and CAIAFFA, M. (2001) *Signage for People with Learning Difficulties*. Working Paper. London: University of London Centre for Transport Studies.

TYLER, N. A. and DEXTRE, J. C. (2001). 'Accesibilidad para todos en el contexto peruano'. *Proc. II Simposio Internacional sobre Facilidades de Transporte y Tránsito para Personas Discapacitadas*, La Habana, September [in Spanish].

TYLER, N. A., CAIAFFA, M. M. and WAINSTEIN, M. (2001). 'Transport information for people with learning difficulties'. *INCLUDE 2001, International Conference on Inclusive Design*, London, April.

2000

SILVA, P. C. M. (2000). 'Simulating bus stops in mixed traffic'. *Traffic Engineering and Control*, Vol. 41, No. 4, pp. 160–7.

SILVA, P. C. M. (2000). 'Simulating bus stops in mixed traffic'. *Proc. UTSG Conference 2000*, Liverpool, January.

TYLER, N. A. (2000). 'Community transport and community development in rural areas'. *Proc. Developing Policies for the Integration of Rural and Community Transport: CTA Scottish Rural Conference*, Edinburgh, June.

TYLER, N. A. (2000). 'El diseño de la ciudad del futuro: ciudadano sostenible?'. *Proc. Jornadas Técnicas de la Asociación de Empresas Gestoras de los Transportes Urbanos Colectivos*, Málaga, 17–18 May [in Spanish].

TYLER, N. A. and BROWN, N. L. C. K. (2000). 'Public participation in transport decisions'. *Traffic Engineering and Control*, Vol. 41, No. 3, pp. 88–92. Correction to misprint: *Traffic Engineering and Control*, Vol. 41, No. 5, p. 192.

TYLER, N. A. and CAIAFFA, M. M. (2000). 'Passenger facilities at fully accessible bus stops'. *Transition*, Vol. 11, pp. 3–13.

1999

BROWN, I. E. W. (1999). *Fully Accessible Rural Bus Shelters and Platforms*. Working Paper. London: University of London Centre for Transport Studies.

BROWN, N. L. C. K. and TYLER, N. A. (1999). 'Catch me if you can: traffic management for accessible rural bus stops'. *Traffic Engineering and Control*, Vol. 40, No. 10, pp. 487–91.

BROWN, I. E. W, TYLER, N. A., SILVA, P.C. M., MARAR, J. R., CAIAFFA, M. and BITARAFEN, F. (1999). *Response to DETR Publication: From Workhorse to Thoroughbred: A Better Role for Bus Travel*. Working Paper. London: University of London Centre for Transport Studies.

CAIAFFA, M. M. and TYLER, N. (1999). 'Projeto EXCALIBUR – um exemplo prático para verificar as inter-relações dos principais elementos da infra-estrutura de pontos de ônibus e o ônibus com piso baixo'. *Proc. X CLATPU – Congreso Latino Americano de Transporte Público*, Caracas, December [in Portuguese].

FERNÁNDEZ, R. (1999). 'Design of bus-stop priorities'. *Traffic Engineering and Control*, Vol. 40, No. 6, pp. 335–40.

FERNÁNDEZ, R. E. and SALAMANCA, Y. M. (1999). 'Aspectos de diseño de paraderos de alto estándar'. *Actas del IX Congreso Chileno de Ingeniería de Transporte*, Santiago, pp. 274–86 [in Spanish].

FERNÁNDEZ, R. and TYLER, N. A. (1999). 'Design of bus stops as part of bus priorities'. *European Transport Conference*, Cambridge, September. Poster.

FERNÁNDEZ, R. E. and VALENZUELA, Y. E. (1999). 'Bases para una gestión ambiental de tránsito'. *Actas del IX Congreso Chileno de Ingeniería de Transporte*, Santiago, pp. 485–95 [in Spanish].

KEAN, A. M. and TYLER, N. A. (1999). *Accessibility and Community-Centred Public Transport: Final Report*. Report to the Department of the Environment, Transport and the Regions.

SILVA. P. C. M. (1999). 'Simulating interactions between buses and other traffic'. *Proc. UTSG Conference 1999*, York, January.

SILVA, P. and TYLER, N. (1999). 'Paradas de ônibus em tráfego misto'. *Proc. X CLATPU – Congreso Latino Americano de Transporte Público*, Caracas, December [in Portuguese].

SILVA, P. C. M. and TYLER, N. (1999). 'Modelagem de interações entre operações de ônibus e fluxos de tráfego'. *Proc. XIII Congresso de Pesquisa e Ensino em Tranportes (ANPET)*, S. Carlos, Brazil, November [in Portuguese].

TYLER, N. A. (1999). 'Accessible bus services in a rural environment'. *Proc. ECMT Seminar Strengthening the Transport Chain*, Gothenberg, September [a slightly updated version of the paper below].

TYLER, N. A. (1999). 'Accessible public transport in rural areas'. *Proc. Rural Transport for All Seminar*, Lancaster University, July.

TYLER, N. A. (1999). *Measuring Accessibility to Public Transport: Concepts*. Working Paper. London: University of London Centre for Transport Studies.

TYLER, N. A. (1999). *Service Specification for the Transport Coordination Centre Hackney*.

TYLER, N. (1999). *Practical Research Collaborations: Universities and Local Government Partnership*. London: The Improvement and Development Agency (formerly the Local Government Management Board).

TYLER, N. A. and BROWN, I. E. W. (1999). *Accessible Public Transport in Rural Areas: Choice of Study Area for the Project*. Working Paper. London: University of London Centre for Transport Studies.

TYLER, N. A. and CAIAFFA, M. (1999). *EXCALIBUR Project – Experiment III: Performance of the Guidance System with Different Low Floor Buses*. Working Paper. London: University of London Centre for Transport Studies.

TYLER, N. A. and CAIAFFA, M. (1999). 'Design of fully accessible bus stops infrastructure elements for buses and drivers'. *Proc. European Transport Conference*, September.

TYLER, N. A., BROWN, I. E. W, BITARAFEN, F., CAIAFFA, M., SILVA, P. C. M. and MARAR, J. R. (1999). *Response to Rural England: A Discussion Document*. Working Paper. London: University of London Centre for Transport Studies.

1998

BROWN, N. L. C. K. (1998). *The Effects of the Americans with Disabilities Act and the Disability Discrimination Act on Urban Bus Services and Social Inclusion*. Working Paper. London: University of London Centre for Transport Studies.

LYNAS, J. R. (1998). *The Hackney Plusbus Scheme Initial Monitoring and Review*. Working Paper. London: University of London Centre for Transport Studies.

TYLER, N. A. (1998). *Transport and Long Term Care for Elderly People*. Evidence to the Royal Commission on Long Term Care for the Elderly.

1997 and before

ARANY, M. C. M., PORTUGAL, L. S. and TYLER, N. (1992) 'Simulação de pontos de ônibus: novos aspectos a serem considerados'. *Revista dos Transportes Públicos – ANTP*, Vol. 57, pp. 119–30.

BROWN, N. L. C. K. (1997). *Accessibility and Public Transport Experiment: Services and Infrastructure*. Working Paper. London: University of London Centre for Transport Studies.

BROWN, N. L. C. K. (1997). *Lincolnshire Travel Diary Survey*. Working Paper. London: University of London Centre for Transport Studies.

BROWN, N. L. C. K. (1997). *Case Study: Operation of Transport Coordination Centres*. Working Paper. London: University of London Centre for Transport Studies.

BROWN, N. L. C. K. and TYLER, N. A. (1997). *Accessible Public Transport Routes in Brighton: Task 2 – Routes 1 and 49 Interim Report*. Report to Brighton and Hove Council.

BROWN, N. L. C. K., FERNÁNDEZ, R., KEAN, A. M., LYNAS, J. R., SILVA, P. C. M. and TYLER, N. A. (1997). *Response to Developing an Integrated Transport Policy*. Working Paper. London: University of London Centre for Transport Studies.

FERNÁNDEZ, R. (1996). *Modelling Bus Stop Interactions*. Working Paper. London: University of London Centre for Transport Studies.

FERNÁNDEZ, R. and TYLER, N. A. (1995). 'Modelación de las interacciones en paraderos de buses'. *Proc. VII Congreso Chileno de Ingeniería de Transporte*, Santiago, October.

FERNÁNDEZ, R., GIBSON, J. and MENDEZ, M. (1995). 'Modelación del comportamiento en parados de alta demanda'. *Proc. VII Congreso Chileno de Ingeniería de Transporte*, Santiago, October.

FERNÁNDEZ, R., BROWN, N. L. C. K. and TYLER, N. A. (1997). *Accessible Public Transport Routes in Brighton: Task 1 – Western Road: Churchill Square Area Improvement*. Report to Brighton and Hove Council.

GIBSON, J., FERNÁNDEZ, R. and ALBERT, A. (1997). 'Operación de paraderos formales en Santiago'. *Proc. VIII Congreso Chileno de Ingeniería de Transporte*, Santiago, November.

LYNAS, J. R. (1997). *The Hackney Plusbus Project*. Working Paper. London: University of London Centre for Transport Studies.

SILVA, P. C. M. (1997). *Buses in Microscopic Traffic Simulation Models*. Working Paper. London: University of London Centre for Transport Studies.

TYLER N.A. (1993) Accessibility and mobility: the means for intermodal comparison? *Proc. Universities' Transport Studies Group Conference*, South-ampton, UK.

TYLER, N. A. (1996). *On Accessibility*. Working Paper. London: University of London Centre for Transport Studies.

TYLER, N. A. (1996). *Accessibility to the Bus System*. Working Paper. London: University of London Centre for Transport Studies.

TYLER, N. A. (1996). *Access Facilities for Buses*. Working Paper. London: University of London Centre for Transport Studies.

TYLER, N. A. (1997). *The Transport Contract*. Working Paper. London: University of London Centre for Transport Studies.

TYLER, N. A. and BROWN, N. L. C. K. (1997). *On Mobility*. Working Paper. London: University of London Centre for Transport Studies.

TYLER, N. A. and FERNÁNDEZ, R. (1996). 'Integracion del diseño de paraderos en las medidas de prioridad a los buses'. *Proc. IX Congreso Panamericano de Ingeniería de Tránsito y Transporte*, Havana, December.

TYLER, N. A., BROWN, N. L. C. K. and LYNAS, J. R. (1997). 'Improving accessibility to bus systems for elderly people'. *Proc. Ville et Vieillissement*, Arles, October.

Contract Document Topics

The topics included in the contract documents for the operations of the bus service are listed below.

Conditions of Contract

- Definitions and interpretation
- assignment and subletting
- contract documents
- validity, legality and enforceability
- jurisdiction
- general obligations
- confidentiality
- intellectual property
- agency
- force majeure
- parent company guarantee
- workmanship
- commencement time
- alterations, additions and omissions
- property in the project vehicle and other equipment
- measurement
- revenue statements and payment
- remedies and powers
- settlement and disputes
- waiver

- termination
- notices.

List of Attachments to Conditions of Contract

A   Contractor's procedures in the event of a road traffic accident, vehicle breakdown or other emergency.
B   Details of route, public timetable and fare charts.
C   List of dates for routine maintenance of project vehicle.
D   Contractor's conditions of carriage.
E   Contractor's working timetable.
F   Parent company guarantee.
G   Sample variation agreement form.
H   Health and safety risk assessment requirements.

Specification

- General
- ticketing equipment operation
- disabled passengers
- the contractor's drivers (including disability awareness training requirements)
- vehicle operation
- advertising the contracted service and other advertising
- contracted service
- revenue
- contract price and contract price adjustment
- monthly statements
- public correspondence
- review meetings.

List of Annexes to Specification

A   Project vehicle details and draft manual.
B   Contract price adjustment formula.
C   Ticketing equipment manuals.
D   Estimated in-service mileage for bus route.
E   Public Service Vehicle Accessibility Regulations 2000 (extract).
F   Contracted service:
number of operating days per annum
in-service attendance period per day.

Bill of Quantities, Including Schedule of Rates

- Preamble and item coverage
- price for estimated in-service mileage per year of contracted service
- price for estimated in-service attendance per year of contracted service
- rate/mile in-service operation of contracted service
- rate/hour in-service operation of contracted service.

The Plusbus service could provide a model for the local public transport necessary for people to retain an independent lifestyle in a remote rural area without needing to depend on access to a car.

Appendix 2

Timetable and Fare Table

The original timetable/fare table leaflet is a two-sided A3 document produced in Lucida Sans Unicode, 12 point, dark green text on cream paper. The reproduction here is 65% of the actual size.

Cumbria Plusbus
Timetable, Fares
and General
Information

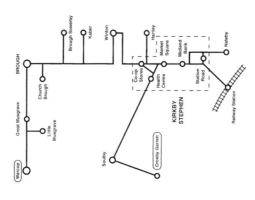

The Cumbria Plusbus – More than just a bus!

The Plusbus:

- is accessible for pushchairs, wheelchairs and shopping trollies.

- is frequent – every 3 hours during the day (Monday – Saturday)

- can carry 13 people, including up to two in wheelchairs.

- has a low floor, wide doors, no steps inside the bus, a wide aisle and comfortable spacing between the seats.

- can also take unaccompanied goods and parcels to points on the route.

- may be hired from the operator by communities along the route when it is not involved in the scheduled service.

The Cumbria Plusbus is part of a research project being carried out by University College London to explore the opportunities for fully–accessible public transport in rural areas. It is funded by:

- The Engineering and Physical Sciences Research Council

- The Countryside Agency

- Cumbria County Council

The project also has the support of Eden District Council.

Please address any comments or queries about the project or any views about rural public transport to:

Centre for Transport Studies
University College London
FREEPOST Lon 14110
London WC1E 6BR

Cumbria Plusbus 571

Fares (Adult single)

	Crosby Garrett	Soulby	Kirkby Stephen Railway Station	Hartley	Nateby	Kirkby Stephen	Winton	Kaber	Brough Sowerby	Church Brough	Brough	Gt. Musgrave	Lt. Musgrave
Soulby	25												
Kirkby Stephen Railway Station	80	55											
Hartley	70	45	40										
Nateby	70	45	25	30									
Kirkby Stephen	55	30	25	30	15								
Winton	70	45	40	30	30	15							
Kaber	85	60	55	45	45	30	15						
Brough Sowerby	100	75	70	60	60	45	30	15					
Church Brough	110	85	80	70	70	55	40	25	10				
Brough	120	95	90	80	80	65	50	35	20	10			
Gt. Musgrave	140	115	110	100	100	85	70	55	40	30	20		
Lt. Musgrave	155	130	125	115	115	100	85	70	55	45	35	15	
Warcop	185	160	155	145	145	130	115	100	85	75	65	45	30

- Each Return fare is 1½ times the relevant single fare.
- Children under 5 years of age travel free of charge.
- The Child (aged 5 – 15 inclusive) fare is three quarters of the relevant Adult fare.
- Each fare is rounded to the nearest 5p.
- Minimum fare 10p.
- A flat fare of 10p per person is charged for a single journey wholly within Kirkby Stephen (boxed area on map) or Warcop.
- An all-day Rover ticket is available (price £2 per adult (£1.50 per child) for unlimited travel during one day on the Cumbria Plusbus Route.
- Unaccompanied parcels up to 13 Kg (28.6 lbs) weight: £1.30. See Operator's Conditions of Carriage for acceptance of items.

All fares in pence unless otherwise stated.
Hail and Ride journeys will be charged the fare from the stop before the boarding point to the stop after the alighting point.

Cumbria Plusbus

571

Crosby Garrett – Warcop
Monday to Saturday

Crosby Garrett	0630	0930	1230	1530
Soulby	0635	0935	1235	1535
Christian Head Health Centre	0641	0941	1241	1541
Kirkby Stephen Co-op	0642	0942	1242	1542
Hartley	0647	0947	1247	1547
Kirkby Stephen Co-op	0651	0951	1251	1551
Kirkby Stephen Midland Bank	0655	0955	1255	1555
Nateby	0700	1000	1300	1600
Kirkby Stephen Station Road	0703	1003	1303	1603
Kirkby Stephen Railway Station	0705	1005	1305	1605
Kirkby Stephen Market Square	0711	1011	1311	1611
Kirkby Stephen Co-op	0713	1013	1313	1613
Winton	0716	1016	1316	1616
Kaber	0721	1021	1321	1621
Brough Sowerby	0725	1025	1325	1625
Church Brough	0728	1028	1328	1628
Brough Clock	0730	1030	1330	1630
Great Musgrave	0736	1036	1336	1636
Little Musgrave	0740	1040	1340	1640
Warcop Shelter	0749	1049	1349	1649
Warcop The Croft	0750	1050	1350	1650
Warcop Post Office	0751	1051	1351	1651

Warcop – Crosby Garrett
Monday to Saturday

Warcop Post Office	0800	1100	1400	1700
Warcop The Croft	0802	1102	1402	1702
Warcop Shelter	0804	1104	1404	1704
Little Musgrave	0811	1111	1411	1711
Great Musgrave	0815	1115	1415	1715
Brough Clock	0821	1121	1421	1721
Church Brough	0823	1123	1423	1723
Brough Sowerby	0826	1126	1426	1726
Kaber	0830	1130	1430	1730
Winton	0835	1135	1435	1735
Kirkby Stephen Co-op	0840	1140	1440	1740
Kirkby Stephen Midland Bank	0842	1142	1442	1742
Kirkby Stephen Railway Station	0847	1147	1447	1747
Kirkby Stephen Station Road	0852	1152	1452	1752
Nateby	0854	1154	1454	1754
Kirkby Stephen Market Square	0859	1159	1459	1759
Kirkby Stephen Co-op	0903	1203	1503	1803
Hartley	0909	1209	1509	1809
Kirkby Stephen Co-op	0914	1214	1514	1814
Christian Head Health Centre	0915	1215	1515	1815
Soulby	0919	1219	1519	1819
Crosby Garrett	0924	1224	1524	1824

The Plusbus will meet the following trains at Kirkby Stephen Railway Station:

Trains / Buses	To Carlisle	From Carlisle	To Settle	From Settle
From Kirkby Stephen (via Nateby)	0728 NS 1029 1628		1020 S 1615 S	
From Kirkby Stephen (direct)		See above services		
To Kirkby Stephen (via Nateby)		1719		1132 S 1428
To Kirkby Stephen (direct)		0950 NS 1246		

S Saturday only   NS Not Saturday

- Passengers may get on or off anywhere along the route on a "hail and ride" basis.
- The Operator of the Cumbria Plusbus is **GRAND PRIX SERVICES**, Main Street, Brough, Kirkby Stephen, Cumbria, CA17 4AY. All enquiries: 017683 41328.
- Journey Planner Enquiry Line: 01228 606000

The Enquiry Line is open: 0900 – 1700 Monday–Friday; 0900 – 1200 Saturday

When the vehicle is being maintained, the service will still operate but the vehicle will not be accessible to wheelchair users and those having difficulty with steps. The scheduled dates for maintenance are:

Tuesday 22 June 1999
Tuesday 31 August 1999
Tuesday 9 November 1999
Tuesday 11 January 2000
Tuesday 21 March 2000

A pocket route map showing the location of bus stops is available from the Tourist Information Centre and Community Centre in Kirkby Stephen, Post Offices and Health Centres.

No service on Sundays or Bank Holidays.

Appendix 3

Bus Stop Locations Leaflet

The original bus stop locations leaflet is a two-sided A3 document produced in Arial, in colour on matt cream paper. The reproduction here is 70% of the actual size.

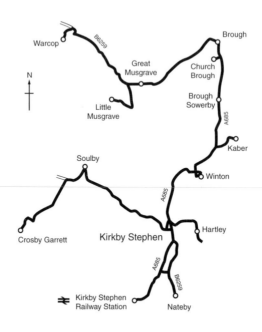

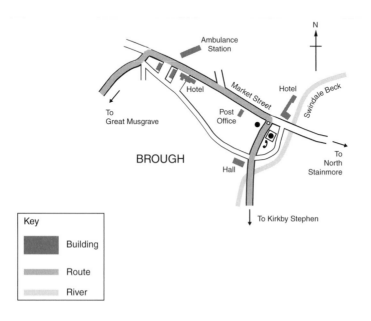

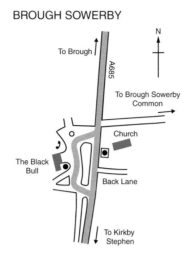

BROUGH SOWERBY

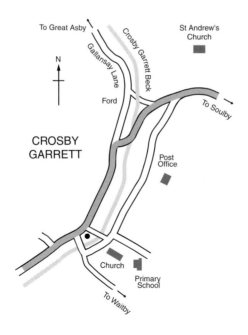

CROSBY
GARRETT

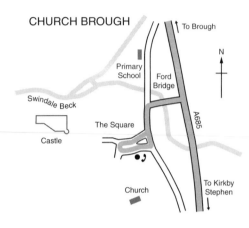

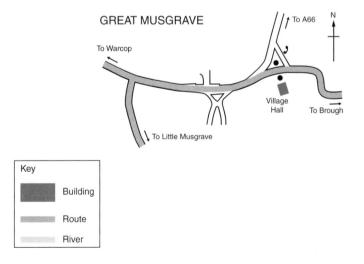

Key

■	Building
▬	Route
▬	River

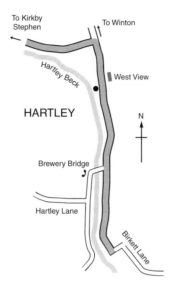

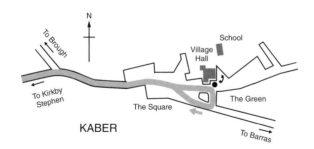

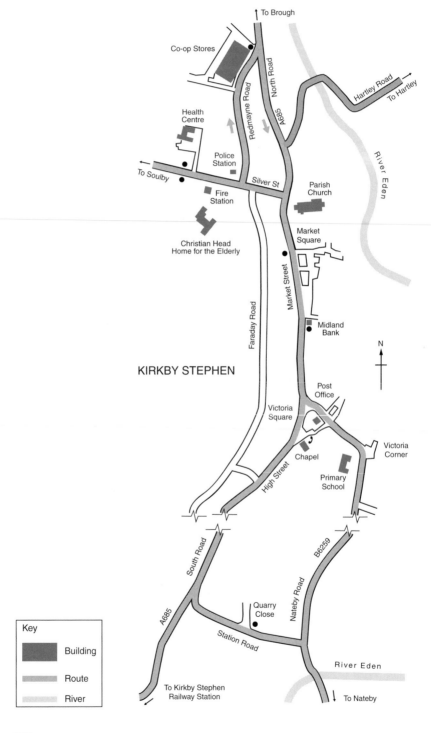

KIRKBY STEPHEN

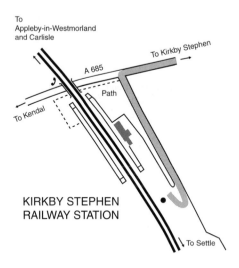

To
Appleby-in-Westmorland
and Carlisle

To Kirkby Stephen

A 685

Path

To Kendal

**KIRKBY STEPHEN
RAILWAY STATION**

To Settle

LITTLE MUSGRAVE

River Eden

N

Swillings Lane

To Great Asby

Eden View
Farm

To Soulby

To Great
Musgrave

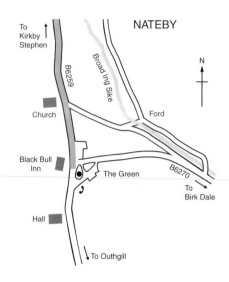

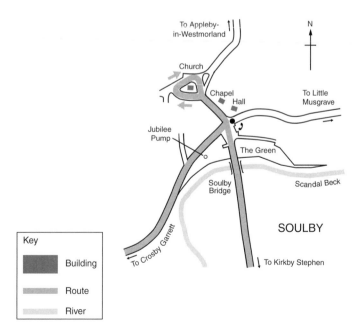

Key

	Building
	Route
	River

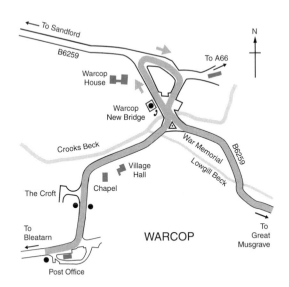

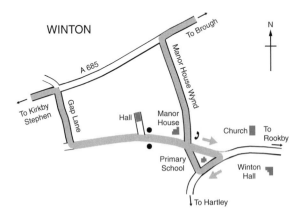

Appendix 4

Braille Timetable

The actual Braille timetable leaflet is part of a six-page B4 (255 mm × 365 mm) booklet. The reproduction here is 45% of the actual size.

For the purposes of reproduction, Braille is treated as a font, with one character being represented by a pattern of dots. In this way text and numbers can be 'translated' into Braille using a standard word processor. However, Braille does not recognise numbers, using the characters a–j instead. As a result, a # symbol is used to inform the reader that the following characters are actually numbers. In this appendix, we have shown the alphabetical text that gives rise to the Braille text. The timetables are the same as those in Appendix 2. Note how the layout (and the way of treating numbers in this case) is explained before presenting the actual Braille timetable. For further information about producing Braille text, contact the Royal National Institute for the Blind.

The Braille text is printed onto special paper which, when heated, expands where black print occurs. Anything printed on the paper thereby becomes tactile.

In this appendix we show the alphabetical text first, followed by the Braille version.

The Cumbria Plusbus4
Bus route map and timetables4

Copyright University College London1 July#aiii

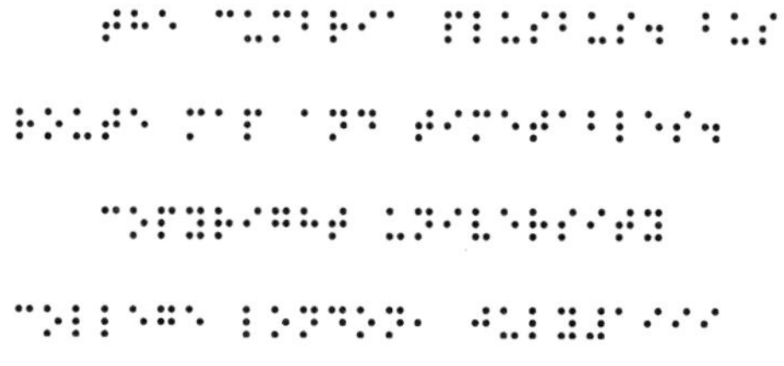

The next two pages are the bus
time tables4 One page for each
direction4 The timetables are
arranged in five columns4 The
first column is a list of the bus
stops4 The other four columns1
columns #b-e1 show the times when
the bus arrives at each stop4
The braille number sign has been
omitted from columns#b-e4

For further information1 please
call Grand Prix Services on
#jagfhc#dacbh

�000 ⠞⠓⠑ ⠝⠑⠭⠞ ⠞⠺⠕ ⠏⠁⠛⠑⠎ ⠁⠗⠑ ⠞⠓⠑ ⠃⠥⠎
⠞⠊⠍⠑ ⠞⠁⠃⠇⠑⠎⠲ ⠕⠝⠑ ⠏⠁⠛⠑ ⠋⠕⠗ ⠑⠁⠉⠓
⠙⠊⠗⠑⠉⠞⠊⠕⠝⠲ ⠞⠓⠑ ⠞⠊⠍⠑⠞⠁⠃⠇⠑⠎ ⠁⠗⠑
⠁⠗⠗⠁⠝⠛⠑⠙ ⠊⠝ ⠋⠊⠧⠑ ⠉⠕⠇⠥⠍⠝⠎⠲ ⠞⠓⠑
⠋⠊⠗⠎⠞ ⠉⠕⠇⠥⠍⠝ ⠊⠎ ⠁ ⠇⠊⠎⠞ ⠕⠋ ⠞⠓⠑ ⠃⠥⠎
⠎⠞⠕⠏⠎⠲ ⠞⠓⠑ ⠕⠞⠓⠑⠗ ⠋⠕⠥⠗ ⠉⠕⠇⠥⠍⠝⠎
⠉⠕⠇⠥⠍⠝⠎ ⠼⠃⠤⠑ ⠎⠓⠕⠺ ⠞⠓⠑ ⠞⠊⠍⠑⠎ ⠺⠓⠑⠝
⠞⠓⠑ ⠃⠥⠎ ⠁⠗⠗⠊⠧⠑⠎ ⠁⠞ ⠑⠁⠉⠓ ⠎⠞⠕⠏⠲
⠞⠓⠑ ⠃⠗⠁⠊⠇⠇⠑ ⠝⠥⠍⠃⠑⠗ ⠎⠊⠛⠝ ⠓⠁⠎ ⠃⠑⠑⠝
⠕⠍⠊⠞⠞⠑⠙ ⠋⠗⠕⠍ ⠉⠕⠇⠥⠍⠝⠎⠼⠃⠤⠑⠲
⠀⠀⠋⠕⠗ ⠋⠥⠗⠞⠓⠑⠗ ⠊⠝⠋⠕⠗⠍⠁⠞⠊⠕⠝⠂ ⠏⠇⠑⠁⠎⠑
⠉⠁⠇⠇ ⠛⠗⠁⠝⠙ ⠏⠗⠊⠭ ⠎⠑⠗⠧⠊⠉⠑⠎ ⠕⠝
⠼⠚⠁⠛⠋⠓⠉⠼⠙⠁⠉⠃⠓

Cumbria Plusbus--#ega
Crosby Garrett--Warcop

Monday to Saturday

Crosby Garrett jfcj jicj abcj aecj
Soulby jfce jice abce aece
Health Centre jfda jida abda aeda
;KS Co-op jfdb jidb abdb aedb
Hartley jfdg jidg abdg aedg
;KS Co-op jfea jiea abea aeea
;KS Midland Bank   jfee jiee abee
aeee
Nateby jgjj ajjj acjj afjj
;KS Station Rd jgjc ajjc acjc afjc
;KS R4 Station jgje ajje acje afje
;KS Market Sq jgaa ajaa acaa afaa
;KS Co-op jgac ajac acac afac
Winton jgaf ajaf acaf afaf
Kaber jgba ajba acba afba
Brough Sowerby jgbe ajbe acbe afbe
Church Brough jgbh ajbh acbh afbh
Brough Clock jgcj ajcj accj afcj
Great Musgrave jgcf ajcf accf afcf
Little Musgrave jgdj ajdj acdj afdj
Warcop Shelter jgdi ajdi acdi afdi

CUMBRIA PLUSBUS--#EGA

CROSBY GARRETT--WARCOP

MONDAY TO SATURDAY

CROSBY GARRETT				
SOULBY				
HEALTH CENTRE				
;S CO-OP				
HARTLEY				
;S CO-OP				
;S MIDLAND BANK				
NATEBY				
;S STATION RD				
;S R4 STATION				
;S MARKET ST				
;S CO-OP				
WINTON				
KABER				
BROUGH SOWERBY				
CHURCH BROUGH				
BROUGH CLOCK				
GREAT MUSGRAVE				
LITTLE MUSGRAVE				
WARCOP SHELTER				
WARCOP CROFT				
WARCOP ;O				

Cumbria Plusbus--#ega
Warcop--Crosby Garrett

Monday to Saturday

Warcop ;PO   jhjj aajj adjj agjj
Warcop Croft   jhjb aajb adjb agjb
Warcop Shelter   jhjd aajd adjd agjd
Little Musgrave   jhaa aaaa adaa agaa
Great Musgrave   jhae aaae adae agae
Brough Clock   jhba aaba adba agba
Church Brough   jhbc aabc adbc agbc
Brough Sowerby   jhbf aabf adbf agbf
Kaber   jhcj aacj adcj agcj
Winton   jhce aace adce agce
;KS Co-op   jhdj aadj addj agdj
;KS Midland Bank   jhdb aadb addb agdb
;KS R4 Station   jhdg aadg addg agdg
;KS Station Rd   jheb aaeb adeb ageb
Nateby   jhed aaed aded aged
;KS Market Sq   jhei aaei adei agei
;KS Co-op   jijc abjc aejc ahjc
Hartley   jiji abji aeji ahji
;KS Co-op   jiad abad aead ahad
Health Centre   jiae abae aeae ahae
Soulby   jiai abai aeai ahai

CUMBRIA PLUSBUS--#EGA

WARCOP--CROSBY GARRETT

MONDAY TO SATURDAY

WARCOP :O				
WARCOP CROFT				
WARCOP SHELTER				
LITTLE MUSGRAVE				
GREAT MUSGRAVE				
BROUGH CLOCK				
CHURCH BROUGH				
BROUGH SOWERBY				
KABER				
WINTON				
:S CO-OP				
:S MIDLAND BANK				
:S R4 STATION				
:S STATION RD				
NATEBY				
:S MARKET ST				
:S CO-OP				
HARTLEY				
:S CO-OP				
HEALTH CENTRE				
SOULBY				
CROSBY GARRETT				

Appendix 5

Tactile Bus Route Map

The actual tactile map leaflet is part of a six-page, B4 booklet. The reproduction here is 45% of the actual size. In this appendix, text is reproduced first in alphabetical characters then in the corresponding Braille (Type 1) font (see page 393).

The Cumbria Plusbus4
Bus route map and timetables4

Copyright University College London1 July#aiii

THE CUMBRIA PLUSBUS4 BUS

ROUTE MAP AND TIMETABLES4

COPYRIGHT UNIVERSITY

COLLEGE LONDON1 JULY#AIII

Following this text is a map of
the Cumbria Plusbus route between
Warcop and Crosby Garrett4 The map
shows each village where the bus
stops and Kirkby Stephen4 The bus
route is indicated by a raised
line4

The following is a key to the
symbols used in the map4

Key3

——— Bus Route

●   Village

     Kirkby Stephen

In Kirkby Stephen1 the Plusbus
stops at the following places3
Health Centre
Market Square
Midland Bank
Station Road

The route through Kirkby
Stephen is a little complicated4
Please ask the bus driver to tell
you the right place to get off4

FOLLOWING THIS TEXT IS A MAP OF THE CUMBRIA PLUSBUS ROUTE BETWEEN WARCOP AND CROSBY GARRETT. THE MAP SHOWS EACH VILLAGE WHERE THE BUS STOPS AND KIRKBY STEPHEN. THE BUS ROUTE IS INDICATED BY A RAISED LINE.

THE FOLLOWING IS A KEY TO THE SYMBOLS USED IN THE MAP.

KEY:

—— BUS ROUTE

● VILLAGE

⬡ KIRKBY

IN KIRKBY STEPHEN, THE PLUSBUS STOPS AT THE FOLLOWING PLACES:
HEALTH CENTRE
MARKET SQUARE
MIDLAND BANK
STATION ROAD

THE ROUTE THROUGH KIRKBY STEPHEN IS A LITTLE COMPLICATED. PLEASE ASK THE BUS DRIVER TO TELL YOU THE RIGHT PLACE TO GET OFF.

This is a map of the Cumbria
Plusbus route between Warcop and
Crosby Garrett4

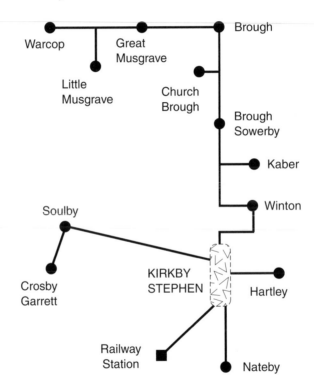

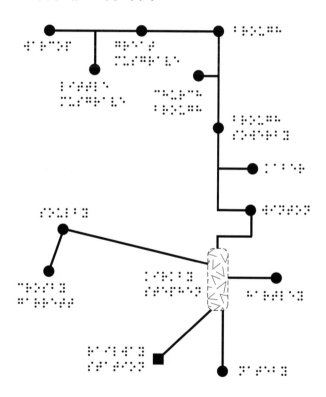

Index